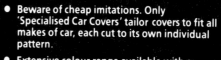

MILLER'S
Collectors Cars
PRICE GUIDE

MILLER'S
Collectors
Cars
PRICE GUIDE

1994-95

Volume IV

Consultants: Judith and Martin Miller

General Editor: Robert Murfin

Foreword by Lord Montagu of Beaulieu

MILLER'S COLLECTORS CARS PRICE GUIDE 1994-95

Created and designed by
Miller's Publications
The Cellars, High Street
Tenterden, Kent TN30 6BN
Telephone: 0580 766411

Consultants: Judith and Martin Miller

General Editor: Robert Murfin
Editorial and Production Co-ordinator: Sue Boyd
Editorial Assistants: Marion Rickman, Jo Wood, Sue Montgomery
Artwork: Stephen Parry, Jody Taylor, Darren Manser
Advertising Executive: Elizabeth Smith
Display Advertisements: Liz Warwick, Melinda Williams
Material Collators: Gillian Charles, Helen Burt
Additional Photographers: Neill Bruce, David Burgess-Wise,
Franco Fiumefreddo, Geoff Goddard, Bob Masters, David Shepherd
Index compiled by: DD Editorial Services, Beccles

First published in 1994
by Miller's Publications, part of Reed Consumer Books Ltd,
Michelin House, 81 Fulham Road, London SW3 6RB

A CIP catalogue record for this book is
available from the British Library

ISBN 1-85732-339-4

Bromide output by Perfect Image, Hurst Green, E. Sussex
Illustrations by G. H. Graphics, St. Leonard's-on-Sea, E. Sussex
Colour origination by Scantrans, Singapore
Printed and bound in England by William Clowes Ltd,
Beccles and London

5

ACKNOWLEDGEMENTS

The publishers would like to acknowledge the great assistance given by our consultants.

Peter Card **Malcolm Welford**	ADT Auctions Ltd, Classic & Historic Automobile Division, Blackbushe Airport, Blackwater, Camberley, Surrey. Tel: 0252 878555
Linden C. T. Alcock	Alcocks, Wyeval House, 42 Bridge Street, Hereford. Tel: 0432 344322
Tom Falconer	Claremont Corvette, Snodland, Kent. Tel: 0634 244444
Arthur Downer	Tenterden, Kent.
Paul Foulkes-Halbard	Foulkes-Halbard of Filching, Filching Manor, Jevington Road, Wannock, Polegate, Sussex. Tel: 0323 487838/487124
David Jones	Graham Walker Ltd., Parkgate Road, Mollington, Chester. Tel: 0244 851144
Tony Leslie	Holmesdale Sevens, Fareham, Chilsham Lane, Herstmonceux, E. Sussex. Tel: 0323 833603
Stanley Mann	Tel: 0923 852505

HOW TO USE THIS BOOK

Miller's Collectors Cars Price Guide presents an overview of the collectors cars market during the past twelve months. The cars are listed alphabetically by make and then chronologically by model within each make. In the case of manufacturers renowned for producing both sports and saloon cars - for example Bentley and MG, we have grouped the sports and saloon cars together and then listed these cars chronologically.

Each illustration is fully captioned and carries a price range which reflects the dealer/ auctioneer sale price. The prefix 'Est.' indicates the estimated price for the cars which did not sell at auction. Each illustration also has an identification code which allows you to locate the source of that particular picture by using the Key to Illustrations.

In the automobilia section, objects are grouped alphabetically by type, for example clothing, garage equipment, and so on, then chronologically within each grouping. Competition cars, commercial vehicles, military vehicles, taxis and tractors all follow the same format. The automobile art section is listed alphabetically.

Also included in *Miller's Collectors Cars Price Guide* are price boxes, compiled by our team of experts from ADT Auctions, car clubs and private collectors, which give the value of a particular model, dependent on condition.

Condition 1. A vehicle in top class condition but not 'Concours d'élégance' standard, either fully restored or in very good original condition.

Condition 2. A good, clean roadworthy vehicle, both mechanically and bodily sound.
Condition 3. A runner, but in need of attention, probably to both bodywork and mechanics. Must have current MOT.

We have also included restoration projects, which cover vehicles that fail to make the condition 3 grading.

Remember, we do not illustrate every classic or collectors car ever produced. Our aim is to reflect the market place, so if, for example, there appears to be a large number of Lotus's and only a few Volvos, then this is an indication of the quantity, availability and, to an extent, the desirability of these cars in the marketplace over the last twelve months. If the car you are looking for is not featured under its alphabetical listing, do look in the colour sections and double-check the index. If a particular car is not featured this year, it may well have appeared in previous editions of *Miller's Collectors Cars Price Guide,* which provide a growing visual reference library.

Lastly, we are always keen to improve the content and accuracy of our books. If you feel that a particular make or model or other aspect of classic and collectable vehicles has not been covered in sufficient detail, if you disagree with our panel of experts, or have any other comments you would like to share with us about our book, please write and let us know. We value feedback from the people who use this guide to tell us how we can make it even better for them.

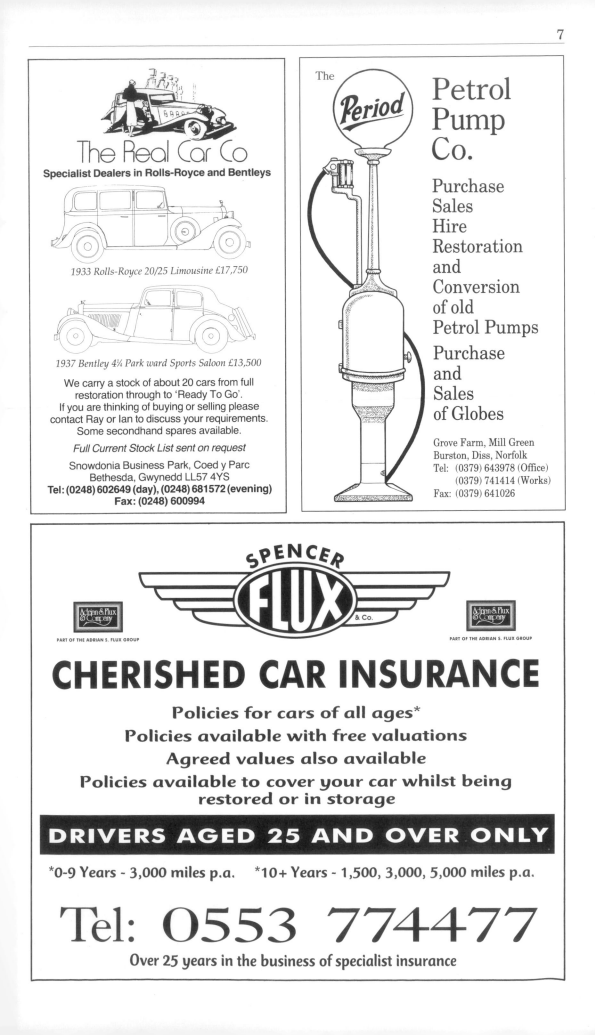

KEY TO ILLUSTRATIONS

Each illustration and descriptive caption is accompanied by a letter-code. The source of any item may be immediately determined by referring to the following list, in which Auctioneers are denoted by *, Dealers by •, Advertisers by †, and Clubs and Trusts by ‡. In no way does this constitute or imply a contract or binding offer on the part of any of our contributors to supply or sell the goods illustrated, or similar articles, at the prices stated.

AD • Arthur Downer, Tenterden, Kent.

ADT †* ADT Auctions Ltd., Classic & Historic Automobile Division, Blackbushe Airport, Blackwater, Camberley, Surrey. Tel: 0252 878555

ALC †* Alcocks, Wyeval House, 42 Bridge Street, Hereford. Tel: 0432 344322

BA †• Balmoral Automobile Co. Ltd., 260 Knights Hill, West Norwood, London, SE27. Tel: 081-761 1155

BC • Beaulieu Cars Ltd, Beaulieu, Hants. Tel: 0590 612689.

BCA • Beaulieu Cars Automobilia, Beaulieu, Hants. Tel: 0590 612689

BGI • Byron Garages International, 70 Grove Road, Sutton, Surrey. Tel: 0737 244567

BKS * Robert Brooks (Auctioneers) Ltd.,
BKS(M) 81 Westside, London SW4. Tel: 071-228 8000

BLE †• Ivor Bleaney, PO Box 60, Salisbury, Wilts. Tel: 0794 390895

Bro †• John Brown, Letchworth, Herts. Tel: 0462 682589

BS • Below Stairs, 103 High Street, Hungerford, Berks. Tel: 0488 682317

C * Christie, Manson & Wood, 8 King Street, St James's, London SW1. Tel: 071-839 9060

C(S) * Christie's Scotland Ltd., 164-166 Bath Street, Glasgow. Tel: 041 332 8134

CARS • Classic Automobilia & Regalia Specialists, 4-4a Chapel Terrace Mews, Kemp Town, Brighton, Sussex. Tel: 0273 601960

Car †• Chris Alford Racing & Sports Cars, Newland Cottage, Hassocks, West Sussex. Tel: 0273 845966

CBG • Cropredy Bridge Garage Ltd., (exclusively Jensen), Riverside Works, Cropredy, Banbury, Oxon. Tel: 0295 758444

CC • Collectors Cars, (Mr D. Connell), Drakeshill, Birmingham Road, Kenilworth, Warwicks. Tel: 0926 57705

CCon †• Canterbury Convertibles. Tel: 0227 720306

CCTC • Classic Car Trade Centre, 47 Ash Grove, Chelmsford, Essex. Tel: 0245 358028

Cen †* Central Motor Auctions PLC, Central House, Pontefract Road, Rothwell, Leeds. Tel: 0532 820707

CGB †• Cars Gone By, Maidstone, Kent. Tel: 0622 630220

CGOC †• Capital & General Omnibus Company Ltd. Tel: 0260 223456

CNY * Christie, Manson & Woods International Inc., 502 Park Avenue, New York, NY 10022. Tel: 212 546 1000 (including Christie's East).

COR †• Claremont Corvette, Snodland, Kent. Tel: 0634 244444

COYS * Coys of Kensington, 2-4 Queens Gate Mews, London SW7. Tel: 071-584 7444

CR †• Classic Restorations, Arch 124, Cornwall Road, Waterloo, London SE1. Tel: 071-928 6613

Cum • Cumbria Classic Car Centre, Windermere Road, Staveley, Nr Kendal, Cumbria. Tel: 0539 534242/0539 821906

CVPG ‡ Chiltern Vehicle Preservation Group, Chiltern House, Ashendon, Aylesbury, Bucks. Tel: 0296 651283

DaD * David Dockree, 224 Moss Lane, Bramhall, Stockport, Cheshire. Tel: 061-485 1258

1910 Cretors Popcorn Wagon, steam driven, fully restored, excellent condition. **£9,000-9,500** *CNY*

DB	† •	David Baldock, North Road, Goudhurst, Kent. Tel: 0580 211326
DDM	*	Dickinson, Davy and Markham, Wrawby Street, Brigg, S. Humberside. Tel: 0652 653666
DF	•	David Foster, 87 Foxley Lane, Purley, Surrey. Tel: 081-668 1246
DJR	•	DJR Services, Unit N4, Europa Trading Estate, Trader Road, Erith, Kent. Tel: 0322 442850
ECC	† *	Eccles Auctions, Unit 4, 25 Gwydir Street, Cambridge. Tel: 0223 561518.
ESM	† •	East Sussex Minors, Bearhurst Farm, Stonegate, Wadhurst, E. Sussex. Tel: 0580 200203
FHD	† •	F. H. Douglass, 1a South Ealing Road, Ealing, London W5. Tel: 081-567 0570
FHF	† •	Foulkes-Halbard of Filching, Filching Manor, Jevington Road, Wannock, Polegate, Sussex. Tel: 0323 487838/487124
FM	•	Franco Macri. Tel: 0227 700555
GML	•	Genevieve Motors Ltd., Cavendish Bridge, Shardlow, Derby. Tel: 0332 799770
GW	† •	Graham Walker Ltd., Parkgate Road, Mollington, Chester, Cheshire. Tel: 0244 851144
H&H	† *	H & H Auctions, Rose Cottage, Roseneath Road, Urmston, Manchester. Tel: 061 747 0561 & 0925 860471
HOLL	† *	Holloway's, 49 Parsons Street, Banbury, Oxon. Tel: 0295 253197
HWA	•	Harry Woodnorth Automobiles, 1650 North Bosworth Avenue, Chicago, Illinois 60622, USA. Tel: 0101 312 227 1340
KSC	† •	Kent Sports Cars, High Street (A257), Littlebourne, Canterbury, Kent. Tel: 0227 832200
L&E	*	Locke & England, Black Horse Agencies, 18 Guy Street, Leamington Spa, Warwicks. Tel: 0926 889100
LF	*	Lambert & Foster, 77 Commercial Road, Paddock Wood, Kent. Tel: 0892 832325
LRT	‡	Dunsfold Landrover Trust, Dunsfold, Surrey. Tel: 0483 200058
MAN	† •	Stanley Mann. Tel: 0923 852505
Mot	•	Motospot, North Kilworth, Lutterworth, Leics. Tel: 0455 552548 or 0831 120498
MR	† *	Martyn Rowe, The Truro Auction Centre, Calenick Street, Truro, Cornwall. Tel: 0872 260020
MSMP	•	Mike Smith's Motoring Past, Chiltern House, Ashendon, Aylesbury, Bucks. Tel: 0296 651283
MSN	•	Murray Scott-Nelson, Classic Sports Car Specialists, Beaconsfield Street, Scarborough, N. Yorks. Tel: 0723 361227
NTC	† •	Northern TR Centre, Sedgefield Industrial Estate, Sedgefield, Cleveland. Tel: 0740 621447
ONS	*	Onslows, Metrostore, Townmead Road, London SW6. Tel: 071-793 0240
P	*	Phillips, Son & Neale, Blenstock House, 101 New Bond Street, London W1. Tel: 071-629 6602
PC		Private Collection.
PiK	† •	Porters in Kensington, 11-14 Atherstone Mews, South Kensington, London SW7. Tel: 071-584 7458
PPP	† •	The Period Petrol Pump Co., Grove Farm, Mill Green, Burston, Diss, Norfolk. Tel: 0379 643978
PS	*	Palmer Snell, 65 Cheap Street, Sherborne, Dorset Tel: 0935 812218
RCC	† •	The Real Car Co., Snowdonia Business Park, Coed y Parc, Bethesda, Gwynedd. Tel: 0248 602649
RJ	*	Roger Jones Co., The Saleroom, 33 Abergele Road, Colwyn Bay, Clwyd. Tel: 0492 532176
S	† *	Sotheby's, 34-35 New Bond Street, London W1. Tel: 071-493 8080
S(NY)	*	Sotheby's New York, 1334 York Avenue, New York, NY 10021. Tel: 212 606 7000
S(Z)	*	Sotheby's Zurich, Bleicherweg 20, CH-8022 Zurich. Tel: 41 (1) 202 0011
SC	•	Sporting Classics, Phil Hacker, The Oast, Shears Farm, North Road, Goudhurst, Kent. Tel: 0580 211275
SJR	† •	Simon J. Robinson (MGA) 1982 Ltd., Ketton Garage, Durham Road, Coatham Munderville, Darlington. Tel: 0325 311232
TSh	*	Thimbleby & Shorland, PO Box 175, 31 Great Knollys Street, Reading, Berks. Tel: 0734 508611
TVR	•	David Gerald TVR Sports Cars Ltd. Tel: 0386 793237
VIC	† •	Vicarys of Battle Ltd., 32 High Street, Battle, East Sussex. Tel: 0424 772425
WBH	*	Walker, Barnett & Hill, Waterloo Road Salerooms, Clarence Street, Wolverhampton. Tel: 0902 773531
WES	† •	Western Classics, 7/8 St George's Works, Silver Street, Trowbridge, Wiltshire. Tel: 0225 751044

CONTENTS

FOREWORD

I am pleased that once again I have been asked to write the foreword to *Miller's Collectors Cars Price Guide*. Now in its fourth edition, this invaluable guide has established its own niche in the great and exciting story of the motor car.

As founder of the National Motor Museum at Beaulieu, I have dedicated much of my life to telling this story. The museum covers a century of automobile history, and I am proud to say that our collection of vehicles and memorabilia is today one of the finest in the world.

Over the years, I have seen at first hand how interest in motoring history has grown. More and more people visit the museum every year and increasing numbers are attracted to our motor-related sales and auto-jumbles, the largest and most successful in Europe. This year our auto-jumbles will be held in May and September.

Whether you are an enthusiast who simply loves looking at wonderful cars, or a collector who wants to buy them, *Miller's Collectors Cars Price Guide* is an essential reference book. It covers the whole sweep of motoring history from the horseless carriage, through the great classic cars of the pre- and post-war periods, to the collectable vehicles of today. The guide includes automobilia and motoring ephemera for every taste, from the grandest silver trophies to the petrol pump. Every entry is verified by a panel of experts.

In all my years at Beaulieu, my fascination for cars and motoring history has never lessened. With the help of *Miller's Collectors Cars Price Guide*, I hope that many more people will be able to share in this passion and find as much enjoyment as I have in the story of the automobile.

Montagu of Beaulieu

1994

STATE OF THE MARKET

Few would deny that 1993 was another difficult year. The one bright spark on the economic front was that we appeared to have inflation somewhat under control - a good thing in itself, except that the market in old vehicles, just as in fine art and real estate, is always more active when inflation is high. Last year will be seen as a buyer's market.

Recession or not - the sheer volume of activity in the classic car market was unprecedented. Events of all types continued to grow, despite a few casualties along the way. Shows, auto-jumbles, historic rallies and races, auctions and social gatherings - there was hardly a weekend in the year not offering a choice of activities for collectors and enthusiasts to enjoy. Indeed, many leading shows reported record attendances with exhibitors booking immediately for 1994. Leading sporting events for vintage and classic vehicles were heavily over subscribed in 1993, at a time when events for modern machinery were often poorly supported.

The continuing success of major events also draws great interest from the more casual observers of our hobby. Just try parking in Brighton on the day of the Veteran Car Run, or find a good vantage point from which to watch a stage of the Rally Britannia! We are fortunate indeed to have a plethora of activities for enthusiasts in this country, with Britian leading the way over Europe.

Another clear trend which emerged in 1993 was the growing association between Britain and the Continent, a factor which is set to increase in 1994 with the opening of the Channel Tunnel. Already coach trips to the major European classic car shows are increasing, whilst the presence of Continental buyers at UK auctions is now commonplace.

Prices generally in 1993 have levelled off. Indeed, some categories rose in the summer of 1993 by 10-15%, but a fall-back in the autumn left few categories more than 10% up overall. Best performers have been cars which are both interesting and easy to maintain, such as tourers or convertibles. If the vehicle in question happens to be eligible for a 'blue form' in VSCC events or for some other competition, so much the better. More important, vehicles now have to be 'right'; doubtful histories, poor workmanship through an over hasty restoration and non-period modifications are definitely out. Only cars with a provenance, an authenticated history and some individuality have been sought by discerning buyers.

In contrast, motoring ephemera has enjoyed a buoyant year with excellent prices realised for art and collectables. Originality is paramount and poor quality goods rarely find a buyer at any price.

In 1993, we were back to an enthusiast-dominated market and most of the dealers and auction houses which are still enjoying success today are run by enthusiasts themselves. That, of course, is where it all began. Paradoxes or not, with lower prices, yet more Continental involvement, collectors and enthusiasts - whatever their particular penchant - there is every reason to view the future with keen anticipation.

Linden C. T. Alcock FRICS, ASVA
Alcocks Vintage Transport &
General Auctioneers

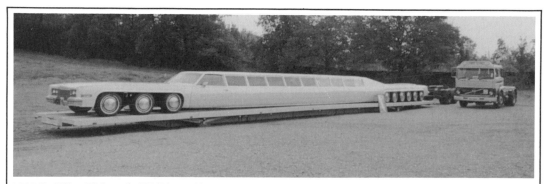

1982 Cadillac Eldorado V8 Limousine, 23m 93cm long, over 7 tons in weight, 18 wheels, seating for 20 passengers, carpetted throughout, fitted with a bar, refrigerator, TV and video, with Volvo type F7 turbo 6 intercooled tractor unit and purpose-built trailer **£18,500-19,000** *S*

REGISTERING OR IMPORTING A CLASSIC CAR

In 1983 the DVLC, later to become the DVLA, requested that all 'older vehicles' have their original registration numbers recorded with their office. However, as many car enthusiasts discovered, one could spend considerable time and expense restoring a classic car only to find that, due to a missing document or the promise of a document from a previous owner which never materialised, one's newly acquired classic car could not be made road legal.

To avoid such pitfalls and disappointments, a few suggestions are offered to those who acquire an older car with no registration number and no old-style log book or, in some cases, if the registration number is not active on the DVLA system. Advice is also given to those wanting to register an imported, non-European car.

If you are intending to register a classic car, be satisfied before you purchase the vehicle that it is genuine. Establish the chassis number of the vehicle, its provenance and particularly the manufacturer of the vehicle in question. More often than not, an old number plate will remain with the car so, in the very first instance, you should take photographs of the vehicle *in situ,* which may help your claim at a later date.

There are about three hundred clubs catering for the needs of the 'old car movement' (most of which are listed in our directory at the back of this book), and very often application to the appropriate club will bring forward a letter confirming that your particular car left the production line on a particular date. If you also add to this that many registration numbers can be dated to within a month of their issue, then it is not unreasonable to believe that if the delivery date and registration issue date are similar then this would constitute a valid claim.

It is also important to note here that you can contact the DVLA at Swansea (Tel: 0792 772134) and ask them whether the registration number on your car has ever been reissued. If the answer is in the negative then this adds benefit to your requests. Needless to say, if they are able to tell you that the registration number has been allocated to another car then clearly you cannot apply for it.

Very often, when a car remains off the road for a considerable period, although the V5 log book may have been applied for before the 1983 deadline, the registration number, due to inactivity, has been archived. You must therefore re-register your vehicle. Reclaiming the old number can involve a V765 application which is handled by the appropriate enthusiasts' club. Your nearest registering office can supply forms V55/5, V765 and V765/1, and will also keep photocopies of your original vehicle documents for you. The V55/5 is used when a vehicle has not previously been registered, where the car has been imported, or has never been driven on the road. The V765 explains how to apply and the V765/1 lists DVLA approved enthusiasts' clubs who will authenticate applications on the DVLA's behalf.

An application must be made to the appropriate club which fits the make and type of your vehicle. The club will decide whether or not to support the application and may wish to inspect the vehicle. If supported, the club will send the papers to the DVLA for final approval and processing. If your application is rejected by the club, or the DVLA, a full explanation will be provided. Although you may not be required to join to make an application, a fee may be charged for the service.

Having acquired a classic or historic car which you want to import to the UK you must receive with the car a customs document C&E386 which demonstrates that customs duties (if payable) have either been paid or that the vehicle is free of duty. Without it, duty and VAT could well be sought again.

Another word of warning is that a similar form, a C&E388, is often offered with a car. This, like the C&E386, demonstrates that the vehicle is free of duty, but in fact was imported as a personal import and its re-sale is not allowed within one year of importation.

It is also worth remembering that some cars, like the De Lorean, for example, are not type-approved. If the vehicle is not legally registered in the UK then problems could exist if you try to register it, particularly if the vehicle is not imported as a private import.

If you encounter problems registering your classic vehicle, remember to contact the enthusiasts' club and the DVLA. They will help and advise you so that you can get on with polishing, pampering and enjoying the finer side of owning a classic vehicle.

Peter W. Card
ADT Auctions Ltd.

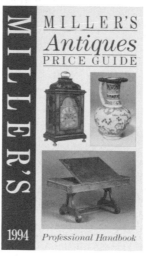
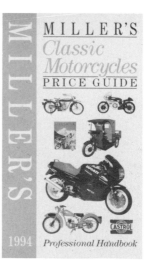
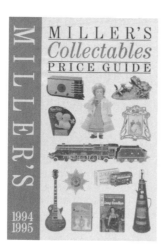

AC

Autocars & Accessories was founded in 1904 by engineers John Weller and John Portwine. Their first major venture was the Autocarrier tri-van of 1904 which was to replace the pony and trap. The tri-van became synonymous with such trade names as Great Western Railways, Maples and Selfridges, and in 1914 a passenger version arrived, the AC Sociable. Although WWI interrupted production, AC continued to make bespoke vehicles.

The company continued after the war with saloons, sports racers and other enterprises, including invalid carriages and the 'bag boy' golf club carrier. AC remained successful in motor racing with the Ace, which, together with the Cobra are still among the most sought after British racing cars.

1926 AC Royal 1½ Litre Anzani, well restored to correct original colour and specifications, full history from new.
£12,000-13,000 *Mot*

1924 AC Royal, 4 cylinders, 1496cc, open 2 seater with dickey, very good original condition.
Est. £11,000-14,000 *COYS*

AC Model	ENGINE cc/cyl	DATES	CONDITION 1	2	3
Sociable	636/1	1907-12	£9,500	£8,000	£4,000
12/24 (Anzani)	1498/4	1919-27	£14,000	£11,500	£7,500
16/40	1991/6	1920-28	£18,000	£15,000	£11,000
16/60 Drophead/Saloon	1991/6	1937-40	£24,000	£21,000	£15,500
16/70 Sports Tourer	1991/6	1937-40	£35,000	£26,000	£18,000
16/80 Competition 2 Seater	1991/6	1937-40	£65,000	£45,000	£35,000

1949 AC Buckland Sports Tourer, 6 cylinder, 2 litre engine, 75bhp, rebuilt engine, partly restored, right hand drive, no weather equipment, unpainted.
£3,500-4,000 *C*

The Sports Tourer was made by the Buckland bodyworks of Buntingford, Hertfordshire.

- The Ace originated from a racing design by John Tojeiro in 1950.
- The lightweight chassis and aluminium body were loosley based on the Ferrari 166MM Barchetta by Touring.
- The AC Ace was available with AC, Bristol and Ford engines.

1954 AC Ace, total chassis-up restoration.
£43,000-47,000 *PiK*

1958 AC Ace-Bristol 2 Litre 2 Seater Sports, with overdrive, body, drive train and suspension restored, side vents have been cut into the lower front wings, good overall condition.
£32,000-34,000 *BKS*

1958 AC Ace 2 Seater Sports Roadster, excellent condition.
£20,000-30,000 *FHF*

1959 AC Ace, open sports coachwork, 6 cylinders, 1991cc, fitted with the later type AC engine, converted to right hand drive, good condition.
£16,500-17,500 *COYS*

1960 AC Ace Bristol,
6 cylinders, 1971cc, chassis and running gear stripped, resprayed to excellent standard, left hand drive.
£42,000-45,000 *COYS*

Launched at the 1953 Earl's Court Motor Show, the Ace was capable of 103mph and 0-60mph in 11.4 seconds.

AC Model	ENGINE cc/cyl	DATES	CONDITION 1	2	3
2 litre	1991/6	1947-55	£5,000	£2,000	£350
Buckland	1991/6	1949-54	£5,500	£3,500	£1,250
Ace	1991/6	1953-63	£26,000	£22,000	£15,000
Ace Bristol	1971/6	1954-63	£30,000	£28,000	£23,000
Ace 2.6	1553/6	1961-62	£35,000	£30,000	£29,000
Aceca	1991/6	1954-63	£21,000	£17,000	£12,000
Aceca Bristol	1971/6	1956-63	£28,000	£21,000	£16,000
Greyhound Bristol	1971/6	1961-63	£13,000	£10,500	£7,000
Cobra Mk II 289	4735/8	1963-64	£85,000	£80,000	£76,000
Cobra Mk III 427	6998/8	1965-67	£115,000	£100,000	£90,000
Cobra Mk IV	5340/8	1987-	£55,000	£40,000	£32,000
428 Frua	7014/8	1967-73	£19,000	£15,000	£11,000
428 Frua Convertible	7014/8	1967-73	£25,000	£20,000	-
3000 ME	2994/6	1976-84	£12,000	£9,000	£6,000

1966 AC Cobra 427 S/C, V8 cylinders, 6998cc, engine still to be run in, sports Holman & Moody heads, Crane 600D camshaft, cross-drilled steel crankshaft and Nascar Le Mans con rods, 550bhp, provenance confirmed by the Shelby Register of the Shelby American Automobile Club, excellent condition.
£165,000-175,000 *COYS*

Motor's road test recorded 165mph and 0-60mph in 4.2 seconds. The 427 sold well to club racers, while 31 competition versions were converted into 427 S/C models, the S/C denoting street competition, quoted 485bhp. AC produced only 75 Cobra 260 models, 560 289s and 310 427s, the latter between 1965 and 1967.

1969 AC 428 2+2 Fastback Coupé, bare metal respray, original upholstery, a 1988 class winner in the ACOC National Concours d'Elegance.
£33,000-35,000 *S*

AC's 428 was powered by Ford's V8, 7016cc engine unit. It came to the market in 1966 adopting the chassis previously used in the Cobra but extended by six inches to enable the car to be offered as a 2+2 Grand Touring Car. The 428cu in engine driving through a Ford automatic 3 speed gearbox with torque convertor and giving the car a top speed of 140mph.

1963 AC Ace 2.6 Litre Ruddspeed, 170bhp Stage 5 Ruddspeed Ford Zephyr 6 engine, with light alloy head and triple Weber 40 DCOE carburettors, excellent condition.
Est. £38,000-45,000 *BKS*

ALFA ROMEO

Alfa Romeo is Italy's oldest sporting car manufacturer, with production commencing in 1910 under the name ALFA. The first cars were sturdy, powerful and well-braked, making them popular from the outset. A year later Alfa's racing aspirations were triggered and several victories followed. However, in 1918 Societa Anonima Italiana Ing Nicola Romeo absorbed Alfa and the newly designed cars bore the badge Alfa-Romeo. Although racing remained a passion, the company branched out into commercial vehicles in 1933 and in 1950 produced its first mass-market car, the 4 cylinder 1900.

1931 Alfa Romeo 6C 1750 Tourismo, cabriolet coachwork by James Young of Bromley, excellent overall condition.
£40,000-45,000 *BC*

• **The first Alfa's were designed by Giuseppe Merosi.**
• **Ugo Zagato started coachbuilding in Milan in 1919. He produced the coachwork for the famous 6C.**
• **Vittorio Jano joined Alfa Romeo in 1923 and was originally responsible for supercharging the P1 and P2 racing cars.**

1930 Alfa Romeo 6C 1750 Gran Sport, coachwork by Zagato, 6 cylinders, 1752cc, original example, one of just 100 6C-1750s produced in 1930, with full competition history, excellent condition.
£225,000-245,000 *COYS*

1954 Alfa Romeo 1900 Super Spring Sports Coupé, coachwork by Touring of Milan, 4 cylinder, 1900cc engine with unibody construction, 5 speed Nardi specification gearbox, original radio and steering wheel, reconditioned mechanical components, bodywork restored, original paperwork and Italian documentation
Est. £38,000-42,000 *S*

1947 Alfa Romeo 6C 2500 Freccia d'Oro, 6 cylinders, 2500cc, totally restored, original Aster radio, original jacking system, excellent condition. **Est. £35,000-45,000** *COYS*

Known as the Freccia d'Oro or Golden Arrow, this 2 door saloon, based on the Sport chassis, was reminiscent of the pre-war 8C 2900 Coupé by Touring which evolved from the 6C 2300B Mille Miglia Coupé.

1949 Alfa Romeo 16C Pinin Farina 2 Door Convertible, 2500 chassis, with new hood. **£16,000-16,500** *HOLL*

1963 Alfa Romeo Giulia Sprint, 5 speed gearbox, right hand drive, in need of restoration. **£3,000-3,500** *C*

1963 Alfa Romeo 101 Giulia Spider 2 Seater Sports, with coachwork by Pininfarina, 4 cylinder, twin overhead camshaft engine, 5 speed gearbox, full ground-up restoration. **£13,000-14,000** *S*

The Giulia was introduced in 1962 with coachwork designed by Bertone. The engine was almost identical to that of the Giulietta, but with the capacity increased to 1570cc.

1963 Alfa Romeo Giulia Spider, left hand drive, Californian import. **£5,500-6,000** *CCTC*

ALFA ROMEO Model	ENGINE cc/cyl	DATES	CONDITION 1	2	3
24HP	4084/4	1910-11	£21,000	£16,000	£12,000
12HP	2413/4	1910-11	£18,000	£11,000	£8,000
40-60	6028/4	1913-15	£32,000	£24,000	£14,000
RL	2916/6	1921-22	£30,000	£24,000	£14,000
RM	1944/4	1924-25	£28,000	£17,000	£13,000
6C 1500	1487/6	1927-28	£14,000	£10,000	£8,000
6C 1750	1752/6	1923-33	£85,000+	-	-
6C 1900	1917/6	1933	£18,000	£15,000	£12,000
6C 2300	2309/6	1934	£22,000	£18,000	£15,000
6C 2500 SS	2443/6	1939-45	£25,000+		

Value is very dependent on sporting history, body style and engine type.

1964 Alfa Romeo Giulia Spider, coachwork by Pininfarina, 4 cylinder, 1570cc engine, complete engine rebuild and body respray, new seats and carpets, suspension and brakes overhauled. **£11,000-12,000** *COYS*

1964 Alfa Romeo Spider 2.6 Litre. £6,500-7,500 *DB*

1964 Alfa Romeo 2600 Spider, with coachwork by Carrozzeria Touring, 6 cylinders, 2584cc, twin overhead camshaft engine, 145bhp at 5900rpm, all-round disc braking, a good example of the model. **£12,500-13,500** *S*

c1960 Alfa Romeo Giulietta Spider Veloce, 4 cylinder, 1290cc in line engine, 90bhp at 6500rpm, 5 speed manual gearbox, Alfin drum brakes all-round, helical springs front suspension, transverse links of unequal length and bar, rear helical springs, triangle above and struts, left hand drive, standard exhaust fitted, original Veloce exhaust manifold is offered with the car, front and rear chrome bumpers missing, good overall condition. **£6,500-7,000** *C*

1964 Alfa Romeo 1.6 Litre Giulia Spider, coachwork by Carrozzeria Pininfarina, right hand drive. **£6,000-7,000** *BKS*

Production of Spiders was just 9,250 between 1962 and 1965, with the tuned Spider Veloce adding a further 1,091 to the total.

1967 Alfa Romeo Duetto Spider, in excellent all-round condition.
£12,000-13,000 *FM*

1969 Alfa Romeo Giulia,
4 cylinders, 1779cc engine, left hand drive, running restoration, the engine and gearbox rebuilt, the engine now has high lift cams, gas flowed manifold.
Est. £2,500-3,500 *ADT*

1972 Alfa Romeo 2000 Spider,
fuel injection, twin overhead camshaft, left hand drive, Californian import.
£4,500-5,000 *CCTC*

1972 Alfa Romeo 1600 Junior Z,
4 cylinder, 1570cc engine, fully restored, Chromodora alloy wheels, excellent overall condition.
£8,500-9,000 *ADT*

All Junior Z models were built as left hand drive cars.

1972 Alfa Romeo Montreal Sports Coupé, V8 2.6 litre engine, Spica fuel injection, electronic ignition and twin overhead camshaft, 200bhp at 6500rpm, bare metal respray, in excellent mechanical condition.
Est. £8,000-10,000 *S*

The Alfa Romeo Montreal was developed from a Bertone styling exercise first displayed at the 1967 Expo 67 Montreal World Fair. The 2+2 featured a practical hatchback and slotted covers shading the quadruple headlamps and in much the same form was the basis of the production model launched in 1971, the Montreal, which remained Alfa's flagship model until 1975.

1973 Alfa Romeo 2000 Spider,
4 cylinder, 1998cc engine, left hand drive, fuel injection, good all-round condition.
£5,500-6,500 *ADT*

1972 Alfa Romeo 1600 GT Junior 2 Door Coupé,
coachwork by Carrozzeria Bertone, engine rebuilt, excellent condition.
£7,200-7,700 *BKS*

1973 Alfa Romeo Junior Zagato 1.6 Litre 2 Door Sports Coupé, resprayed, good condition throughout, average interior. **£6,500-7,000** *BKS*

1971 Alfa Romeo Montreal 3 litre Sports Coupé, left hand drive, original specification. **Est. £7,000-10,000** *S*

1975 Alfa Romeo 2000 GT Veloce Sports Coupé, twin overhead camshaft engine, twin side draught carburettors, Auto Delta high lift cams, 5 speed gearbox, paintwork good, mechanically very good. **£3,000-3,500** *S*

Introduced originally in 1968, the 1750 series replaced Alfa Romeo's 1600 series, and in GT Veloce guise was first offered with a 1779cc engine. This was later uprated to 1962cc as the 2000 and is considered to be the best of the GTVs.

1975 Alfa Romeo 2000 Veloce Spider, right hand drive, major restoration, repainted, gearbox rebuilt, very good overall condition. **£7,000-7,500** *S*

ALFA ROMEO Model	ENGINE cc/cyl	DATES	CONDITION 1	2	3
2000 Spider	1974/4	1958-61	£14,000	£9,000	£4,000
2600 Sprint	2584/6	1962-66	£11,000	£7,500	£4,000
2600 Spider	2584/6	1962-65	£14,000	£12,000	£8,000
Giulietta Sprint	1290/4	1955-62	£10,000	£7,000	£4,000
Giulietta Spider	1290/4	1956-62	£9,000	£5,000	£3,500
Giulia Saloon	1570/4	1962-72	£3,500	£2,000	£300
Giulia Sprint (rhd)	1570/4	1962-68	£10,500	£6,000	£2,000
Giulia Spider (rhd)	1570/4	1962-65	£9,500	£7,000	£2,500
Giulia SS	1570/4	1962-66	£15,000	£13,000	£10,000
GT 1300 Junior	1290/4	1966-72	£7,000	£5,500	£4,000
1300GT Junior	1290/4	1973-75	£4,000	£2,000	£750
Giulia Sprint GT (105)	1570/4	1962-68	£7,500	£5,000	£3,000
1600GT Junior	1570/4	1972-75	£7,000	£4,000	£1,400
1750/2000 Berlina	1779/ 1962/4	1967-77	£2,750	£1,700	£1,000
1750GTV	1779/4	1967-72	£8,250	£6,500	£2,500
2000GTV	1962/4	1971-77	£8,000	£6,500	£2,500
1600/1750 (Duetto)	1570/ 1779/4	1966-67	£8,500	£8,000	£5,500
1750/2000 Spider (Kamm)	1779/ 1962/4	1967-78	£8,000	£6,000	£3,000
Montreal	2593/8	1970-77	£10,000	£8,000	£5,000
Junior Zagato 1290	1290/4	1968-74	£11,000	£10,000	£5,000
Junior Zagato 1600	1570/4	1968-74	£13,000	£11,000	£6,000
Alfetta GT/GTV (chrome)	1962/4	1974-84	£2,500	£1,500	£350
Alfasud	1186/ 1490/4	1972-83	£1,500	£600	£250
Alfasud ti	1186/ 1490/4	1974-81	£2,500	£1,000	£500
Alfasud Sprint	1284/ 1490/4	1976-85	£3,000	£2,000	£500
GTV6	2492/6	1981-	£3,500	£2,000	£500

1973 Alfa Romeo Montreal,
8 cylinder, 2593cc engine,
bodyshell in excellent order,
interior in good condition.
£9,500-10,500 *ADT*

**1981 Alfa Romeo Alfetta GTV
2000 Coupé,** mechanically good,
upholstery average.
Est. £1,500-1,800 *S*

1976 Alfa Romeo Spider,
4 cylinder, 1962cc engine, good
restored condition.
Est. £8,400-9,400 *ADT*

**1981 Alfa Romeo 2000 2.0 Litre
Spider Veloce 2 Seater Sports
Convertible,** coachwork by
Pininfarina, left hand drive,
chrome wire wheels, very good
overall condition.
£9,000-9,500 *BKS*

ALLARD

Allard made its début as a car manufacturer
in 1937, despite the fact that Sydney Allard
had been engaged in trials since 1930, using
modified Ford V8 engines. Twelve more
Allard Specials were built before the war,
ranging from trials specials to four seater
sports tourers. Production continued to
thrive until 1948 when Jaguar presented its
XK120 which stole the show from Allard's.

**1950 Allard J2 Sports Racing
Car. £36,000-38,000** *FHF*

**1949 Allard M-Type Drophead
Coupé,** Ford V8, 3622cc engine,
85bhp at 3800rpm, 3 speed
manual gearbox with column
change, 4 wheel hydraulic drum
brakes, independent front
suspension, swinging half axle
type with transverse leaf spring,
rear transverse leaf spring, right
hand drive, complete restoration
of the bodywork and frame,
interior original, good overall
condition.
£10,000-12,000 *CGB*

CROSS REFERENCE
Racing Cars ⟶ p301

ALLARD Model	ENGINE cc/cyl	DATES	CONDITION 1	2	3
K/K2/L/M/M2X	3622/8	1947-54	£17,000	£9,000	£5,500
K3	var/8	1953-54	£22,000	£13,000	£10,000
P1	3622/8	1949-52	£16,000	£10,000	£5,500
P2	3622/8	1952-54	£22,000	£18,000	£11,000
J2/J2X	var/8	1950-54	£70,000	£60,000	£45,000
Palm Beach	1508/4, 2262/6	1952-55	£10,000	£7,500	£4,500
Palm Beach II	2252/ 3442/6	1956-60	£22,500	£18,000	£11,000

1954 Allard K3, original Cadillac V8 engine, 331cu in, 300bhp at 6000rpm, 3 speed automatic gearbox, 4 wheel hydraulic drum brakes, independent front suspension with coil springs, swinging half axles, radius arms and hydraulic shock absorbers, rear transverse leaf springs with rigid axle, hydraulic shock absorbers, left hand drive, very low mileage, excellent original paint and interior.
Est. £27,000-34,000 *CNY*

ALVIS

Alvis started production in Coventry in 1920 with the side valve 1.5 litre 4 cylinder 10/30. The year 1923 heralded the launch of the 12/50, with a 1496cc sports and a 1598cc touring model. Sales of the sports car soared after it won the Brooklands 200 mile race. The 12/50, along with the 10/30 and other models, such as the TF21 (1966), earned Alvis the reputation of handsome, well-made vehicles.

Although Rover took controlling interest in 1965, Alvis still produce a range of armoured fighting vehicles.

1931 Alvis 12/50 TJ, 2 seater, fully restored.
£22,000-23,000 *Mot*

- **The Alvis Firebird, introduced in 1934, had a 1842cc 4 cylinder engine and an all-synchromesh Borg and Beck clutch.**
- **The Alvis Silver Eagle, announced in 1929, was a 6 cylinder version of the Alvis Firebird with a similar range of 3 body styles - saloon, drophead coupé and sports.**
- **The Alvis Crested Eagle of 1933 was the first British car to carry independent front suspension.**

1934 Alvis Firebird, 14hp, 4 door saloon, preserved to original specification.
£6,000-6,500 *S*

1934 Alvis Silver Eagle, 3 Position Drophead Coupé, 6 cylinders, 2511cc, coachwork by Cross and Ellis, very good restored condition throughout.
£12,000-13,000 *ADT*

ALVIS Model	ENGINE cc/cyl	DATES	CONDITION 1	2	3
12/50	1496/4	1923-32	£14,000	£9,000	£6,000
Silver Eagle	2148	1929-37	£14,000	£10,000	£8,000
Silver Eagle DHC	2148	1929-37	£16,000	£11,000	£8,000
12/60	1645/4	1931-32	£15,000	£10,000	£7,000
Speed 20 (tourer)	2511/6	1932-36	£35,000	£28,000	£18,000
Speed 20 (closed)	2511/6	1932-36	£22,000	£15,000	£11,000
Crested Eagle	3571/6	1933-39	£10,000	£7,000	£4,000
Firefly (tourer)	1496/4	1932-34	£12,000	£10,000	£6,000
Firefly (closed)	1496/6	1932-34	£7,000	£5,000	£4,000
Firebird (tourer)	1842/4	1934-39	£13,000	£10,000	£6,000
Firebird (closed)	1842/4	1934-39	£7,000	£5,000	£4,000
Speed 25 (tourer)	3571/6	1936-40	£38,500	£30,000	£20,000
Speed 25 (closed)	3571/6	1936-40	£20,000	£15,000	£12,000
3.5 litre	3571/6	1935-36	£35,000	£25,000	£18,000
4.3 litre	4387/6	1936-40	£44,000	£30,000	£22,000
Silver Crest	2362/6	1936-40	£14,000	£10,000	£7,000
TA	3571/6	1936-39	£18,000	£12,000	£8,000
12/70	1842/4	1937-40	£15,000	£10,000	£7,000

1939 Alvis 12/70 Sports Saloon,
4 cylinders, 1842cc,
0-60mph acceleration in 26.7
seconds, 26mpg, original brown
leather upholstery.
£10,500-11,000 *S*

*Alvis, who had previously used
Cross and Ellis and Charlesworth
for much of their post-1930
coachwork, entrusted the
coachwork for the 12/70 to
Arthur Mulliner. Being a later
model this example has the spare
wheel set into the boot lid giving
additional space.*

1946 Alvis TA 14 Shooting Brake, good overall
condition.   **Est. £4,000-5,000** *LF*

**1952 Alvis TA21 3 Position
Drophead Coupé,** coachwork by
Tickford, 6 cylinders, overhead
valve, 2993cc, 90bhp at 4000rpm,
4 speed manual gearbox,
synchromesh on top 3 gears,
drum brakes all round,
independent front suspension,
rear semi-elliptic leaf springs,
right hand drive, good condition
throughout, interior needs some
attention.
£9,000-9,500 *C*

**1952 Alvis TA21 Tickford
Drophead Coupé,** 6 cylinders, 3
litre, fully restored condition
throughout.
£19,500-20,500 *Mot*

1961 Alvis TD21, automatic
transmission, aluminium bodied,
bare metal respray, interior
restored.
£8,250-8,750 *Bro*

**1954 Alvis TC21/100 'Grey
Lady' Saloon,** 6 cylinders,
2993cc, very good restored
condition overall.
£5,000-7,000 *ADT*

1960 Alvis TD21 2 Door Saloon,
right hand drive, resprayed and
fair overall condition.
£5,400-5,800 *C*

*The last all-new Alvis was the
3 litre, launched at the Geneva
Salon in 1950, which remained in
production until 1967, 2 years
after Rover acquired the Alvis
company.*

1961 Alvis TD21 Drophead Coupé, coachwork by Park Ward, 6 cylinders, 2993cc, excellent panelwork, original leather seats, carpeting and door trim, standard centre lock wire wheels. **£18,000-20,000** *ADT*

1961 3 Litre Alvis TD21 2 Door Saloon, coachwork by Graber/Park Ward, rebuilt automatic gearbox, bare metal respray, original leather trim. **£7,500-8,000** *BKS*

1966 Alvis TE21, coachwork by Graber/Park Ward, 6 cylinders, 2993cc, good original condition. **£8,500-9,000** *COYS*

ALVIS Model	ENGINE cc/cyl	DATES	CONDITION 1	2	3
TA14	1892/4	1946-50	£9,000	£7,000	£3,000
TA14 DHC	1892/4	1946-50	£14,000	£12,000	£5,000
TB14 Roadster	1892/4	1949-50	£14,000	£9,000	£7,000
TB21 Roadster	2993/6	1951	£15,000	£9,000	£6,000
TA21/TC21	2993/6	1950-55	£15,500	£9,500	£4,000
TA21/TC21 DHC	2993/6	1950-55	£18,000	£15,000	£11,500
TC21/100 Grey Lady	2993/6	1953-56	£16,000	£11,000	£4,500
TC21/100 DHC	2993/6	1954-56	£24,000	£20,000	£14,000
TD21	2993/6	1956-62	£15,000	£12,000	£7,000
TD21 DHC	2993/6	1956-62	£24,000	£20,000	£12,000
TE21	2993/6	1963-67	£18,000	£15,000	£12,000
TE21 DHC	2993/6	1963-67	£28,000	£23,000	£15,000
TF21	2993/6	1966-67	£16,000	£12,000	£9,500
TF21 DHC	2993/6	1966-67	£28,000	£18,000	£12,000

AMERICAN LAFRANCE

1914 American LaFrance Speedster, open sports coachwork, 6 cylinders, 17900cc, good condition and full running order. **£5,500-6,000** *COYS*

Founded in 1903 in New York, the American LaFrance Fire Engine Company initially experimented with both petrol and steam engines. A 6 cylinder engine had been fitted to the Type 19 fire appliance truck with 130bhp. To generate publicity for the new model 22 examples were stripped to the chassis and rebodied with speedster coachwork. The 17.9 litre engine, with single Schebler carburettor and magneto/coil ignition was fitted with 3 speed manual transmission with twin chain drive to the rear axle. Like the original 22 Speedsters it started life as a Type 19 ladder truck, subsequently being similarly converted.

AMILCAR

The creation of Amilcar in 1921 was due mainly to the collapse of Le Zèbre. One of the technicians of Borie and Co., which manufactured the Le Zèbre, with a friend, combined efforts to produce a car small enough to invoke French tax advantages for lightweight vehicles. The first car, a 903cc 4 cylinder, with solid rear axle, became popular and won several races. By 1925 Amilcar was producing 3,700 cars annually.

1924 Amilcar C4 Petit Sport 3 Seater, older restoration to good all round condition.
Est. £12,000-15,000   *BS*
The early Type CC of 1921 had a 903cc engine, was developed to 970cc for the CS of 1922 and the C4 had an engine of 58 x 95mm, 1004cc.

1922 Amilcar 5hp Type 4C 3 Seater Skiff, coachwork attributed to Carrosserie Labourdette, good original condition.
Est. £20,000-30,000   *BKS(M)*

> **Did you know?**
> **MILLER'S Collectors Cars Price Guide** *builds up year-by-year to form the most comprehensive photo library system available.*

AMPHICAR

The Amphicar was the only true amphibian vehicle manufactured for private use and sold worldwide. In 1961 Deutsche Industrie-Werke in Lübeck-Schlutup was set up to mass-produce the Amphicar, with production being transferred to Wuppertal-Elberfield, Berlin, where it remained until 1968.

1967 Amphicar 1.4 Litre Amphibious Touring Car, 4 cylinder Triumph unit mounted in the rear and driving to the rear wheels for land use, 1147cc, 2 water screw propellers for marine propulsion, being driven by specially tailored gearing when afloat.
Est. £4,000-7,000   *BKS(M)*

ARIES

The Société Anonyme Ariès of Courbevoie on the Seine were manufacturers in France from 1903 until 1938, displaying their first car at the Paris Salon in 1903. This had twin cylinders, but 4 cylinder cars were also offered by 1905, powered by Aster engines. In 1907, 2 models - the 18/22 and the 14/18 - were listed, both with 4 cylinder engines.

c1907 Aries 4½ Litre 5 Seater Open Touring Car, body in fair to good condition, upholstery good, wooden wheels, 140in wheelbase, good running order.
Est. £20,000-25,000   *S*
A rare car, the Veteran Car Club listing no other Aries of this model. Aries cars do not appear to have been imported into the UK at any time until 1925, when Taylor's Motor Mart of Surbiton were appointed agents.

> **Locate the source**
> *The source of each illustration in Miller's can be found by checking the code letters below each caption with the list of contributors.*

ARMSTRONG-SIDDELEY

Armstrong-Siddeley produced their first car, a 30hp 6 cylinder model, in 1919, quickly followed by a 2.3 litre 18hp in 1922, and a 1.8 litre 4 cylinder 14hp in 1924. In 1933, the company entered the Rolls-Royce and Daimler market with the Siddeley Special. Despite producing further high quality cars they effectively priced themselves out of the market.

1931 Armstrong-Siddeley Tickford Cabriolet.
£12,000-17,000 *FHF*

1948 Armstrong-Siddeley Hurricane, 6 cylinders, 1990cc, excellent original all-round condition.
Est. £7,000-8,000 *ADT*

1947 Armstrong-Siddeley Hurricane Drophead Coupé, only 2 owners from new, good overall condition.
£10,000-11,000 *S*

The Hurricane featured a 6 cylinder overhead valve engine of 2309cc, rated at 18hp, and had synchromesh on 2nd, 3rd and top gears. The drophead coupé had 2 doors, comfortable seating for 4/5 passengers and a 3 position hood which can be furled to give a coupé de ville effect.

ARMSTRONG-SIDDELEY Model	ENGINE cc/cyl	DATES	CONDITION 1	2	3
Hurricane	1991/6	1945-53	£10,000	£5,500	£2,500
Typhoon	1991/6	1946-50	£7,000	£3,000	£1,500
Lancaster/Whitley	1991/ 2306/6	1945-53	£6,000	£3,500	£1,250
Sapphire 234/236	2290/4 2309/6	1955-58	£5,000	£3,500	£1,500
Sapphire 346	3440/6	1953-58	£7,500	£5,000	£2,000
Star Sapphire	3990/6	1958-60	£8,000	£5,500	£2,500

ASTER

1903 Aster, single cylinder.
£16,000-17,000 *DB*

ASTON MARTIN

Aston Martin found popularity on the racing circuit, with works cars achieving successes such as the Rudge Whitworth Cup in the 1928 Le Mans race. 1959 saw the introduction of the 3.7 litre DB4 and the end of the Atom chassis and Bentley designed engine. The 4 litre DB5, DB6 and DBS followed, and a 5.3 litre V8 engine with DBS body was produced in 1969.

However, the company went into insolvency in 1974, but was rescued 6 months later, after which the Vantage and Volante were launched, followed in 1976 by a new Lagonda 4 door saloon. In 1987 Ford took control of the company.

1937 Aston Martin 15/98 2 litre Bertelli Two-Seater Tourer.
£32,000-35,000 *S*

1934 Aston Martin 1.5 litre Mk II, to Ulster specification, coachwork by Morntane Engineering, excellent all-round restored condition.
Est. £45,000-55,000 *BKS*

This car started life as a long-chassis 4-seater tourer but was converted to its present Ulster Replica form in 1986-87.

ASTON MARTIN Model	ENGINE cc/cyl	DATES	CONDITION		
			1	2	3
Lionel Martin Cars	1486/4	1921-25	£26,000	£18,000	£16,000
International	1486/4	1927-32	£28,000	£18,000	£16,000
Le Mans	1486/4	1932-33	£52,000	£38,000	£32,000
Mk II	1486/4	1934-36	£40,000	£30,000	£25,000
Ulster	1486/4	1934-36	£65,000	£50,000	-
2 litre	1950/4	1936-40	£18,000	£14,000	£9,000

Value is dependent upon racing history, originality and completeness. Add 40% if a competition winner.

1950 Aston Martin DB2 Drophead Coupé, 6 cylinder in line, overhead camshaft, 2,580cc, 105bhp at 5000rpm, David Brown 4 speed manual gearbox, 4 wheel drum brakes, front suspension coil springs and trailing arms, rear coil springs and parallel arms with Panhard rod, right hand drive, recent ground-up restoration, excellent overall condition.
£50,000-55,000 *CNY*

1954 Aston Martin DB2/4 Mk I Drophead Coupé.
£47,000-48,000 *BGI*

1958 Aston Martin DB Mk III, total restoration, engine and gearbox overhaul, fitted with optional overdrive from new, excellent overall condition.
£26,000-27,000 *COYS*

1958 Aston Martin DB Mk III,
regularly maintained, new tyres
and a stainless steel exhaust, good
condition.
£14,500-15,500 *COYS*

- **Aston Martin has suffered more than almost any other car company during the recent price slump.**
- **Many bargains are still available and the rarer models, e.g. DB5 Convertible, still retain their value.**
- **Aston Martins can be expensive to maintain, but spares are readily available from specialist dealers.**

1959 Aston Martin DB4 Series I Sports Saloon, coachwork by Touring of Milan, 6 cylinders, 3670cc, good condition.
£21,000-23,000 *COYS*

1959 Aston Martin DB Mk III Drophead Coupé, 6 cylinders, 2922cc, complete restoration.
£31,000-33,000 *COYS*

This is one of just 47 DB Mk IIIs to have been fitted from new with the Special Series engine. However, this has been fitted with a DB2 cylinder head and twin rather than triple SU carburettors.

1960 Aston Martin DB4 Sports Coupé, older restoration, further work includes retrimming, repainting and rechroming, wire spoked wheels repainted.
£26,000-28,000 *S*

1960 Aston Martin 3.7 litre DB4 Series II Superleggera Saloon, original trim, good condition throughout, although the paintwork needs attention. **£16,500-17,500** *BKS*

1961 Aston Martin DB4 Series IV Coupé, coachwork by Touring of Milan, 6 cylinders, 3670cc, good original condition.
£16,000-17,000 *COYS*

1963 Aston Martin DB5 Sports Coupé, 6 cylinders, 3995cc, 282bhp at 5500rpm, 4 speed manual gearbox with overdrive, 4 wheel servo disc brakes, front suspension independent coil, rear coil, left hand drive, excellent condition throughout.
Est. £22,000-28,000 *C*

1961 Aston Martin DB4 Series II, rebuilt original engine.
Est. £20,000-25,000 *COYS*

1964 Aston Martin DB5 Superleggera Saloon, excellent condition throughout.
£30,000-32,000 *S*

DB5s were broadly similar in appearance to their DB4 predecessor with aluminium coachwork constructed under Touring Superleggera licence, but had enlarged engines that developed 282bhp in standard form.

1962 Aston Martin DB4 Series IV Convertible, no major restoration, but properly maintained, 47,000 miles.
Est. £20,000-25,000 *S*

From a total production of 1,113 DB4 cars only 70 were convertibles, making this model one of the rarest Aston Martins.

1963 Aston Martin DB4 Convertible Series V, 6 cylinder in line engine, twin overhead camshaft, 3670cc, 240bhp at 5500rpm, 4 speed manual gearbox, 4 wheel disc brakes, all coil spring suspension independent at front, right hand drive, period radio, fully illustrated history file documenting the restoration, superb restored condition.
£72,000-75,000 *C*

1965 Aston Martin DB5 Convertible, coachwork by Touring, 6 cylinders, 3995cc, fully restored, excellent condition throughout.
£92,000-95,000 *COYS*

1967 Aston Martin 4 litre DB6 Mark I 2 Door Grand Touring Coupé, very good overall condition. **£25,000-26,000** *RKS*

1969 Aston Martin DB6 Mk I Sports Coupé, coachwork by Touring, 6 cylinders, 3995cc, fitted with optional automatic transmission, good condition. **£16,000-17,000** *COYS*

1967 Aston Martin DB6 Vantage, left hand drive. **£31,000-33,000** *DJR*

1969 Aston Martin DB6 Volante, very good, totally original condition. **£35,000-37,000** *COYS*

1969 Aston Martin DBS Coupé, 6 cylinders, 3995cc, resprayed, engine completely rebuilt, in good condition. **£8,250-8,750** *COYS*

Designed by William Towns, this elegant aluminium-bodied coupé employed a widened version of the DB6 floorpan using steel pressings for the body frame rather than the lightweight steel tubing of previous Touring styled models. The rear was also new with an independent coil sprung de Dion tube rear axle, complete with limited slip differential and in-board disc brakes, located by radius arms and Watt linkage; at the front the coil spring/wishbone set-up and discs were as the DB6.

1969 Aston Martin DB6 Sports Coupé, 6 cylinders, 3995cc, twin overhead camshafts, 325bhp at 5750rpm, Borg Warner automatic gearbox, 4 wheel servo disc brakes, coil spring independent front suspension, right hand drive, original car requiring some cosmetic attention. **£18,000-19,000** *C*

1970 Aston Martin 4 litre DB6 Mk II Vantage 2 Door Grand Touring Saloon, 2 owners from new, 22,000 recorded mileage, resprayed, excellent condition. Est. £30,000-40,000 *BKS*

> ### Make the most of Miller's
> *Condition is absolutely vital when assessing the value of a vehicle. Top class vehicles on the whole appreciate much more than less perfect examples. However a rare, desirable car may command a high price even when in need of restoration.*

1970 Aston Martin DBS, 6 cylinders, 3995cc, good useable condition. £10,500-11,500 *ADT*

1971 Aston Martin DBS V8, 8 cylinders, 5340cc, fuel injection with automatic transmission, good overall condition. £6,500-7,500 *ADT*

1970 Aston Martin DB6 Coupé, 6 cylinders, 3995cc, total body restoration by GTC, mechanical restoration by Aston Martin, with service history. £25,000-26,000 *COYS*

1972 Aston Martin AM Vantage, 6 cylinders, 3995cc, very good condition. £9,750-10,750 *ADT*

Only 70 or so 6 cylinder AM Vantages were built and modifications over the standard DBS included a dished, leather covered steering wheel and specific gear ratios in the manual 5 speed box.

1974 Aston Martin V8 Series III Coupé, 5340cc, converted to V8 Vantage Series I, total restoration, condition as new.
£21,000-23,000 *COYS*

After David Brown sold Aston Martin in February 1972 the DBS V8 was replaced by the Series II model, now simply called the Aston Martin V8. In August 1973 the Series III arrived with quadruple Weber carburettors, larger bonnet bulge, improved seats and central locking; power rose to 304bhp in June 1977. Later that year the V8 Vantage was launched, boasting special camshafts, larger valves and Weber IDA carburettors; with 380bhp at 6000rpm it provided 0-60 and 0-100mph in 5.3 and 12.7 seconds respectively, and a 170mph maximum.

1976 Aston Martin V8 Coupé, 5 speed gearbox.
£18,000-20,000 *HWA*

1973 Aston Martin AM Vantage, 6 cylinders, 3995cc, very good overall condition.
£13,500-14,500 *ADT*

Did you know?
MILLER'S Collectors Cars Price Guide *builds up year-by-year to form the most comprehensive photo library system available.*

1977 Aston Martin V8 Saloon, 8 cylinders, 5340cc, good condition, although some attention required.
£9,500-10,500 *ADT*

1978 Aston Martin V8 Saloon, 8 cylinders, 5340cc.
£13,000-14,000 *ADT*

1979 Aston Martin Volante.
£34,000-36,000 *BGI*

1979 Aston Martin V8, with Vantage front air dam and driving lights.
£28,000-30,000 *BGI*

Miller's is a price Guide not a price List

The price ranges given reflect the average price a purchaser should pay for a similar vehicle. Condition, rarity, provenance, racing history, originality and any restoration are factors that must be taken into account when assessing values. When buying or selling, it must always be remembered that prices can be greatly affected by the condition of any vehicle. Unless otherwise stated, all cars shown in Miller's are of good merchantable quality, and the valuations given reflect this fact. Vehicles offered for sale in exceptionally fine condition or in poor condition may reasonably be expected to be priced considerably higher or lower respectively than the estimates given herein.

1981 Aston Martin V8 Vantage, 3 owners.
£30,000-32,000 *DJR*

1986 Aston Martin Volante Convertible, 3,160 miles.
£63,000-66,000 *HWA*

1983 Aston Martin Lagonda, 28,000 miles, left hand drive, excellent condition throughout.
£25,000-30,000 *HWA*

1983 Aston Martin Lagonda, 14,880 miles, excellent condition throughout.
£20,000-25,000 *HWA*

1983 Aston Martin Lagonda V8 Sports Saloon, very good condition throughout.
£19,000-20,000 *S*

1990 Aston Martin Zagato Volante, one of only 25 made, 1,500 miles, full service history.
£120,000-130,000 *DJR*

ASTON MARTIN Model	ENGINE cc/cyl	DATES	CONDITION		
			1	2	3
DB1	1970/4	1948-50	£15,000	£13,000	£9,500
DB2	2580/6	1950-53	£19,000	£14,000	£10,000
DB2 Conv	2580/6	1951-53	£28,000	£18,000	£14,000
DB2/4 Mk I/II	2580/2922/6	1953-57	£17,000	£13,000	£10,000
DB2/4 Mk II Conv	2580/2922/6	1953-57	£28,000	£14,000	£11,000
DB2/4 Mk III	2580/2922/6	1957-59	£16,000	£12,000	£11,000
DB2/4 Mk III Conv	2580/2922/6	1957-59	£30,000	£17,000	£15,000
DB Mk III	2922/6	1957-59	£33,000	£24,000	£17,500
DB Mk III Conv	2922/6	1957-59	£30,000	£19,000	£16,000
DB4	3670/6	1959-63	£22,000	£16,000	£12,000
DB4 Conv	3670/6	1961-63	£45,000	£30,000	-
DB4 GT	3670/6	1961-63	£75,000	£70,000	-
DB5	3995/6	1964-65	£32,000	£25,000	£18,000
DB5 Conv	3995/6	1964-65	£42,000	£30,000	-
DB6	3995/6	1965-69	£22,000	£17,000	£9,000
DB6 Mk I auto	3995/6	1965-69	£18,000	£13,000	£8,000
DB6 Mk I Volante	3995/6	1965-71	£35,000	£28,000	£22,000
DB6 Mk II Volante	3995/6	1969-70	£36,000	£30,000	£24,000
DBS	3995/6	1967-72	£11,000	£9,000	£6,500
AM Vantage	3995/6	1972-73	£14,000	£10,000	£7,000

ATCO

c1935 Atco Junior Trainer 98cc 2 Seater, original overall condition, finished in 'lawn mower' green, in working order.
£3,750-4,000 *S*

Adopting the 98cc Villiers petrol engine, the Trainer boasted a top speed of 10mph and was equipped with one forward gear and reverse. Final drive to the rear wheels was by chain.

AUBURN

Auburn commenced production of motor vehicles in 1903. Cord took over Auburn in 1924 with a range of cars designed by J.M. Crawford. He produced some wonderful vehicles which represented the best of American design.

ATLANTA

Atlanta Motors, based in Staines, Middlesex, began producing cars in 1937. Using a tubular steel chassis, they featured independent torsion bar front suspension while employing coil springs. The rear suspension was also independent, making the Atlanta the only so-equipped British car available pre-war.

c1929 Auburn 6-80 5 Passenger Tourer, left hand drive, re-upholstered interior.
£8,000-10,000 *S*

1939 Atlanta V12 Roadster, 4279cc, extensively restored and in excellent condition.
£42,000-44,000 *COYS*

AUDI

1931 Auburn Model 8-98A 2 Door 4 Seater Coupé, very good condition throughout.
Est. £14,000-20,000 *S*

Miller's is a price GUIDE not a price LIST.

1939 Audi 225 Sports Cabriolet, coachwork by Glaser of Dresden, little used since restoration, museum stored. **£58,000-62,000** *S*

1935 Auburn 851 Supercharged Speedster, totally original, restored, rare right hand drive.
£125,000-140,000 *BC*

1985 Audi Quattro Turbo-charged 2 Litre 2 door Sports Coupé, 4 wheel drive, outstanding condition, full service history.
Est. £30,000-40,000 *BKS*

AUSTIN

The Austin Motor Company was founded in 1905 by a former Wolseley employee, Herbert Austin. Production increased dramatically at their Longbridge, Birmingham, factory during WWI and continued with a range of reliable, rugged, but somewhat uninteresting motor cars. The introduction of the ubiquitous Austin 7 in the 1920s was probably one of the most significant events in the history of the motor car.

By 1952 Austin, together with Morris, had formed part of the British Motor Corporation, making it the fourth largest motor manufacturer in the world. BMC merged with Leyland, which already controlled Triumph, Rover and Alvis, to form British Leyland in 1968. By 1982 it had become the Austin Rover Group Ltd.

1928 Austin 7, coachwork by Mulliner of Birmingham, 4 cylinders, 747cc, exceptionally well restored, wooden body frame has been serviced and re-skinned in red leatherette.
£6,000-6,500 *ADT*

1910 Austin 18/24hp Cabriolet, 4 cylinders, 4400cc, side valve, water-cooled separate cylinders, 3 speed manual gearbox, rear wheel brakes only, front suspension, semi-elliptic leaf springs, rear fully elliptic leaf springs, right hand drive, good condition throughout. **Est. £30,000-40,000** *C*

1928 Austin 12/4 Golfer's Roadster, coachwork by Mulliner of Birmingham, with trap door for golf bags on side of body.
£18,000-19,000 *FHF*

The Austin 12 appeared in 1922 and was one of the company's most successful pre-war vehicles. They sold for £550.

1929 Austin 7 Chummy, very good condition.
£6,250-6,750 *CC*

1929 Austin 7 Top Hat Saloon, 747cc, above average condition.
£3,700-4,000 *BKS*

1929 Austin 7 Chummy.
£3,800-4,200 *DB*

1929 Austin 7 Chummy Tourer, 4 cylinders, 747.5cc, side valve, 10.5bhp at 2400rpm, 3 speed manual gear box, drum brakes all-round, front transverse leaf springs, rear quarter elliptic leaf springs, right hand drive, very good restored condition. **£6,000-6,500** *C*

**1930 Austin 7 Chummy
4 Seater Tourer,** very good all- round condition.
£6,500-7,000 *DDM*

1931 Austin 7, good condition.
£3,800-4,300 *ECC*

1931 Austin 7 Chummy,
totally rebuilt.
£6,000-7,000 *LF*

The Austin 7 Tourers were known as 'Chummies'. Only about 42,500 were built from 1922 onwards, plus approximately 13,000 bare chassis for special bodies.

1931 Austin 7 Box Saloon,
short wheelbase, very good condition throughout.
£5,750-6,250 *CC*

1931 Austin 7 Saloon,
4 cylinders, 747cc, good working order, interior in need of some restoration.
£2,500-2,700 *ADT*

A rebuilt car is not necessarily of more value than a car in good original condition, even if the restoration has cost thousands of pounds.

1931 Austin 7 Tourer, very good
all-round condition.
£7,250-7,750 *CC*

**1931 Austin 7 Box
De Luxe Saloon.
£4,500-5,500** *FHF*

1931 Austin 7 Chummy,
very good condition.
£5,750-6,250 *CC*

*The Austin 'Big 7' range,
introduced in 1937, was so called
simply because it had a larger
engine than the Austin 7.*

1932 Austin 7 'RN' Saloon,
fitted with engine and gearbox
from a later Austin 7, good
restored condition.
Est. £3,500-4,500 *ADT*

1934 Austin 7 Box Saloon,
good condition throughout.
£4,200-4,500 *S*

1933 Austin 7 2 Door Saloon,
747cc, with optional sunshine
roof and original equipment spare
wheel, excellent condition.
£5,250-6,000 *BKS*

1934 Austin 7 Box Saloon,
good condition throughout.
Est. £3,000-4,000 *S*

*The long running Austin 7 made
its debut in 1922, the product of
18 year old draughtsman Stanley
Edge, and reputedly designed by
him in the billiard room at
Austin's home, Lickey Grange.
By 1934 the Austin 7 had grown
in size and reputation and the
slightly larger 81in wheelbase
made the Box Saloon a spacious
family car at a price of only £125.*

AUSTIN Model	ENGINE cc/cyl	DATES	CONDITION 1	2	3
25/30	4900/4	1906	£35,000	£25,000	£20,000
20	3600/4	1919-27	£18,000	£12,000	£6,000
12	1661/4	1922-26	£8,000	£5,000	£2,000
7	747/4	1924-39	£8,000	£4,000	£1,500
7 Coachbuilt	747/4	1924-39	£12,000	£9,000	£7,000
12/4	1861/4	1927-35	£5,500	£4,000	£2,000
16	2249/6	1928-36	£9,000	£7,000	£4,000
20/6	3400/6	1928-38	£12,500	£10,000	£8,000
12/6	1496/6	1932-37	£6,000	£4,000	£1,500
12/4	1535/4	1933-39	£5,000	£3,500	£1,500
10 and 10/4	1125/4	1932-47	£4,000	£3,000	£1,000
10 and 10/4 Conv	1125/4	1933-47	£5,000	£3,500	£1,000
18	2510/6	1934-39	£8,000	£5,000	£3,000
14	1711/6	1937-39	£6,000	£4,000	£2,000
Big Seven	900/4	1938-39	£4,000	£2,500	£1,500
8	900/4	1939-47	£3,000	£2,000	£1,000
28	4016/6	1939	£6,000	£4,000	£2,000

1934 Austin 7 Saloon, long wheelbase, excellent condition, fully restored. **Est. £5,000-6,000** *ADT*

1934 Austin 7 Box Saloon, excellent condition. **£4,500-5,000** *ECC*

1937 Austin 7 Opal 2 Seater Tourer, excellent condition. **£4,750-5,250** *CC*

1934 Austin 7 Box Saloon, 747cc, 4 speed gearbox, older restoration, reconditioned mechanics. **£4,250-4,700** *Mot*

1935 Austin 7 Opal 2 Seater Tourer, fully restored condition. **£5,250-5,750** *ADT*

1936 Austin 7 Opal 2 Seater Tourer, older restoration, excellent condition. **£6,000-6,500** *S*

1935 Austin 7 Ruby Saloon,
original specification.
£2,500-2,750 *S*

**1936 Austin Ruby
7.5hp Saloon.**
£2,800-3,200 *Cum*

**1936 Austin 7 Fixed Roof
Saloon,** excellent restored
condition.
£6,750-7,500 *ADT*

1937 Austin 7 Ruby Saloon,
good all-round condition.
£4,800-5,200 *HOLL*

1937 Austin 7 Ruby Saloon,
slight exterior cosmetic work
required, overall good condition.
£2,400-2,800 *HOLL*

1937 Austin 7 Ruby Saloon,
very good all-round condition.
£3,800-4,300 *CC*

1937 Austin 7 Ruby Saloon,
good overall condition.
£2,400-2,800 *CC*

1931 Austin 10/4 4 Door Saloon.
£4,200-4,600 *Bro*

1938 Austin 7 Ruby,
66,700 miles, very good
condition throughout.
£6,200-6,600 *ADT*

CROSS REFERENCE
Replica Vehicles ➔ p303

**1926 Austin 7 Brooklands
Super Sports Replica,** restored
in 1974, excellent condition.
£8,250-8,750 *ADT*

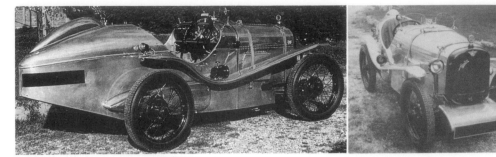

**1926 Austin 7 Brooklands
Super Sports,** replica coachwork
by Gordon England, very good
condition, full documentation.
£13,000-14,000 *S*

1933 Austin 10/4 Saloon,
excellent condition throughout.
£4,250-4,750 *CC*

1935 Austin 10/4 Tourer,
good condition.
£5,250-5,750 *CC*

1922 Austin 12/4 Clifton,
very good condition.
£16,500-17,500 *CC*

**1935 Austin 10 Lichfield
Saloon,** 4 cylinders, 1296cc.
£3,250-3,750 *ADT*

*The 4 door Lichfield saloon
possessed several innovations for
1935 which included improved
adjustment for the bucket seats,
flush fitting direction indicators,
louvres in the bonnet and
redesigned radiator cowl.*

**1929 Austin 12/4 4 Door
Tourer,** 4 cylinder, side valve,
1861cc engine, 4 speed manual
gearbox, all-round drum brakes,
semi-elliptic suspension, right
hand drive, brass radiator, Lucas
King of the Road lamps, Smith's
instruments, a Tetra fire
extinguisher, Boyce motor meter,
in original condition,
re-upholstered, museum stored.
£10,250-11,250 *C*

1929 Austin 20hp Saloon.
£17,000-19,000 *FHF*

c1925 Austin 12/4 Windsor saloon, in original condition, original upholstery, requires restoration.
£13,000-15,000 *S*

1929 Austin Clifton Heavy 12/4 Tourer, good restored condition.
£13,500-14,500 *Mot*

1933 Austin Light 12/4 Harley, excellent overall condition.
£6,250-6,750 *CC*

1933 Austin 12/4 Berkeley Saloon, excellent condition.
£8,750-9,250 *CC*

1934 Austin Eton, 6 cylinders, 15.9hp, good restored condition.
£8,750-9,250 *Mot*

1931 Austin 16/6 2 Seater, Convertible, plus 2 seater dickey, original car, unrestored.
£9,750-10,000 *Bro*

1947 Austin 10, 1200cc.
£1,000-1,200 *ECC*

1937 Austin 18, excellent overall condition.
£7,250-7,750 *CC*

1948 Austin A40 Devon,
4 cylinders, 1187cc, total respray,
generally good condition.
£2,250-2,750 *ADT*

1952 Austin A40 Convertible,
3 owners from new, requires very
minor cosmetic attention.
£3,750-4,000 *Bro*

> **Miller's is a price GUIDE
> not a price LIST.**

1959 Austin A30, very good
overall condition.
£700-800 *CC*

**1955 Austin Cambridge A50
4 Door Saloon,** good bodywork
and overall sound condition.
£700-900 *DDM*

AUSTIN Model	ENGINE cc/cyl	DATES	CONDITION 1	2	3
16	2199/4	1945-49	£3,000	£2,000	£1,000
A40 Devon	1200/4	1947-52	£1,500	£1,000	£750
A40 Sports	1200/4	1950-53	£6,000	£4,000	£2,000
A40 Somerset	1200/4	1952-54	£2,000	£1,500	£750
A40 Somerset DHC	1200/4	1954	£5,000	£4,000	£2,500
A40 Dorset 2 door	1200/4	1947-48	£2,000	£1,500	£1,000
A70 Hampshire	2199/4	1948-50	£1,750	£1,500	£1,000
A70 Hereford	2199/4	1950-54	£1,850	£1,500	£1,000
A90 Atlantic DHC	2660/4	1949-52	£8,000	£6,000	£3,000
A90 Atlantic	2660/4	1949-52	£5,000	£3,000	£2,000
A40/A50 Cambridge	1200/4	1954-57	£1,200	£750	£500
A55 Mk I Cambridge	1489/4	1957-59	£1,000	£750	£500
A55 Mk II	1489/4	1959-61	£1,000	£750	£500
A60 Cambridge	1622/4	1961-69	£1,000	£750	£500
A90/95 Westminster	2639/6	1954-59	£2,000	£1,500	£750
A99 Westminster	2912/6	1959-61	£1,500	£1,000	£500
A105 Westminster	2639/6	1956-59	£2,000	£1,500	£750
A110 Mk I/II	2912/6	1961-68	£2,000	£1,500	£750
Nash Metropolitan	1489/4	1957-61	£2,500	£1,500	£750
Nash Metropolitan DHC	1489/4	1957-61	£4,000	£3,000	£1,500
A30	803/4	1952-56	£1,000	£500	-
A30 Countryman	803/4	1954-56	£1,500	£1,000	-
A35	948/4	1956-59	£1,000	£500	-
A35 Countryman	948/4	1956-62	£1,500	£1,000	-
A40 Farina Mk I	948/4	1958-62	£1,250	£750	£200
A40 Mk I Countryman	948/4	1959-62	£1,500	£1,000	£400
A40 Farina Mk II	1098/4	1962-67	£1,000	£750	-
A40 Mk II Countryman	1098/4	1962-67	£1,200	£750	£300
1100	1098/4	1963-73	£1,000	£750	-
1300 Mk I/II	1275/4	1967-74	£750	£500	-
1300GT	1275/4	1969-74	£1,250	£1,000	£750
1800/2200		1964-75	£1,500	£900	£600
3 litre	2912/6	1968-71	£3,000	£1,500	£500

1959 Austin A55 Cambridge Saloon, second-hand fully reconditioned engine fitted, in need of further restoration.
£575-650 *S*

The Cambridge adopted the B-Series 4 cylinder 1489cc engine shared by other marques in the BMC range. Although it was priced at less than the contemporary Wolseley, MG and Riley, it nevertheless offered a good quality interior.

CROSS REFERENCE
**Restoration
Projects** ――――→ p305

1959 Austin Cambridge A55 Mk II, right hand drive, manual gearbox.
Est. £1,500-2,000 *LF*

1960 Austin Cambridge Saloon, 4 cylinders, 1622cc, 41,750 miles from new, very good original condition throughout.
£2,500-3,500 *ADT*

1961 Austin A40 2 Door Saloon, styled by Pininfarina, 948cc, 36,704 miles, good condition throughout.
£825-875 *BKS*

Don't forget!
If in doubt please refer to the 'How to Use' section at the beginning of this book.

1965 Austin Princess Vanden Plas, 4 cylinders, 1098cc, good overall condition, resprayed but some cosmetic attention required.
£725-775 *ADT*

1967 Austin A40 Farina Countryman, approximately 35,000 recorded miles, good original condition.
£850-950 *DDM*

1971 Austin 1100, 4 cylinders 1098cc, manual gearbox, original interior, very good condition.
£575-650 *ADT*

1974 Austin Allegro Vanden Plas, 4 cylinders, 1500cc, 42,000 miles, very good unrestored condition throughout.
£625-675 *ADT*

AUSTIN HEALEY

Donald Healey first found fame in the world of motor sport in the early 1920s. He joined Riley in 1933, but moved again to become Technical Director at Triumph in 1937.

During WWII Healey worked for Humber and planned the car he had intended for Triumph. However, in 1945 they rejected his design, and Healey formed the Donald Healey Motor Company in Warwick.

The first Healey was an open 4 seater tourer, followed by the Healey Silverstone of 1949. In 1957 production started on the 948cc 'frog-eye' Austin Healey Sprite sports car, joined in 1961 by the similar MG Midget.

1960 Austin Healey 'Frog-eye' Sprite, rust free Californian car, new paintwork, new interior trim, mechanically good, left hand drive.
£4,750-5,250 *CCTC*

1960 Austin Healey 'Frog-eye' Sprite Mk I, very good original body, repainted, trimmed and mechanically overhauled.
£6,750-7,250 *MSN*

Produced concurrently with the MG Midget with which it shared similar body and mechanical specification. The Healey Sprite was built as an inexpensive 2 seater sportscar to complement the existing 100/6 Healey and MGA. The BMC 'A' series engine was the mainstay of this model.

1966 Austin Healey Sprite, 4 cylinders, 1098cc, complete restoration, very good condition.
£2,800-3,400 *ADT*

1953 Austin Healey 100/4, 4 cylinders, 2660cc, excellent restored condition.
£10,500-11,500 *ADT*

The Austin Healey 100 was built between 1953 and 1955, and more than 10,000 were made.

1954 Austin Healey 100/4 Modified, heavily adapted V8 Moroso engine, left hand drive, much modified body with flared arches, bumpers removed, prepared for competition and sprint/hill climb.
£6,250-6,700 *ADT*

CROSS REFERENCE
Racing Cars ———➤ p301

1955 Austin Healey 100/4 BN1 Sports 2 Seater, 4 speed gearbox, genuine UK car, very good original unrestored condition.
£11,000-12,000 *S*

1954 Austin Healey 100, 3 speed gearbox, fold flat windscreen, engine totally rebuilt, steering and suspension rebuilt, converted from left to right hand drive, bodyshell totally stripped, re-metalled and painted.
£13,000-14,000 *ADT*

1954 Austin Healey 100/4, 4 cylinders, 2660cc, left hand drive, total body restoration including new leather trim, carpets and chrome, finished to concours standards.
£15,000-16,000 *COYS*

Only 50 of the 100S cars were built but subsequent demand for a faster road-going model led to the launch of the 110bph 100M (type BN2) in 1955. Distinguished by a louvred bonnet with transverse leather retaining strap and 2 tone paintwork, the 100M was capable of 118mph and 0-60mph in 10 seconds, while uprated suspension improved handling.

1955 Austin Healey 100M, 4 cylinders, 2660cc, restored, in good condition.
£9,000-10,000 *COYS*

1958 Austin Healey 100/6, original wire wheels and overdrive, left hand drive, good condition.
£9,250-9,750 *CCTC*

1957 Austin Healey 100/6, expertly rebuilt as a rally/race car, since when it has been virtually unused. **£20,000-22,000** *COYS*

In September 1956 the Austin Healey 100/6 was introduced using the 6 cylinder BMC 2638cc engine from the new Austin Westminster, which produced 102bhp at 4600rpm.

1960 Austin Healey 3000 Mk I, wire wheels and overdrive, left hand drive, first class condition throughout. **£19,000-21,000** *MSN*

Only the Mk II 3000 had the competition proven triple SU carburettor set-up. This proved difficult for garages to maintain and service, and subsequent models reverted to twin carburettors.

1961 Austin Healey 3000 Mk I, 6 cylinders, 2912cc, fitted with optional overdrive, hard top and wire wheels, body-off restoration, full mechanical rebuild, excellent condition. **£15,000-16,000** *COYS*

1964 Austin Healey 3000 Mk III, 6 cylinders, 2912cc, left hand drive, good overall condition. **£9,000-9,500** *ADT*

AUSTIN-HEALEY Model	ENGINE cc/cyl	DATES	CONDITION		
			1	2	3
100 BN 1/2	2660/4	1953-56	£20,000	£12,000	£8,000
100/6, BN4/BN6	2639/6	1956-59	£21,000	£13,500	£8,000
3000 Mk I	2912/6	1959-61	£22,000	£14,000	£8,500
3000 Mk II	2912/6	1961-62	£22,000	£15,000	£9,000
3000 Mk IIA	2912/6	1962-64	£23,000	£15,000	£11,000
3000 Mk III	2912/6	1964-68	£24,000	£17,000	£11,000
Sprite Mk I	948/4	1958-61	£5,000	£4,000	£2,000
Sprite Mk II	948/4	1961-64	£3,000	£2,000	£500
Sprite Mk III	1098/4	1964-66	£3,500	£2,000	£500
Sprite Mk IV	1275/4	1966-71	£3,500	£1,500	£500

BENJAMIN

1922 Benjamin Type B Cyclecar, 750cc, 4 cylinders.   **Est. £15,000-20,000** *ADT*

BENTLEY

Walter Owen Bentley formed Bentley Motors Ltd. in 1919, and soon produced a 3 litre car, with a 4 cylinder, single overhead cam engine. By 1924 the company had achieved its first Le Mans victory, and between 1926 and 1931 had 4 more successive wins. To rival the Rolls-Royce market, the 8 litre car was launched at the 1930 London Show, but only 100 were made and the company collapsed.

Although W. O. Bentley went to work for Rolls-Royce, he left in 1935 to join Lagonda. In 1931 a new company was formed, Bentley Motors (1931) Ltd., which was a wholly-owned subsidiary of Rolls-Royce. Bentley Motors produced 2 great sports cars - the 'Silent Sports Car' and the 4¼ litre, which used the 25/30 engine.

1924 Bentley 3 Litre Tourer, replica Vanden Plas 4 seater touring coachwork, supplied with a saloon body by Weymann, twin SU sloping carburettors, engine rebuilt, very good overall condition. **£55,000-58,000** *ADT*

1926 Bentley 3/4½ Litre 4 Seater Tourer, restored, full history notes. **£65,000-70,000** *S*

1924 Bentley 3/4½ Litre 2 Seater Sports, chassis-up rebuild, new Brooklands style body, recently used for film work in the television series *House of Eliott*. **£75,000-77,000** *S*

The 3 litre was introduced in 1919 and was produced until 1927, but by then it was becoming outclassed by other 3 litre cars such as the Sunbeam and Type 44 Bugatti. Bentley produced a 4½ litre unit with a longer wheelbase which was heavier than its predecessor. To offset this, the lighter chassis of the 3 litre engine was used with the engine of the 4½ litre. H. M. Bentley then designed a cut down 2 seater version in an effort to keep the Bentley movement alive after the failure of the company in 1930.

1929 Bentley 4½ Litre Vanden Plas Open Tourer, excellent condition. **£148,000-152,000** *MAN*

1929 Bentley 4½ Litre 4 Seater Tourer, originally fitted with Sportsman's Coupé coachwork by J. Gurney Nutting, now has open touring fabric covered 3 door replica bodywork in the manner of Vanden Plas by Richard Moss, equipped with a side mounted spare wheel and twin aeroscreens. **£105,000-110,000** *BKS*

1929 Bentley Speed 6, fully
rebuilt with engine uprated to
8 litre.
£320,000-330,000 *MAN*

CROSS REFERENCE
Colour Section ⟶ p69

**1931 Bentley 4 Litre Vanden
Plas Tourer,** totally original car
in excellent running order.
£82,000-87,000 *PiK*

1930 Bentley Speed 6,
outstanding condition.
£320,000-330,000 *MAN*

*The first product of the 1931
Rolls-Royce takeover of Bentley,
the 3½ Litre was introduced in
1933 and was a sporting version
of the Rolls-Royce 20/25.*

**1934 Bentley 3½ Litre
Drophead Coupé,** coachwork
by James Young, 6 cylinders,
3699cc, refurbished leather
interior, new hood.
£38,000-40,000 *COYS*

**1933 Bentley 3½ Litre
3 Position Drophead Coupé,**
coachwork by Barker, excellent
condition throughout.
£78,000-82,000 *FHF*

**1934 Bentley 3½ Litre Hooper
Sports Saloon,** basically original
and complete car, running and
driving well, original leather
interior needs some restoration.
£14,500-15,500 *RCC*

1934 Bentley 3½ Litre Sports Saloon, coachwork by Thrupp & Maberly, right hand drive, incorrect engine and gearbox, in need of restoration.
£7,500-8,000 *C*

1935 Bentley 3½ Litre Drophead Coupé, 3 position coachwork by Thrupp & Maberly, 6 cylinders, 3669cc, much restoration work, in very good condition.
Est. £34,000-38,000 *COYS*

1935 Bentley 3½ Litre Sports Saloon, coachwork by Thrupp & Maberly, 6 cylinders, 3699cc, completely restored, excellent condition.
£16,000-17,000 *COYS*

1936 4¼ Litre Bentley.
£17,000-18,000 *DB*

1935 Bentley 3½ Litre Park Ward Saloon.
£14,000-16,000 *DB*

1937 Bentley 4¼ Litre All Weather Tourer, coachwork by Vanden Plas, 6 cylinder in line engine, 4257cc, 125bhp at 4500rpm, 4 speed manual gearbox, 4 wheel drum brakes assisted by mechanical servo, semi-elliptic leaf spring suspension with hydraulic shock absorbers to front and rear, right hand drive, excellent restored condition.
Est. £60,000-80,000 *C*

1937 Bentley 4¼ Litre 4 seater, rebodied in vintage style, good overall condition.
£19,000-20,000 *Mot*

BENTLEY Model	ENGINE cc/cyl	DATES	CONDITION		
			1	**2**	**3**
3 litre	2996/4	1920-27	£110,000	£75,000	£50,000
Speed Six	6597/6	1926-32	£450,000	£250,000	£160,000
4.5 litre	4398/4	1927-31	£175,000	£125,000	£80,000
4.5 litre Supercharger	4398/4	1929-32	£500,000	£300,000	£200,000
8 litre	7983/6	1930-32	£350,000	£250,000	£100,000
3.5 litre	3699/6	1934-37	£65,000	£30,000	£15,000
4.25 litre	4257/6	1937-39	£70,000	£35,000	£20,000
Mark V	4257/6	1939-41	£45,000	£25,000	£20,000

Prices are very dependent on engine type, body style and original extras like supercharger, gearbox ratio, history and originality.

1940 Bentley 4½ Litre Sports Saloon, coachwork by Park Ward, 6 cylinders, 4257cc, 135bhp, 4500rpm, 4 speed manual gearbox with overdrive, 4 wheel drum brakes, semi-elliptic leaf springs front and rear suspension, right hand drive, very good order.
£30,000-32,000 *C*

This car was one of the last produced and is from the MX series.

1937 Bentley 4¼ Litre Sports Saloon, coachwork by Park Ward, 6 cylinders, 4257cc, brakes converted to hydraulic operation, original interior, engine fully rebuilt.
£17,000-17,500 *COYS*

In March 1936 the new Bentley 4¼ litre was introduced, using a similar chassis to that of the 3½ litre but with the enlarged engine and hence more power. 1,241 4½ litre chassis were produced before production ceased in 1939.

1947 Bentley Mk VI Drophead Coupé, coachwork by Duncan Industries, 6 cylinders, 4275cc, repainted and re-chromed.
Est. 25,000-30,000 *COYS*

1937 Bentley 4¼ Litre Park Ward Sports Saloon, complete and original, in running order, some corrosion on the steel body, good upholstery.
£13,250-13,750 *RCC*

1947 Bentley Mk VI 4 Door Saloon, coachwork by H. J. Mulliner, right hand drive, goes well but requires overall restoration.
£2,750-3,500 *C*

1948 Bentley Saloon.
£20,000-21,000 *HWA*

1947 Bentley Mk VI, coachwork by Freestone & Webb.
£3,750-4,250 *DB*

1948 Bentley Mk VI.
£8,500-9,500 *Cum*

1948 Mk VI Bentley.
£4,500-5,000 *DB*

1949 Bentley Mk VI.
£3,500-3,800 *ADT*
This vehicle has been inappropriately stored and needs restoration.

1950 Bentley Mk VI 4¼ Litre 4 seater Touring Special, Vanden Plas style coachwork by John Thomas, bodywork of coachbuilt aluminium, constructed to a very high standard, fabric covered to give the traditional Vanden Plas appearance, Bentley instruments, engine turned aluminium dashboard, whip-corded steering wheel, P100 headlamps, 18in wire wheels.
£26,500-28,000 *BKS*

- **Standard post-war Bentleys are currently very good value for money.**
- **Spares, although expensive, are readily available from specialist dealers, with the exception of radiators which can prove difficult to locate.**

1950 Bentley Mk VI Donnington Special, fitted with 6.3 litre V8 Rolls-Royce engine by Johnard Vintage Cars, manufacturer of the Donnington, originally a Bentley Mark VI Standard Steel factory bodied saloon, body conversion is styled loosely on the SS 100 Jaguar and is built of fibreglass.
£14,000-15,000 *S*

1950 Bentley Mk VI, 6 cylinders, 4256 cc, some body deterioration, substantial amount of restoration work carried out.
Est. £5,000-6,000 *ADT*

1951 Bentley Mk VI Coupé,
coachwork by Park Ward,
6 cylinders, 4566cc, 3 owners
from new, immaculate original
condition.
£23,500-25,000 *COYS*

**1950 Bentley Mk VI Standard
Steel Saloon,** right hand drive,
good overall condition.
£6,000-6,500 *C*

*The 4¼ litre Bentley Mk VI was
the first model to be supplied by
Bentley with standard coachwork.*

1952 Bentley Mk VI, good
condition overall.
£3,800-4,000 *CC*

1952 Bentley Mk VI, fitted
factory sunroof, original working
valve radio and original tool kit,
2 owners from new.
£11,500-12,500 *Bro*

1952 Bentley Mark VI, very
good condition.
£37,000-38,000 *HWA*

1952 Bentley Mk VI, 6 cylinders,
4566cc, good condition but
requires running restoration.
£5,000-5,500 *ADT*

1952 Bentley R-Type, coachwork
by James Young, very good
original condition.
£13,750-14,250 *Bro*

1952 Bentley 4½ Litre Mk VI, coachwork by Park Ward.
£34,000-36,000 *BLE*

1952 Bentley Mark VI Saloon, coachwork by H. J. Mulliner, 4566cc, re-upholstered, very good original condition.
Est. £12,000-15,000 *S*

1953 Bentley R-Type Drophead Coupé, coachwork by Park Ward, 6 cylinders, 4566cc, power hood.
£35,000-37,500 *COYS*

This vehicle was first registered in April 1953, and its original owner was HRH Prince Frederick of Prussia. In 1992 a £60,000 restoration was completed.

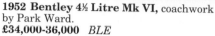

- All motor car production was moved from Derby to Crewe in 1946.
- Cars were supplied complete with standardised bodywork.

1953 Bentley R-Type Standard Steel Saloon, restored condition.
Est. £12,000-14,000 *S*

1953 Bentley R-Type Drophead Convertible.
£37,000-38,000 *HWA*

From late 1953 all models had 4 speed automatic transmission fitted as standard, replacing the 4 speed manual gearbox. Previously automatic transmission was only available on cars for export.

Miller's is a price GUIDE not a price LIST.

1954 Bentley R-Type Automatic.
£10,000-12,000 *DB*

1953 Bentley R-Type Standard Steel Saloon, maintained to original specification, stored in the USA, generally in good condition.
Est. £8,000-10,000 *S*

Bentley's first new post-war model, the Mark VI, featured in-house factory built coachwork for the first time and was an elegant car from every angle. It was well received by Bentley customers and its original 4¼ litre engine was soon upgraded to 4566cc for later cars.

1954 Bentley R-Type 4 Door Saloon, coachwork by H. J. Mulliner, 6 cylinder in-line engine, 4566cc, 135bhp at 4000rpm, 4 speed manual gearbox, independent front suspension by coil springs and wishbones with lever arm hydraulic dampers, rear live axle with semi-elliptic springs and adjustable lever arm hydraulic dampers, right hand drive, paintwork needs a final coat, but good restored condition.
Est. £10,000-15,000 *C*

The owner-driver Bentleys of the post-war years commenced with the Mk VI, and was succeeded by the R-Type in 1952. The chassis was lengthened to give more boot space and improve the lines of the car. Other improvements included the relocation of the rear suspension and fitting the engine with a cold start system.

1956 Bentley S1 Standard Steel Saloon, very good original condition.
£11,000-12,000 *S*

1955 Bentley R-Type Standard Steel Saloon, automatic transmission, original valve radio, good original condition.
£8,750-9,500 *S*

1956 Bentley S1 4.9 Litre 4 Door Standard Steel Saloon, restored and resprayed, needs further attention.
£7,000-8,000 *BKS*

The S-Type Bentley shared its bodywork with the Rolls-Royce Silver Cloud, and was similarly powered by the company's 6 cylinder overhead inlet/side exhaust valve engine. The model made way for the V8 engined S2 in 1959, by which time some 3,072 examples had been built.

1956 Bentley S1 Continental Fastback Coupé, coachwork by H. J. Mulliner, 6 cylinders, 4887cc, very good original condition.
£35,000-37,000 *COYS*

1958 Bentley S1 Continental Convertible Drophead Coupé, coachwork by Park Ward, 6 cylinders, 4187cc, power steering, power operated hood and high compression engine, maintained to a high standard, very good original condition.
£78,000-82,000 *COYS*

1959 Bentley S2 4 Door Saloon, right hand drive, excellent condition, recent major restoration.
£14,000-16,000 *CGB*

1958 Bentley S1 Continental 2 Door Fastback, coachwork by H. J. Mulliner, 6 cylinders, 4887cc, 4 speed automatic gearbox, 4 wheel drum brakes, front independent coil springs, rear live axle with semi-elliptic springs, right hand drive, very good condition throughout.
£30,000-32,000 *C*

1960 Bentley S2 Continental Flying Spur, coachwork by H. J. Mulliner, fitted with later S3 wings with headlight conversion, very good original condition.
Est. £25,000-28,000 *S*

1960 Bentley S2 Continental Flying Spur Sports Saloon, coachwork by H. J. Mulliner, right hand drive, restored, good condition.
Est. £22,000-30,000 *COYS*

All Continental versions of the Bentley S1 and S2 were aluminium bodied and produced mainly by Mulliner and Park Ward. With the Flying Spur of 1958, Mulliner incorporated 4 doors into what had traditionally been 2 door coachwork; subsequently a handful of similar examples were built by James Young.

Of the 2,130 S2s produced, only 57 were long wheelbase, with less than 30 as touring bodies.

1960 Bentley S2 Touring Limousine, V8 engine, overhead valve, single central camshaft, 6230cc, 200bhp at 4500rpm, 4 speed automatic GM/Rolls-Royce Hydra-Matic gearbox, drum brakes, hydraulic, mechanical servo, front independent suspension, rear elliptic, right hand drive, excellent original condition. **£14,800-15,200** *CNY*

1960 Bentley S2 Continental Flying Spur, coachwork by H. J. Mulliner, V8 engine, 6230cc, unrestored, good original condition.
£20,000-22,000 *COYS*

1960 Bentley S2 4 Door Standard Steel Saloon, good condition.
£4,500-6,500 *BA*

1961 Bentley S2 Series C Standard Steel Saloon, interior, bodywork, transmission, gearbox and chassis fair to good throughout.
£9,500-10,000 *S*

1960 Bentley S2 Continental Saloon, coachwork by James Young, overall good condition.
£30,000-35,000 *S(Z)*

An all new V8 engine was ready for the Rolls-Royce Silver Cloud II in 1959 developed from the General Motors unit. It had taken 4 years to modify and bore little resemblance to the original GM product when it entered service. It was coupled with a standard automatic transmission also from GM and the Bentley S2 produced alongside the Silver Cloud used the same power train assembly.

1963 Bentley S3 Continental, coachwork by Park Ward, very good condition.
£12,000-15,000 *VIC*

BENTLEY Model	ENGINE cc/cyl	DATES	CONDITION 1	2	3
Abbreviations: HJM = H J Mulliner; PW = Park Ward; M/PW = Mulliner/Park Ward					
Mk VI Standard Steel	4257/4566/6	1946-52	£18,000	£10,000	£6,000
Mk VI Coachbuilt	4257/4566/6	1946-52	£30,500	£20,000	£15,000
Mk VI Coachbuilt DHC	4566/6	1946-52	£40,000	£30,000	£22,000
R Type Standard Steel	4566/6	1952-55	£18,000	£12,000	£7,000
R Type Coachbuilt	4566/6	1952-55	£32,000	£20,000	£15,000
R Type Coachbuilt DHC	4566/4887/6	1952-55	£50,000	£35,000	£25,000
R Type Cont (HJM)	4887/6	1952-55	£60,000	£40,000	£29,000
S1 Standard Steel	4887/6	1955-59	£18,000	£12,000	£7,000
S1 Cont 2 door (PW)	4877/6	1955-59	£30,000	£25,000	£20,000
S1 Cont Drophead	4877/6	1955-59	£90,000	£75,000	£50,000
S1 Cont F'back (HJM)	4877/6	1955-58	£45,000	£35,000	£25,000
S2 Standard Steel	6230/8	1959-62	£15,000	£9,000	£6,000
S2 Cont 2 door (HJM)	6230/8	1959-62	£50,000	£40,000	£30,000
S2 Flying Spur (HJM)	6230/8	1959-62	£45,000	£33,000	£22,000
S2 Conv (PW)	6230/8	1959-62	£65,000	£50,000	£35,000
S3 Standard Steel	6230/8	1962-65	£16,000	£11,000	£9,000
S3 Cont/Flying Spur	6230/8	1962-65	£35,000	£30,000	£22,000
S3 2 door (PW)	6230/8	1962-65	£30,000	£25,000	£18,000
S3 Conv (modern conversion - only made one original)	6230/8	1962-65	£30,000	£24,500	£19,500
T1	6230/6, 6750/8	1965-77	£12,000	£9,000	£4,000
T1 2 door (M/PW)	6230/6, 6750/8	1965-70	£16,000	£12,000	£9,000
T1 Drophead (M/PW)	6230/6, 6750/8	1965-70	£25,000	£18,000	£12,000

1961 Bentley S2 Standard Steel Saloon, V8 engine, overhead valve, 6230cc, 200bhp at 5000 rpm, automatic gearbox, servo-assisted drum brakes all-round, independent front suspension, wishbones and coil springs, anti-roll bar, rear semi-elliptic leaf springs, right hand drive, genuine low mileage, generally good condition.
£12,000-12,500 *C*

1960 Bentley S2 Saloon, 8 cylinders, 6230cc, good condition.
Est. £5,000-7,000 *ADT*

1961 Bentley S2, one owner from new, excellent condition.
£13,750-14,250 *Bro*

1964 Bentley S3 4 Door Saloon, 51,000 miles, full service history, very good condition.
£20,000-24,000 *VIC*

1964 Bentley S3 Drophead Coupé, coachwork by H. J. Mulliner, 8 cylinders, 6230cc, good condition generally.
Est. £30,000-32,000 *ADT*

When the twin headlamp S3 Bentley was introduced in 1963, only 2 drophead coupés were manufactured. This vehicle represents a high quality conversion that was completed several yeas ago.

1963 Bentley S3 Continental Flying Spur, coachwork by H. J. Mulliner, V8 engine, 6230cc, excellent overall condition.
Est. £28,000-35,000 *COYS*

1965 Bentley S3 Continental Sports Saloon, coachwork by James Young, V8 engine, 6230cc, very good original condition.
£40,000-42,000 *COYS*

1966 Bentley T-Type 2 Door Fixed Head Coupé, coachwork by Mulliner Park Ward, good condition throughout. **Est. £15,000-18,000** *S*

1967 Bentley 2 Door Saloon, coachwork by James Young. **£11,000-12,000** *DB*

There were only about 40 made.

1967 Bentley T1, excellent overall condition. **£8,750-9,250** *Bro*

1968 Bentley T Series. **£3,800-4,200** *DB*

1969 Bentley T1 2 Door Mulliner Park Ward Saloon, good overall condition. **£15,000-16,000** *S*

1969 Bentley T1 Saloon, fair to good condition. **Est. £6,300-6,800** *S*

1970 Bentley T1 Series Saloon, very good condition throughout. **£10,000-11,000** *S*

1981 Bentley Mulsanne. **£14,000-16,000** *VIC*

1985 Bentley Mulsanne Sports Saloon,
very good condition throughout.
Est. £32,000-34,000 *S*

Rolls-Royce introduced a new model range in 1980 based upon the T2 Series floorpan, but with a new body style designed by Fritz Feller, the Rolls-Royce being named the Silver Spirit and the corresponding Bentley, the Mulsanne. When launched, the top speed of the Bentley was about 120mph and it was named after the famous Le Mans straight where 50 years previously the Bentley team had recorded a famous victory. Power came from a V8 engine of 6750cc with GM 3 speed automatic transmission.

1988 Bentley 8, 12,850 miles.
£32,000-36,000 *HWA*

BENZ

1989 Bentley Mulsanne S,
V8 engine, overhead valve,
6750cc, 240bhp at 4300 rpm,
3 speed GM Hydramatic gearbox,
disc brakes front and rear, with
ABS, independent front and rear
suspension with automatically
controlled hydraulic dampers, left
hand drive, flawless condition
throughout, 15,000 miles.
£43,000-45,000 *CNY*

1898 Benz Velo, fully restored.
£48,000-52,000 *FHF*

Introduced in 1912, the 33/75 model Benz was a 4 cylinder model, with the cylinders pair-cast, fitted with a 4 speed gearbox, driving through a leather lined cone clutch by shaft to a bevel gear rear axle. It was sold in the UK as the Model A5 from Benz Motors (England) Ltd., in Grafton Street, off Bond Street, London.

c1914 Benz 33/75 3 Door Open Touring Car, right hand drive,
very good condition throughout, open touring bodywork largely
rebuilt, discovered in East Germany in mechanically unrestored
condition. **Est. £50,000-60,000** *S*

1959 AC Ace 2 Seater Sports, 6 cylinders, 1991cc, 85bhp, independent transverse leaf suspension front and rear, drum brakes, 4 speed gearbox, excellent condition.
£23,000-24,000 *COYS*

1931 Alfa Romeo Tourismo, 6 cylinders, 1750cc, coachwork by James Young, good original condition.
£38,000-42,000 *BC*

1931 Alfa Romeo Gran Sport, 6 cylinders, 1750cc, Zagato Spider coachwork, Brooklands history.
£190,000-210,000 *BC*

1959 AC Ace-Bristol Open Sports, 6 cylinder, 1971cc straight 6 engine, 85bhp, optional Borrani aluminium wheels, 42,000 miles, resprayed, converted to right hand drive, excellent condition.
£42,000-44,000 *COYS*

1930 Alfa Romeo 6C Supercharged Gran Sport 2 Seater Drophead Coupé, coachwork by James Young, 6 cylinders, 1750cc, older restoration.
£77,000-78,000 *BKS*

1932-33 Alfa Romeo Tipo 8C, 8 cylinders, 2300cc, replica Monza Corsa coachwork.
Est. £300,000-350,000 *BKS*

1964 Alfa Romeo Giulia SS, race prepared, excellent condition.
£19,000-21,000 *PiK*

l. and above.
1943 Alfa Romeo 6C Superleggera Sports Saloon, coachwork by Touring of Milan, 6 cylinders, 2500cc, Veglia instruments, sliding Plexiglass door windows, wire wheels, Pirelli tyres, 118in wheelbase, right hand drive, engine restored, good condition.
£62,000-65,000 *S(Z)*

1964 Alfa Romeo Giulia Spider, coachwork by Pininfarina, 4 cylinders, 1570cc, 5 speed gearbox, disc brakes, restored by Hexagon, excellent condition.
£13,500-14,500 *COYS*

1963 Alfa Romeo 1.6 Litre Giulia Sprint Speciale, coachwork by Carrozzeria Bertone, mechanically restored in USA, repainted in Britain, air-conditioning. **£15,500-16,500** *BKS*

1926 Amilcar CGSS 'Surbaisse', 1087cc, original unrestored and sound condition.
£14,000-15,000 *BKS(M)*

1951 Allard J2, Mercury V8 engine, 3917cc, 120bhp at 3600rpm, 3 speed La Salle gearbox, hydraulic drum brakes all-round, left hand drive, restored, excellent condition.
Est. £55,000-60,000 *CNY*

1961 Aston Martin DB4 Series II Sports Saloon, coachwork by Touring of Milan, 6 cylinders, 3670cc, David Brown 4 speed gearbox, 240bhp at 5500rpm, all-round disc brakes, very good condition.
£25,000-27,000 *COYS*

1935 Aston Martin Mk II 2 Seater Sports, ex-LM12, 1.5 litres, 'Ulster' type coachwork by Ecurie Bertelli.
£58,000-62,000 *BKS*

1965 Aston Martin DB5 Sports Coupé, coachwork by Touring of Milan, 6 cylinders, 3995cc, all-alloy engine, 4 speed gearbox with overdrive, Girling disc brakes.
Est. £25,000-30,000 *COYS*

1962 Aston Martin DB4 Series IV, original condition.
£30,000-34,000 *PiK*

1964 Aston Martin DB5 Superleggera Saloon, 4 litres, overhauled by Scott Moncrieff in 1988, good condition.
£32,000-34,000 *BKS*

1952 Aston Martin DB2 2 Door Grand Touring Saloon, now with 2.9 litre engine, total rebuild, very good overall condition.
£30,000-32,000 *BKS*

1966 Aston Martin DB6 Mk I Vantage Grand Touring Coupé, coachwork by Carrozzeria Touring Superleggera, 6 cylinders, 4 litres, original condition. **Est. £22,000-30,000** *S*

1967 Aston Martin DB6 Mk I Vantage Grand Touring Coupé, coachwork by Carrozzeria Touring Superleggera, 6 cylinders, 4 litres, 5 speed ZF gearbox, left hand drive, excellent condition. **£30,000-35,000** *S(Z)*

1979 Aston Martin V8 Volante Convertible, 5340cc, good original condition. **£48,000-50,000** *COYS*

r. **1928 Austin 'Chummy' 7hp Open Tourer,** good all-round condition. **Est. £5,000-6,000** *S*

1948 Austin 16 4 Door Saloon, 2.2 litres, with sunroof, very good condition. **Est. £2,000-3,000** *BKS*

l. **1929 Austin 7 Ulster Replica,** Phoenix crank, racing cylinder block, close ratio gearbox, new wheels, all correct weather equipment, only 2,000 miles recorded since re-build. **Est. £9,000-10,000** *LF*

1958 Austin Healey 100/6, 6 cylinders, 2639cc, 102bhp at 4600rpm, ground-up restoration, very good condition. **£16,000-17,000** *COYS*

1935 Auburn Supercharged Model 851 Speedster, Lycoming GG 8 cylinder in line engine, 150bhp at 4000rpm, wheelbase 127in. **£68,000-70,000** *S(NY)*

1959 Austin Healey 'Frog-eye' Sprite Mk I, 4 cylinders, 948cc, 43bhp at 5200rpm, 4 speed manual gearbox, rebuilt and restored. **£8,000-9,000** *C*

1959 Austin Healey 100/6, excellent condition, imported from California. **Est. £11,000-15,000** *ECC*

1962 Austin Healey 3000 Mk II, 6 cylinders, 2912cc, 3 carburettors, 132bhp at 4750rpm, restored to Concours standard, right hand drive, with new hood and tonneau cover.
£22,000-24,000 *COYS*

1964 Austin Healey 3000 Mk III 'Phase 1' Sports 2 Seater, 6 cylinders, 2.9 litres, 150bhp, servo-assisted brakes, right hand drive.
£36,000-38,000 *BKS*

1955 Austin Healey 100/4 BN1, right hand drive, restored, very good condition.
£11,000-13,000 *MSN*

1922 Bentley 3 Litre, Harrison body, full engine rebuild, fully restored.
£78,000-80,000 *MAN*

1966 Austin Healey 3000 Mk III 'Phase 2' Sports, right hand drive, restored, excellent condition.
£26,000-28,000 *MSN*

1923 Bentley TT Model 3 litre Open Tourer, mechanically overhauled, requires further restoration.
£47,000-49,000 *S*

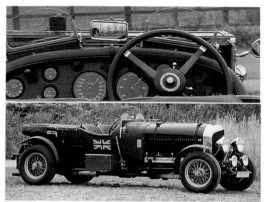

1928 Bentley 6.5 litre Le Mans Replica, older restoration, very good condition.
£190,000-210,000 *MAN*

1926 Bentley 3 litre Vanden Plas Tourer, fitted with 4½ litre engine, superb older restoration.
£90,000-110,000 *MAN*

Above and right:
**1929 Bentley 4½ Litre
2 Seater Tourer,** coachwork
by R. Harrison & Son,
4 cylinders, 4398cc, 4 speed
and reverse C-Type gearbox.
£75,000-78,000 *C*

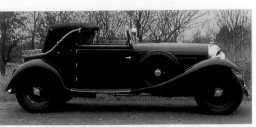

1931 Bentley Blower Drophead Coupé,
Vanden Plas body, long range petrol tank,
excellent condition.
£340,000-360,000 *MAN*

1934 Bentley 3½ Litre Sports Saloon,
coachwork by Park Ward, 4 cylinders, 3669cc,
in working order, requires further restoration.
£13,500-14,500 *ADT*

1929 Bentley Speed 6, coachwork by
Abbott, excellent condition.
£240,000-260,000 *MAN*

**1931 Bentley 4½ Litre Supercharged 4 Seater
Sports Tourer,** coachwork by Vanden Plas, fully
restored condition.
£400,000+ *S*

**1952 Bentley R-Type Drophead
Coupé,** coachwork by Mulliner.
£33,000-36,000 *BLE*

1937 Bentley 4¼ Litre Roadster,
coachwork by Park Ward, 6 cylinders,
4257cc, rebodied as a boat-tail 4 seater
tourer, rear tonneau cover.
£19,000-20,000 *COYS*

r. **1934 Bentley 3½ Litre Open Tourer,**
6 cylinders, 3699cc, originally a saloon,
rebodied as a Vanden Plas style open
tourer, restored, good condition.
Est. £33,000-38,000 *COYS*

1937 Bentley 4¼ litre All-Weather Tourer, coachwork by Vanden Plas, owned by one family only, mechanically well maintained but bodywork requires restoration. **£33,000-35,000** *BKS*

1939 Bentley 4¼ Litre Pillarless Saloon, coachwork by Park Ward, 6 cylinders, 4250cc, original interior, good condition. **£14,500-15,500** *ADT*

1953 Bentley 4.5 Litre R-Type Standard Steel Saloon, 6 cylinder, 4556cc engine, automatic gearbox, completely overhauled by Barry Price in 1991, resprayed. **£8,500-9,500** *BKS*

1949 Bentley Mk VI Sedanca Coupé, coachwork by Hooper, 6 cylinders, 4257cc, original interior intact, in need of restoration. **£26,000-28,000** *ADT*

1959 Bentley S1 Continental Flying Spur, coachwork by H. J. Mulliner, optional power steering, restored, in very good condition. **£45,000-50,000** *S(Z)*

1962 Bentley S2 Continental Drophead Coupé, coachwork by Park Ward, V8 engine, automatic gearbox, requires some restoration. **Est. £30,000-40,000** *S*

1955 Bentley R-Type Continental Fastback Sports Saloon, coachwork by H. J. Mulliner, manual gearbox, complete body-off restoration, excellent condition. **Est. £90,000-110,000** *S*

l. **1954 Bentley R-Type Continental Fastback Sports Saloon,** coachwork by H. J. Mulliner, 4566cc engine, mechanically restored, good condition. **£82,000-85,000** *S*

r. **1987 Bentley Turbo R-Type,** long wheelbase, electronric fuel injection, anti-lock braking system, 53,000 miles recorded, excellent condition, full service history.
£34,000-38,000 *VIC*

1958 BMW 507 3.2 Litre V8 2 Seater Sports, 150bhp at 5000rpm, 5 speed gearbox, steel knock-on wheels, left hand drive, restored, good condition.
£100,000-150,000 *S(Z)*

c1898 Benz 1.05 Litre 'Velo' 2 Seater Voiturette, 3.5hp, rear mounted horizontal engine, 2 speed belt drive, maximum speed of 12mph at 450-500rpm.
£37,000-39,000 *BKS*

1954 Bristol 403 2 Litre 2 Door Saloon, 6 cylinder engine, Alfin brake drums, anti-roll bar, brakes overhauled, restored, only 300 of these cars were produced.
£18,000-19,000 *BKS*

1981 BMW M1 Coupé, 6 cylinders, 3423cc, coachwork by Ital Design, electric windows, air conditioning, excellent condition, 13,000 recorded miles. **£48,000-50,000** *COYS*

1930 Bugatti Type 46 2 Door Saloon, 8 cylinders, 5.3 litres, rear mounted gearbox, cast alloy vane type 20in wheels, sliding sunroof, Marchal headlights, Telecontrol shock absorbers, original Jaeger instrumentation, engine recently rebuilt. **Est. £80,000-100,000** *S(Z)*

1921 Bugatti Type 13 Brescia Sports 2 Seater, restored using BOC approved replica chassis frame, original complete 16 valve engine.
Est. £30,000-40,000 *S*

l. **1926 Bugatti Type 38,** 8 cylinders, 1991cc, Torpedo Tourer coachwork by Lavocat & Marsaud, twin Solex carburettors, 4 speed gearbox, Marchal headlights, Grand Prix wheels, 2-piece folding windscreen.
Est. £60,000-70,000 *COYS*

1958 Cadillac Coupé de Ville, V8 engine, overhead valve, 365cu in, 310bhp at 4800rpm, 3 speed automatic gearbox, 4 wheel drum brakes, independent coil front suspension, coil springs rear, left hand drive, original and excellent condition. **Est. £12,000-15,000** *CNY*

1939 Chevrolet Master 85 Businessman's Coupé, straight 6 engine, 3.5 litres, 3 speed gearbox, engine rebuilt, imported from New Zealand in 1991. **£4,500-5,500** *BKS*

1963 Chevrolet Corvette 327 Split Window Coupé , 5 speed manual gearbox, full restoration and modified for maximum road performance.
£26,000-28,000 *COR*

1961 Chevrolet Corvette Roadster, 8 cylinders, 230bhp, 4 speed manual gearbox. **£16,000-17,000** *ADT*

1963 Chevrolet Corvette Stingray Split Window Coupé, V8, overhead valve engine, 340bhp, 4 speed manual gearbox, knock-off wheels, left hand drive, restored, good condition. **£20,000-25,000** *CNY*

l. **1982 Chevrolet Corvette T-top 350 Automatic.**

1980 Chevrolet Corvette T-top 350 Automatic, low mileage, excellent condition. **£9,000-11,000** *COR*

1963 Chevrolet Corvette Stingray Convertible, V8 engine, 5358cc, Offenhauser manifold and competition cams, Edelbrock rocker/valve covers, Holly carburettors, fully restored, resprayed, good condition.
Est. £13,500-15,500 *ADT*

l. **1982 Chevrolet Corvette T-top 350 Automatic,** 8,000 miles, excellent condition.
£15,000-17,000 *COR*

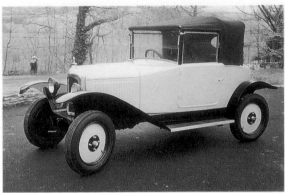

1923 Citroën 5CV Boat-tail 2 Seater,
855cc, 6 volt coil ignition, right hand drive,
fully restored in 1986, good condition.
£6,000-7,000 *BKS*

1949 Citroën Light 15, Slough built, 1950cc,
right hand drive, small boot model, original
condition throughout.
Est. £5,000-5,500 *DDM*

1974 Citroën 2.7 Litre SM Sports Saloon, 90° V6
engine, resprayed, very good overall original condition.
£6,250-6,750 *BKS*

1952 Daimler DE36, 8 cylinders,
5500cc, coachwork by Hooper,
extensively restored, engine
rebuilt, very good conditon.
Est. £15,000-18,000 *ADT*

Above: Interior
detail of **1952
Daimler DE36.**

1964 Daimler SP 250, factory wire wheels,
immaculate condition throughout.
£13,000-15,000 *CGOC*

1975 Daimler Double Six Coupé,
bare shell Concours rebuild.
£13,000-15,000 *SC*

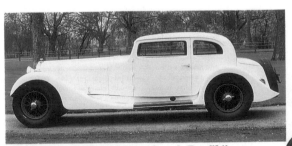

1933 Delage D8S 4.1 Litre 'Coach Profilé',
coachwork by Carrosserie Letourner & Marchand,
excellent condition. **£77,000-79,000** *BKS*

r. **1932 Delage D6 3.1 Litre Faux Cabriolet,**
designed by Maurice Gaultier, 6 cylinders, 4 speed
gearbox, restored, replacement electric fuel pump.
£18,000-20,000 *BKS*

1948 Delahaye 135M Drophead Coupé, coachwork by Pennock, 6 cylinder in line monobloc engine, 3557cc, 130hp, 43 speed Cotal gearbox, Gleason rear axle, original condition. **£25,000-30,000** *S(NY)*

1966 Ferrari 275 GTB Series II 2 Door Coupé, coachwork by Scaglietti, 3286cc, 280bhp at 7500rpm, all-synchro 5 speed and reverse gearbox, disc brakes, restored. **£110,000-130,000** *S(Z)*

1939 Delage D6-75 Drophead Coupé, 2.8 litres, Marchal Aerolux headlamps, Lucas driving lamps, miniature fingertip Cotal gate change on steering column, upholstery restored, new hood and head lining. **£23,000-24,000** *S*

1965-66 Ferrari 275 GTB/2 3.3 Litre 'Shortnose' 2 Door Gran Turismo Berlinetta, coachwork by Pininfarina/Scaglietti, V12 engine, 280bhp at 7600rpm, restored. **Est. £80,000-120,000** *BKS*

1964 Ferrari 500 Superfast Series I Berlinetta, coachwork by Pininfarina, 5 litre, V12 engine, 400bhp at 6500rpm, Borrani wheels, restored, excellent condition. **£110,000-120,000** *S(Z)*

1970 Ferrari 365 GTC Berlinetta, coachwork by Pininfarina, 4 litre, disc brakes, 94in wheelbase, knock-on wheels, restored, left hand drive. **£38,000-40,000** *S(Z)*

1968 Ferrari 365 GT 2+2 Coupé, coachwork by Pininfarina, 4 litre, V12 engine, 4 speed in-unit gearbox, 300bhp at 6600rpm, good original condition. **Est. £45,000-48,000** *S*

r. **1967 Ferrari 330 GTC Berlinetta Speciale,** V12 engine, 300bhp at 7000rpm, 5 speed gearbox, restored, good condition. **£100,000-120,000** *S(Z)*

1975 Ferrari 365 GT4 Berlinetta Boxer,
12 cylinders, 4390cc, 0-100mph in 13.5 seconds, air
conditioning, electric windows, good condition.
Est. £45,000-50,000 *ADT*

1972 Ferrari 246 Dino GTS, Spyder coachwork by
Pininfarina, rebuilt V6 engine, 2418cc, 5 speed
gearbox, right hand drive, excellent condition.
Est. £34,000-38,000 *COYS*

l. **1968 Fiat
Dino 2000
Coupé,** V6
engine,
rebuilt
gearbox,
original
alloy wheels,
good
condition.
£7,000-9,000
CCTC

1956 Ford Thunderbird, Concours
condition.
£19,000-21,000 *BLE*

1968 Ferrari 330 GTS Spyder, coachwork by
Pininfarina, 4 litre, 60° V12 engine, 5 speed
gearbox, 3 x 40DCZ6 Weber carburettors giving
320bhp at 7000rpm, restored, excellent condition.
£85,000-95,000 *S(Z)*

1991 Ferrari 348ts, V8 engine, 3405cc, 300bhp
at 7000rpm, 5 speed manual gearbox, vented disc
brakes with ABS, 17in wheels, left hand drive,
excellent condition.
£55,000-60,000 *CNY*

1939 Fiat Topolino, right hand drive,
very good condition.
£3,250-3,750 *CC*

**1911 Model T Ford 2 Seater Runabout with
Mother-in-Law Seat,** 2.9 litres, engine
overhauled and reconditioned, imported from
US, restored. **£10,000-11,000** *BKS*

1959 Ford Consul Low Line De Luxe, 1700cc,
excellent condition.
Est. £1,800-2,000 *ECC*

1914 Hispano-Suiza 8/10hp 4 Seater Open Tourer, 4 cylinder, side valve engine, 1847cc, leather lined cone clutch, 3 speed and reverse gearbox, magneto ignition, thermo-syphon cooling, brass radiator, original Tarrida brass lamps, wooden artillery wheels, original condition, good running order. **£35,000-37,000** *S*

1921 Hispano Suiza H6 All Weather Tourer, coachwork by Belvallette, Paris, 6 cylinder in line engine, 6597cc, water-cooled monobloc, 120bhp at 2000rpm, 3 speed gearbox, 4 wheel mechanical with servo brakes. **£62,000-65,000** *S(NY)*

1935 Hispano-Suiza J-12 Pillarless Sedan, coachwork by Kellner, Paris, 60° V12 overhead valve pushrod engine, 9424cc, 220bhp at 3000rpm, dual-two Scintilla Vertex magnetos, 2 sets of 12 spark plugs, 3 speed gearbox, 2 twin choke carburettors, 4 wheel servo-assisted brakes, good condition. **£110,000-130,000** *S(NY)*

1934 Invicta 12/45 1.5 Litre 4 Seater Tourer, coachwork by Carbodies, 6 cylinder Blackburne engine, 1498cc, gearbox bearings replaced, brakes relined, very good condition throughout. **£21,000-22,000** *BKS*

1934 Invicta 12/45, coachwork by Carbodies, Blackburne overhead camshaft engine. **£13,500-14,500** *CVPG*

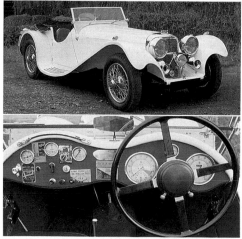

1939/1940 SS Jaguar '100' Roadster, 6 cylinders, 2.5 litres, gearbox overhauled, new clutch, reconditioned fuel gauge, QK headlights, very good condition. **Est. £90,000-100,000** *S*

1946 Jaguar 3½ Litre 3 Position Drophead Coupé, 6 cylinders, 3485cc, 125bhp at 4250rpm, 4 speed synchromesh gearbox, restored, excellent condition. **Est. £24,000-26,000** *COYS*

r. Dashboard and interior detail of **1953 Jaguar XK120M Drophead Coupé.**

1954 Jaguar XK120 Drophead Coupé, 6 cylinder in line engine, double overhead camshaft, 3422cc, 160bhp at 5250rpm, 4 speed manual gearbox, fully restored, very good condition. **£48,000-50,000** *C*

1953 Jaguar XK120M Drophead Coupé, 3.4 litres, 190bhp, wire wheels, twin spotlamps, reconditioned engine, fully restored. **£40,000-42,000** *BKS*

1950 Jaguar XK120 Roadster, 6 cylinder in line twin cam engine, 3422cc, 160bhp at 5250rpm, 4 speed manual gearbox, 4 wheel drum brakes, left hand drive, fully restored, very good condition. **Est. £28,000-32,000** *C*

1958 Jaguar XK150 Fixed Head Coupé, 6 cylinders, 3442cc, Dunlop disc brakes, resprayed, engine rebored, new stainless steel exhaust, good condition. **Est. £16,000-18,000** *ADT*

1950 Jaguar XK120 Roadster, 6 cylinder in line engine, 3442cc, 160bhp at 5000rpm, 4 speed manual gearbox, fully restored. **Est. £37,000-43,000** *CNY*

1959 Jaguar XK150 'S' 3.8 Coupé, 6 cylinders, 210bhp, twin SU carburettors, all-round disc brakes, top speed 125mph, restored, very good condition. **£22,000-24,000** *COYS*

1962 Jaguar 3.8 Mk II, manual gearbox with overdrive, later type chrome wheels, otherwise original condition. **£8,250-9,000** *CCTC*

l. **1959 Jaguar XK150 'S' Fixed Head Coupé,** 6 cylinders, 3482cc, manual gearbox, rebuilt engine, body-off restoration, very good condition. **Est. £21,000-24,000** *ADT*

1967 Jaguar E-Type 4.2 litre Series I Drophead Coupé, restored to Concours condition.
£40,000-45,000 *SC*

1969 Jaguar E-Type 4.2 litre Series II Fixed Head Coupé, right hand drive, well preserved, good condition.
£9,500-10,500 *BKS*

1964 Jaguar Mk II Saloon, 6 cylinders, 3781cc, Coombs modifications to carburettor air intake, carburettors, front suspension, steering box, engine and gearbox rebuilt, resprayed.
£13,000-14,000 *ADT*

1961 Jaguar E-Type 3.8 litre Series I 'Flat Floor' Fixed Head Coupé, triple SU carburettors, imported from USA, converted to right hand drive, rebuilt and restored, very good condition.
£16,000-17,000 *BKS*

1967 Jaguar Mk II 3.4 litre 4 Door Saloon, automatic gearbox, chrome wire wheels, fold-down wooden picnic tables in back of front seats, engine and bodywork rebuilt, good condition.
£13,500-14,500 *BKS*

1965 Jaguar E-Type Series I Roadster, 6 cylinders, 4235cc, synchromesh gearbox, servo-assisted system brakes, fully restored, excellent condition throughout.
£34,000-35,000 *ADT*

1972 Jaguar E-Type Series III Roadster, V12 engine, 5343cc, 272bhp at 5850rpm, 4 Stromberg carburettors, new clutch, very good condition.
£25,000-27,000 *COYS*

1973 Jaguar E-Type Series III Roadster, V12 engine, 5343cc, 272bhp at 5850rpm, 4 Stromberg carburettors, left hand drive, fully restored, imported from USA, excellent condition.
£22,000-24,000 *COYS*

1973 Jaguar E-Type Series III Fixed Head Coupé, V12 engine, 5.3 litres, 272bhp, automatic gearbox, converted to right hand drive, resprayed, restored. **£12,000-13,000** *LF*

1974 Jensen Interceptor III Convertible, 8 cylinders, 7212cc, electric windows and folding hood, engine rebuilt, new steering rack, starter motor and alternator, restored, good condition. **Est. £23,000-28,000** *ADT*

1965 Jensen CV8 Mk III Coupé, V8 engine, 6276cc, 330bhp at 4600rpm, dual circuit brakes, reclining seats, front seats retrimmed, restored, excellent condition. **£8,500-9,500** *COYS*

1956 Jensen 541 Sports Coupé, 6 cylinders, 4 litres, 4 speed manual gearbox with overdrive, 125bhp, optional wire wheels, good all-round condition. **£14,000-15,000** *S*

1935 Lagonda M45 4.5 Litre Sports Tourer, 115bhp, cycle mudguards, fold-flat screen, good weather equipment, centre spotlight, twin horns, restored. **Est. £30,000-35,000** *S*

l. Rear view showing hood of **1952 Lagonda DB 2.6 Litre.**

1937 Lagonda LG45 Le Mans Replica, 6 cylinders, 4453cc, 125bhp, originally drophead coupé, engine uprated to Rapide specification, excellent condition. **£36,000-39,000** *COYS*

1952 Lagonda DB 2.6 Litre Drophead Coupé, 6 cylinders, 2580cc, semaphore arm indicators, fully restored, good condition. **£12,000-13,000** *ADT*

1939 Lagonda LG6 Drophead Coupé,
4.5 litre V12 engine, torsion bar independent
front suspension, originally painted black,
restored in USA, good condition.
£55,000-58,000 *BKS*

1924 Lancia Lambda 4th Series Tourer, V4 engine,
60bhp, wing mounted battery and tool boxes, rear
tonneau cover, black hood, sidescreens, older interior
restoration, engine rebuilt, good condition.
Est. £35,000-38,000 *S*

1934 Lancia Belna Cabriolet, coachwork by Paul
Nee, Paris, V4 engine, single overhead camshaft,
1196cc, 35bhp at 4000rpm, 4 speed dog engagement
gearbox, 4 wheel hydraulic drum brakes, imported
from France, restored. **£9,500-10,500** *C*

1962 Lagonda Rapide 4 litre Sports Saloon,
coachwork by Touring of Milan, 6 cylinders,
3995cc, 4 speed manual gearbox, 236bhp at
5000rpm, right hand drive, restored, good
condition. **£15,500-16,500** *C*

**1964 Lancia Flaminia 2.8 litre Super Sport
Coupé,** coachwork by Zagato, V6 engine, 148bhp at
5900rpm, Weber 40 DCN carburettors, left hand drive,
original specification, good condition.
£23,000-25,000 *S(Z)*

**1957 Lancia B20 Aurelia Gran Turismo
2 Door Coupé,** coachwork by Pininfarina,
V6, 2.4 litre engine, 110bhp, Nardi floor
change gearbox, very good condition.
£17,500-18,500 *BKS*

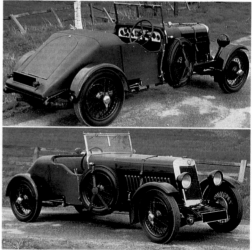

1974 Lancia Stratos HF Coupé, V6 Ferrari Dino
engine, only 727km from new and never registered,
stored in a heated garage, excellent condition.
Est. £50,000-60,000 *S(Z)*

**1930 Lea-Francis S-Type Hyper Replica
Supercharged 2 Seater,** built around a 1930
12hp P Type chassis, SU carburettor, Jaeger
instruments, excellent condition.
Est. £30,000-35,000 *S*

BMW

BMW (Bayerische Motoren Werke) officially entered the motor car market in 1927 with the Dixi 3/15PS, based on the Austin 7. Pre-war production was very low with only about 55,000 vehicles being produced from 1928 to 1939.

BMW produced the Isetta Bubble Car from 1955 which nearly resulted in their bankruptcy. However, the new series of sports saloons, which began to be produced in the 1960s, soon restored BMW's fortunes and has led to a range of highly respected and prestigious motor cars.

1928 BMW Dixi Type 3/15 Model DA-1 IHLE Sport 2 Seater, fully restored, excellent overall condition.
Est. £8,000-10,000 *S(Z)*

The Austin 7 was built under licence by a number of manufacturers outside the United Kingdom, including Dixi in Germany. In October 1928, BMW purchased Dixi-Werke and thus progressed from motorcycles to car production, and the DA-1 Model was the first BMW type - basically a re-badged Dixi, not revised in any way.

CROSS REFERENCE
Austin ——————————▶ p40

1937 BMW 328 Sports 2 Seater Roadster, left hand drive, fully restored throughout, excellent condition.
£85,000-90,000 *S*

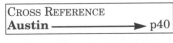

1937 BMW 328, 2 litre, high twin cam, Figoni Falachi coachwork.
£35,000-37,000 *FHF*

Very rare, only a very few wre made.

1939 2 Litre BMW 327/28 2 Seater Cabriolet Sport, engine completely rebuilt, interior re-upholstered and trimmed, good and useable condition.
Est. £30,000-40,000 *BKS(M)*

Mechanically the 327/28 was identical to the 328, using the triple Solex carburettor 6 cylinder engine with BMW's unique and effective cross pushrod valve gear in an aluminium cylinder head. While the basic 327 had first been produced in 55bhp form, the 328 engine could produce as much as 90bhp.

BMW Model	ENGINE cc/cyl	DATES	CONDITION 1	2	3
Dixi	747/4	1927-32	£5,000	£3,000	£1,500
303	1175/6	1934-36	£11,000	£8,000	£5,000
309	843/4	1933-34	£6,000	£4,000	£2,000
315	1490/6	1935-36	£9,000	£7,000	£5,000
319	1911/6	1935-37	£10,000	£9,000	£6,000
326	1971/6	1936-37	£12,000	£10,000	£8,000
320 series	1971/6	1937-38	£12,000	£10,000	£8,000
327/328	1971/6	1937-40	£18,000	£15,000	£10,000
328	1971/6	1937-40	£50,000+		

1938 BMW 327 Cabriolet,
mechanical and body restoration,
engine overhauled.
£34,000-36,000 *S(Z)*

1952 BMW 501 Saloon, left hand
drive, dry stored, requires
restoration.
Est. £2,000-3,000 *S*

*BMW introduced its first post-war
passenger car, the 501, in October
1952. The bodies were initially
constructed at Bauer in Stuttgart
before the Munich factory became
fully operational, and the car was
fitted with a 6 cylinder, 2 litre
engine based upon the pre-war
326. Only 1,706 units were
produced before the factory
introduced the 501A and 501B
derivatives.*

> CROSS REFERENCE
> **Restoration
> Projects ⟶ p305**

1972 BMW 3.0 CS, 6 cylinders,
2985cc, alloy wheels, sills
replaced, excellent solid condition
with a good chassis.
Est. £8,500-9,500 *ADT*

1973 BMW 3.0 CS Coupé,
right hand drive, automatic
transmission, good condition
throughout.
Est. £3,500-4,500 *LF*

1973 BMW 2002 Cabriolet,
4 cylinders, 1990cc, new wings,
sills, valance and under pan,
extremely good condition.
Est. £5,000-6,000 *ADT*

- **BMW was the first manufacturer to
  offer a road-going turbo-charged
  production car.**
- **BMW Isetta 250, introduced in 1955,
  was built under licence from Renzo
  Rivolta of ISO Milan.**

1974 BMW 3.0 CS, 6 cylinders,
2985cc, bare metal respray and
engine rebuilt, very good overall
condition.
Est. £4,500-5,000 *ADT*

1974 BMW 3.0 CSi, 6 cylinders,
2985cc, manual gearbox, Alpina
side striping, extensively
restored, superb condition.
Est. £5,500-6,500 *ADT*

**1975 BMW 2.0 Litre 2002
Turbo 2 Door Coupé,**
engine rebuilt, extensive
body overhaul.
Est. £7,000-9,000 *BKS*

*The BMW 2002 Turbo was the
first European production car to
be equipped with a turbocharger.
Just 1,672 were built.*

CROSS REFERENCE
Colour Section ⟶ p71

**1985 BMW 3.4 Litre 745i
Turbocharged 4 Door Saloon,**
left hand drive, good overall
condition.
Est. £8,000-12,000 *BKS*

*The car was created because of
homologation rules requiring the
construction of 400 examples in
order to compete in the sports
racing category. The simple goal
was to build a car to compete
with the Porsche 911.*

1981 BMW M1, 6 cylinder in line engine, double overhead camshaft,
3453cc, 277bhp, ZF 5 speed gearbox, 4 wheel vented disc brakes, 4 wheel
independent coil and shock suspension, left hand drive, excellent example,
thoroughly original inside and out. **£68,000-70,000** *CNY*

BMW Model	ENGINE cc/cyl	DATES	CONDITION 1	2	3
501	2077/6	1952-56	£7,500	£5,500	£2,000
501 V8/502	2580, 3168/8	1955-63	£8,000	£6,000	£3,000
503	3168/8	1956-59	£25,000	£20,000	£15,000
507	3168/8	1956-59	£85,000	£70,000	-
Isetta (4 wheels)	247/1	1955-62	£3,000	£2,000	£1,000
Isetta (3 wheels)	298/1	1958-64	£4,000	£2,000	£1,000
Isetta 600	585/2	1958-59	£1,000	£600	£300
1500/1800/2000	var/4	1962-68	£1,100	£700	£200
2000CS	1990/4	1966-69	£5,500	£4,000	£1,500
1500/1600/1602	1499/1573/4	1966-75	£2,000	£1,000	£300
1600 Cabriolet	1573/4	1967-71	£6,000	£4,500	£2,000
2800CS	2788/6	1968-71	£5,000	£4,000	£1,500
1602	1990/4	1968-74	£2,000	£1,500	£600
2002	1990/4	1968-74	£3,000	£2,000	£750
2002 Tii	1990/4	1971-75	£4,500	£2,500	£800
2002 Touring	1990/4	1971-74	£3,000	£2,000	£500
2002 Cabriolet	1990/4	1971-75	£4,000	£3,000	£2,500
2002 Turbo	1990/4	1973-74	£8,000	£5,500	£4,000
3.0 CSa/CSi	2986/6	1972-75	£9,000	£6,000	£4,000
3.0 CSL	3003/3153/6	1972-75	£17,000	£12,000	£9,500

BMW ISETTA

In 1954 the Italian firm of Iso Isetta introduced a tiny 2 seater vehicle. It had a narrow rear track, no differential and a single front door. BMW subsequently acquired both the licence to build it and the press tools needed to manufacture the body parts. The noisy 2 stroke engine was replaced with a modified version of their single cylinder R25 motorcycle 4 stroke engine with numerous other improvements.

The bubble car was at once a practical means of transport in the 1950s and 1960s, with manufacturers such as Heinkel, Isetta and Messerschmitt vying for a share of a lucrative market.

Isetta GB was formed to build the BMW 300 bubble car under licence in Brighton. The 3 wheeled version was rated as a motorcycle for road tax purposes with some 32,000 being built between 1957 and 1963.

1961 BMW Isetta Superplus 300 Bubble Car, 6 year restoration with care to retain originality and catalogue specification.
Est. £3,000-3,500 *S*

1962 BMW Isetta 300 Coupé, good overall condition.
£2,800-3,200 *BKS*

1962 BMW Isetta 300 Super Plus Bubble Car, good overall condition.
Est. £4,000-5,000 *S*

The engine size had grown from 245cc to 298cc by 1962 and the BMW built engine offered a top speed in excess of 50mph with 70mpg economy.

BMW Isettas were successful in motor sport with remarkable endurance performances in such events as the Mille Miglia. The 300cc engine of the Isetta Superplus would rev to some 5200rpm developing 13bhp. Seating for 2/3 people was standard with a front opening door, sliding side windows, a sunshine roof and cowhorn bumpers.

CROSS REFERENCE
Messerschmitt ──────▶p188

1961 BMW Isetta 300, one cylinder, 298cc, good all-round condition.
Est. £2,000-2,500 *ADT*

BOND

1971 Bond Bug 700 ES, 4 cylinder, 700cc, good condition.
£1,100-1,300 *ADT*

BORGWARD

Carl Borgward produced the Hansa and Lloyd cars in his Bremen works, and with the announcement of his new 1½ litre car in 1949, he gave his own name to the new model, the Borgward Hansa. The marque was renowned for its dramatic styling and was offered in both 4 and 6 cylinder models and also with a diesel engine. The first Isabella appeared in 1954.

1961 Borgward Isabella 2 Door Coupé, no bumpers or rear screen, coachwork and original upholstery need attention, restoration project. **Est. £1,500-2,500** *S*

CROSS REFERENCE
Restoration Projects ───────▶ p305

BRASIER

1912 Brasier 12hp Tourer. Est. £15,000-18,000 *S*

BRISTOL

The Bristol Company was founded in 1910 by Sir George White as The British and Colonial Aeroplane Company at Filton, Bristol. In 1920 it became the Bristol Aeroplane Co.

The Type 400, introduced in 1947, was the first production Bristol motor car, derived from a BMW of pre-war design. The 401, 402 and 403 models became more mechanically developed and with superior aerodynamic bodies. In 1968, Bristol adopted the Chrysler V8 engine and produced fast luxurious vehicles.

1948 Bristol 400, 6 cylinders, 1971cc, completely restored, superb example, excellent condition. **£18,000-20,000** *COYS*

1948 Bristol 400 Sports Saloon, 6 cylinders, 1971cc, fully restored, outstanding condition. **£20,000-22,000** *COYS*

Power was provided by Bristol's own version of the BMW 328 engine, an efficient 2 litre, 6 cylinder unit with hemispherical combustion chambers and a complex 18 pushrod system operating the valves. Producing 80bhp at 4200rpm and driving through a 4 speed gearbox, the Bristol 400 could achieve 0-60mph in 19.1 seconds.

1954 Bristol 403 Saloon, bodywork good, but requires restoration. **£3,500-4,000** *S*

BRISTOL Model	ENGINE cc/cyl	DATES	CONDITION		
			1	2	3
400	1971/6	1947-50	£13,000	£12,000	£8,000
401	1971/6	1949-53	£14,000	£9,000	£5,500
402	1971/6	1949-50	£18,000	£16,000	£10,000
403	1971/6	1953-55	£15,000	£10,000	£7,000
404 Coupé	1971/6	1953-57	£17,000	£12,000	£9,000
405	1971/6	1954-58	£12,000	£10,000	£8,000
405 Drophead	1971/6	1954-56	£18,000	£16,000	£13,000
406	2216/6	1958-61	£9,000	£7,500	£4,500
407	5130/8	1962-63	£7,000	£6,000	£4,000
408	5130/8	1964-65	£8,000	£7,000	£4,000
409	5211/8	1966-67	£9,500	£7,500	£4,500
410	5211/8	1969	£11,500	£9,000	£5,000
411 Mk 1-3	6277/8	1970-73	£11,000	£8,000	£6,000
411 Mk 4-5	6556/8	1974-76	£12,000	£9,000	£7,000
412	5900/ 6556/8	1975-82	£14,500	£8,500	£5,500
603	5211/ 5900/8	1976-82	£12,000	£8,000	£5,000

1950 Bristol 400, 6 cylinders, 1971cc, good restoration, very good condition.
Est. £17,000-19,000 *ADT*

A Bristol 400 finished in 3rd place overall in the first post-war Monte Carlo rally.

1952 Bristol 401 2.0 Litre 2 Door Coupé, an older restoration, would benefit from a respray, otherwise very good condition throughout.
Est. £8,000-12,000 *BKS*

The Bristol 401's body was inspired by the work of Touring of Milan and developed in the wind tunnel of the parent Bristol Aeroplane Co. With an aluminium body over a tubular steel frame, the 401 weighed a mere 2700lb.

1962 Bristol 407, engine overhauled, fully restored including chrome.
£10,500-11,000 *Bro*

1961 Bristol 407, very good original condition, with service history.
£9,750-10,000 *Bro*

BSA

1924 BSA 4 Seater Tourer, 10hp, first class condition.
Est. £7,000-8,000 *HOLL*

BUGATTI

The history of Bugatti is really the history of Ettore Bugatti who founded the company in 1909. The first motor car was delivered in 1910. Ettore Bugatti died in 1947, and the company eventually was acquired by Hispano-Suiza and then by SNECMA, the French aerospace combine.

Bugattis fall into two main categories; the road cars and the racing cars. Beware of fake Bugattis, especially the racing cars, some of which date back to before the war, and buy only from reputable sources.

1920 Bugatti Type 22 4 Seater Sport Torpedo, replica coachwork in the style of Durr, complete restoration building up the car on a replica chassis, confirmed by the BOC, original engine, gearbox, clutch and steering but replica front and rear axles, very good condition throughout.
£25,000-28,000 *S*

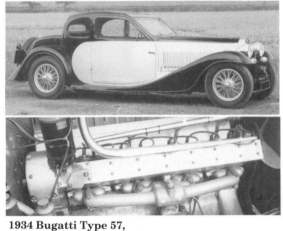

1934 Bugatti Type 57, coachwork by Ventoux Coupé Profilé, 8 cylinders, 3300cc, well maintained, excellent condition.
£75,000-80,000 *COYS*

The 3.3 litre engine was similar in specification to that used in the Type 49 which the Type 57 succeeded. The straight 8 twin overhead camshaft unit developed 140bhp at 4800 and was made in hand-polished aluminium.

1928 Bugatti T38, coachwork by Lavercette et Marcand, original condition.
£150,000-175,000 *FHF*

BUGATTI Model	ENGINE cc/cyl	DATES	CONDITION		
			1	2	3
13/22/23	1496/4	1919-26	£40,000	£32,000	£25,000
30	1991/8	1922-36	£45,000	£35,000	£30,000
32	1992/8	1923	£45,000	£35,000	£30,000
35	1991/8	1924-30	£110,000	£90,000	£80,500
38 (30 update)	1991/8	1926-28	£44,500	£34,000	£28,000
39	1493/8	1926-29	£120,000	£90,000	£80,000
39A Supercharged	1496/8	1926-29	£140,000+	-	-
35T	2262/8	1926-30	£140,000+	-	-
37 GP Car	1496/4	1926-30	£110,000	£90,000	£75,000
40	1496/4	1926-30	£50,000	£42,000	£35,000
38A	1991/8	1927-28	£48,000	£40,000	£35,000
35B Supercharged	2262/8	1927-30	£17,000+	-	-
35C	1991/8	1927-30	£17,000+	-	-
37A	1496/4	1927-30	£125,000+	-	-
44	2991/8	1927-30	£50,000	£40,000	£35,000
45	3801/16	1927-30	£150,000+	-	-
43/43A Tourer	2262/8	1927-31	£180,000+	-	-
35A	1991/8	1928-30	£140,000	£110,000	£90,000
46	5359/8	1929-36	£140,000	£110,000	£90,000
40A	1627/4	1930	£55,000	£45,000	£35,500
49	3257/8	1930-34	£55,000	£45,000	£35,500
57 Closed	3257/8	1934-40	£40,000	£35,000	£30,000
57 Open	3257/8	1936-38	£80,000	£60,000	£55,000
57S	3257/8	1936-38	£250,000+	-	-
57SC Supercharged	3257/8	1936-39	£250,000+	-	-
57G	3257/8	1937-40	£250,000+	-	-
57C	3257/8	1939-40	£140,000+	-	-
Bugatti continues to be popular with not much movement in prices during 1993/4.					

1939 Bugatti 57C 3 Position Drophead Coupé, coachwork
by James Young, Bromley, Kent, recently restored throughout to a
high standard. **£134,000-144,000** *S*

BUICK

1910 Buick Roadster, superb
overall condition.
£24,000-26,000 *FHF*

**1918 Buick 6 Series
44 Roadster,** right hand drive,
engine and body rebuilt, the
wings and wheels are not
original, trial condition, sack
cloth seats, poor paintwork.
Est. £6,000-8,000 *C*

*The first 6 cylinder, overhead
valve engined Buick to be
marketed was the Model B55
which appeared in 1914. In 1916
a revised 6 cylinder model was
launched and the popularity of
these cars helped Buick to a
record year of production with
an output of 124,834 cars.*

CROSS REFERENCE
Racing Cars ⟶ p301

1923 Buick Sports Roadster,
sliding gear transmission, rear
wheel brakes and 3 speed
gearbox, substantially renovated.
£17,500-20,500 *ADT*

*The Buick Motor Car Co. of Flint,
Michigan, was one of the earliest
acquisitions by Durant for his
General Motors Corporation and
despite never being the cheapest
product offered by GM, the Buick
earned a loyal following from its
qualities of reliability and
performance. The 1927 Standard
6 model displaced some 207cu in
and developed 63bhp at 2800rpm.
The sedan sold for $1,295
and some 40,272 sedans were
sold in that production year.*

1929 Buick, left hand drive,
very good overall condition.
£9,500-10,000 *CC*

**1934 Buick McLaughlin S60
4 Door Club Sedan,** overhead
valve, straight 8, IFS, syncromesh
and servo assisted brakes.
£8,000-10,000 *CGB*

**1927 Buick Standard 6
4 Door Sedan,** right hand
drive, original specification,
comprehensive restoration.
£7,000-9,000 *S*

- **David Buick, a Scottish plumber,
  built his first prototype in 1903.**
- **The Buick company was acquired by
  General Motors and the name still
  survives today.**

1928 Buick Golfer's Coupé,
manual 3 speed gearbox, left
hand drive, bodywork, mechanics
and interior all good.
Est. £10,000-12,000 *LF*

*The Golfer's Coupé was a special
model built to accommodate golf
clubs. The cubby hole for these
can be seen between the driver's
seat and the rumble seat or
dickey.*

**1935 Buick (Series 90)
8 Saloon,** 8 cylinders, 5634cc,
right hand drive, unused and
kept in dry storage for the past
20 years, very good original
condition.
Est. £15,000-18,000 *ADT*

*The McLaughlin bodied vehicle
was referred to as the Club Sedan.*

**1935 Buick McLaughlin 3.8 Litre Series 40
6-light Sedan,** good overall condition.
£7,000-8,000 *BKS*

*The marque built official cars for the Royal
Tours of Canada by the Prince of Wales in 1928
and by King George VI and Queen Elizabeth in
1939, and it was a Buick McLaughlin
limousine which King Edward VIII drove
into exile in France after his abdication.*

BUICK Model	ENGINE cc/cyl	DATES	CONDITION		
			1	2	3
Veteran	various	1903-09	£18,500	£12,000	£8,000
18/20	3881/6	1918-22	£12,000	£5,000	£2,000
Series 22	2587/4	1922-24	£9,000	£5,000	£3,000
Series 24/6	3393/6	1923-30	£9,000	£5,000	£3,000
Light 8	3616/8	1931	£18,000	£14,500	£11,000
Straight 8	4467/8	1931	£22,000	£18,000	£10,000
50 Series	3857/8	1931-39	£18,500	£15,000	£10,000
60 Series	5247/8	1936-39	£19,000	£15,000	£8,000
90 Series	5648/8	1934-35	£20,000	£15,500	£9,000
40 Series	4064/8	1936-39	£19,000	£14,000	£10,000
80/90	5247/8	1936-39	£25,000	£20,000	£15,000
McLaughlin	5247/8	1937-40	£22,000	£15,000	£10,000

Various chassis lengths and bodies will affect value. Buick chassis fitted with English bodies
previous to 1916 were called Bedford-Buicks. Right hand drive can have an added premium of 25%.

**1948 Buick Rigid Body
Saloon,** 5 litre, very good
condition.
Est. £4,000-5000 *ECC*

1954 Buick Skylark Convertible, V8, 322cu in,
200bhp, 3 speed automatic gearbox, hydraulic drum
brakes all round, independent coil springs suspension,
rear live axle, leaf springs, telescopic dampers,
left hand drive, 122in wheelbase, body off restoration.
Est. £40,000-47,000 *CNY*

*Skylarks were supplied with chrome plated 40 spoke
Kelsey-Hayes wheels, leather interior, a 4 way power
seat and a power radio antenna.*

**1953 Buick Riviera Super
8 Coupé,** left hand drive, low
mileage, original car, excellent
condition.
£7,000-9,000 *CGB*

**1957 Buick Special
Convertible,** V8, 364cu in,
250bhp at 4400rpm, Dynaflow 3
speed automatic gearbox, 4 wheel
drum brakes, front independent
direct action coil suspension, rear
coil springs, left hand drive,
power steering, power brakes
and a radio, very well
maintained, recently overhauled
including refurbished
transmission, brakes and torque
converter.
£8,000-10,000 *CNY*

**1959 Buick Electra 6.5 Litre
4 Door Sedan,** overhauled
3 speed Dynaflow automatic
transmission, left hand drive,
generally good bodywork, chassis
rust-proofed.
£5,000-5,500 *BKS*

**1960 Buick Le Sabre 2 Door
Hard Top**, left hand drive, very
good condition, interior needs
attention.
£3,500-4,500 *CGB*

BUICK Model	ENGINE cc/cyl	DATES	CONDITION 1	2	3
Special/Super 4 door	248/ 364/8	1950-59	£6,000	£4,000	£2,000
Special/Super Riviera	263/ 332/8	1950-56	£8,000	£6,000	£3,000
Special/Super convertible	263/ 332/8	1950-56	£7,500	£5,500	£3,000
Roadmaster 4 door	320/ 365/8	1950-58	£11,000	£8,000	£6,000
Roadmaster Riviera	320/ 364/8	1950-58	£9,000	£7,000	£5,000
Roadmaster convertible	320/ 364/8	1950-58	£14,500	£11,000	£7,000
Special/Super Riviera	364/8	1957-59	£10,750	£7,500	£5,000
Special/Super convertible	364/8	1957-58	£13,500	£11,000	£6,000

CADILLAC

In 1904 the Cadillac Motor Car Company was formed by Leland and Faulconer. By 1906 they claimed to have the biggest car factory in the world, producing technically advanced, well-made and powerful cars. Although production fell during the Depression, by introducing power brakes and independent suspension, sales exceeded that of Packard by 1936.

During WWII car production was suspended and the Cadillac factories began to build light tanks and gun carriages with V8 engines and Hydramatic. The factories expanded during the 1960s, producing the Eldorado, but production fell sharply following the 'gas guzzling' Seville of 1975.

1930 Cadillac V8 Series 353 Roadster Replica, V8, 353cu in, 95bhp, 3 speed manual gearbox, mechanical drum brakes all-round, rigid axle front suspension, rear live axle, left hand drive, complete ground-up restoration, fitted with replica body that is indistinguishable from the original.
£44,500-45,500 *CNY*

1931 Cadillac V12 Series 370A 7 Passenger Sedan, right hand drive, original condition, museum stored.
£14,000-16,000 *S*

The V12 cars appeared in September 1930 and were technically similar to the V8, but offered outstanding smoothness and power out-performing the larger V16 car.

CADILLAC (pre-war) Model	ENGINE cc/cyl	DATES	CONDITION 1	2	3
Type 57-61	5153/8	1915-23	£20,000	£14,000	£6,000
Series 314	5153/8	1926-27	£22,000	£15,000	£6,000
Type V63	5153/8	1924-27	£20,000	£13,000	£5,000
Series 341	5578/8	1928-29	£22,000	£15,000	£6,000
Series 353-5	5289/8	1930-31	£32,500	£22,000	£12,000
V16	7406/16	1931-32	£40,000	£32,000	£18,000
V12	6030/12	1932-37	£42,000	£25,000	£15,000
V8	5790/8	1935-36	£18,000	£12,000	£6,000
V16	7034/16	1937-40	£45,000	£30,000	£18,000

1949 Cadillac 5.5 Litre Series 62 Convertible, 56,000 miles, never been repainted, trim, carpets and soft top are completely original, unused and in dry storage for the past 3 years.
£24,000-26,000 *BKS*

1953 Cadillac Fleetwood 60 Special, 5.7 litre engine, automatic transmission and power steering, electric windows, very original, no major restoration.
£6,000-6,500 *Cen*

1962 Cadillac Sedan De Ville, electric windows, air conditioning, power seats and radio aerial, original Cadillac floor mats, 19,500 miles, original condition.
Est. £9,000-10,000 *Cen*

1959 Cadillac Coupé De Ville,
2 door hardtop, fully restored.
Est. £11,000-15,000 *CGB*

*As early as 1952, automatic
transmission (as featured on this
example) was standard
specification, and a year later
12 volt electrics were introduced.
Output by 1954 was 230bhp,
wrap around windscreens and
power steering were also
standardised.*

**1958 Cadillac Fleetwood 60
Special 4 Door Saloon,** in
excellent condition throughout.
Est. £9,000-12,000 *S*

1962 Cadillac Coupé De Ville,
2 door, original Wonderbar radio,
excellent interior, good condition.
Est. £2,000-3,000 *Cen*

CADILLAC Model	ENGINE cc/cyl	DATES	CONDITION 1	2	3
4 door sedan	331/8	1949	£8,000	£4,500	£3,000
2 door fastback	331/8	1949	£10,000	£8,000	£5,000
Convertible coupé	331/8	1949	£18,000	£10,000	£7,000
Series 62 4 door	331/365/8	1950-55	£7,000	£5,500	£3,000
Sedan de Ville	365/8	1956-58	£8,000	£6,000	£4,000
Coupé de Ville	331/365/8	1950-58	£12,500	£9,500	£3,500
Convertible coupé	331/365/8	1950-58	£25,000	£20,000	£10,000
Eldorado	331/8	1953-55	£35,000	£30,000	£18,000
Eldorado Seville	365/8	1956-58	£11,500	£9,000	£5,500
Eldorado Biarritz	365/8	1956-58	£30,000	£20,000	£15,000
Sedan de Ville	390/8	1959	£12,000	£9,500	£5,000
Coupé de Ville	390/8	1959	£15,000	£9,000	£5,500
Convertible coupé	390/8	1959	£28,000	£20,000	£10,000
Eldorado Seville	390/8	1959	£13,000	£10,000	£6,000
Eldorado Biarritz	390/8	1959	£30,000	£20,000	£14,000
Sedan de Ville	390/8	1960	£10,000	£8,000	£4,500
Convertible coupé	390/8	1960	£27,000	£14,000	£7,500
Eldorado Biarritz	390/8	1960	£25,000	£17,000	£10,000
Sedan de Ville	390/429/8	1961-64	£7,000	£5,000	£3,000
Coupé de Ville	390/429/8	1961-64	£8,000	£6,000	£4,000
Convertible coupé	390/429/8	1961-64	£15,000	£9,000	£7,000
Eldorado Biarritz	390/429/8	1961-64	£19,500	£14,000	£9,000

CALCOTT

Calcott Bros. Ltd., of Far Gosford Street, Coventry, was one of a number of light car manufacturers who entered the booming motor car industry prior to WWI. Previously they had been engaged in bicycle and motorcycle manufacture, using White and Poppe engines for their early motorcycles.

1915 Calcott 10.5hp 2 Seater with Dickey, 4 cylinders, side valve, 3 speed gearbox, pistons are currently removed ready for a rebore, well upholstered. **Est. £8,500-10,500** *S*

c1920 Calcott 11.9hp 2 Seater with Dickey, good original condition.
Est. £6,500-8,000 *S*
This car has been in the same ownership for some 30 years.

CHEVROLET

Louis Chevrolet and William C. Durant formed the Chevrolet Company in 1911 to produce a prototype car, the Chevrolet. General Motors took control of the company in 1918. In 1935 the 10 millionth Chevrolet rolled off the assembly line.

The Corvette sports car, produced since 1953, typifies the American sports car.

1929 Chevrolet Tourer, right hand drive, excellent condition.
£8,750-9,250 *CC*

1934 Chevrolet Master 6,
6 cylinders, 3358cc, good engine and ancillary equipment, restored.
£10,000-12,000 *ADT*

1934 Chevrolet Master 2 Door Saloon, 6 cylinders, 2800cc, chassis in excellent condition, generally good overall but bodywork requires some attention.
Est. £7,000-8,000 *ADT*

CHEVROLET Model	ENGINE cc/cyl	DATES	CONDITION		
			1	2	3
H4/H490 K Series	2801/4	1914-29	£9,000	£5,000	£2,000
FA5	2699/4	1918	£8,000	£5,000	£2,000
D5	5792/8	1918-19	£10,000	£6,000	£3,000
FB50	3660/4	1919-21	£7,000	£4,000	£2,000
AA	2801/4	1928-32	£5,000	£3,000	£1,000
AB/C	3180/6	1929-36	£6,000	£4,000	£2,000
Master	3358/6	1934-37	£9,000	£5,000	£2,000
Master De Luxe	3548/6	1938-41	£9,000	£6,000	£4,000
Value is very much dependent on being a right or left hand drive car (LHD 15% less).					

1947 Chevrolet Special De Luxe Fleetline Aerosedan, original right hand drive, fine restored condition throughout. **Est. £10,000-12,000** S

Chevrolet entered its post-war production with uprated versions of pre-war models and quickly established itself as America's best selling manufacturer, the value leaders in the low priced field. The Fleetline, Stylemaster and Fleetmaster models were fitted with 6 cylinder in line, 3.5 litre, engines and 3 speed gearbox. The 2 door Aerosedan was introduced initially in 1942 with 'fastback' 2 door coachwork.

1956 Chevrolet Bel Air 2 Door Sedan, original V8 engine, major restoration work. **£4,000-4,750** S

Chevrolet's Bel Air of 1956 was catalogued in 2 and 4 door specifications and also as a 9 passenger Station Wagon. Typifying the American car of the period, the model featured heavy wide doors, wide bench seating front and rear, column mounted 3 speed gear shift, V8 overhead valve 265cu in capacity engine and chrome trim in profusion. The V-emblem on the bonnet represented the 'V' configuration of the engine. At a little over $2,000 the Bel Air represented excellent value for money and over 100,000 examples of the 2 door Sedan left the factory in the 1956 season.

1954 Chevrolet Corvette,
6 cylinder in line engine, 235cu in, 160bhp at 4200rpm, 3 speed automatic gearbox, semi-elliptical leaf springs supporting a hypoid bevel live rear axle, left hand drive, complete frame-off restoration, excellent condition throughout. **£21,000-22,000** CNY

1960 Corvette Convertible 283 Automatic, total restoration. **£18,500-19,500** COR

1963 Chevrolet Corvette Sting Ray, 5.4 litre, 2 seater roadster, good condition throughout. **£12,500-13,500** BKS

1961 Chevrolet Corvette,
8 cylinders, 4640cc, 4 speed gearbox, brakes need servicing, largely in good order throughout. **£9,000-10,000** ADT

1964 Chevrolet Corvette Sting Ray Convertible 327, 250hp, fully restored, knock-off wheels. **£19,000-21,000** COR

1966 Chevrolet Corvette Convertible 327 Automatic, factory knock-off wheels, side exhausts, hard and soft tops, extensive restoration. £19,000-21,000 *COR*

1966 Chevrolet Corvette Sting Ray Big Block, 8 cylinders, 6997cc, Softray tinted glass, fitted radio, hard top and cast aluminium knock-off wheels, panelwork chassis and floorpans in good undamaged condition, excellent order throughout. £16,000-17,000 *ADT*

1969 Chevrolet Corvette Stingray Sports Coupe, 4 speed floor shift gearbox, fitted with supercharer, only known major modification from standard specification. Est. 7,500-8,500 *S*

1969 Chevrolet Corvette 427 Convertible, rebuilt 390hp big block engine, restored hard and soft tops. £18,500-19,500 *COR*

1971 Chevrolet Corvette 350 T-Top, 5.7 litre, automatic gearbox, good condition throughout. £9,750-10,250 *COR*

1973 Chevrolet Corvette Stingray, customised wheels and paint. £14,000-14,500 *FHF*

**1974 Chevrolet Corvette 454
T-Top Big Block,** automatic
gearbox, very good condition.
£10,500-11,500 *COR*

**1986 Chevrolet Corvette 350
Coupe,** automatic gearbox, low
mileage, leather interior.
£11,500-12,500 *COR*

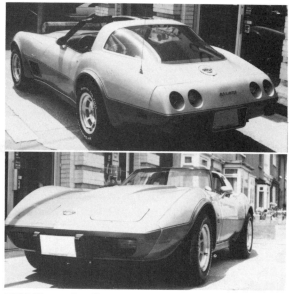

**1978 Chevrolet Corvette 350
T-Top,** optional L-82 engine,
manual gearbox.
£9,500-10,500 *COR*

**1990 Chevrolet Corvette
Coupe,** 6 speed manual gearbox,
excellent condition throughout.
£17,000-19,000 *COR*

CHEVROLET Model	ENGINE cu in/cyl	DATES	CONDITION 1	2	3
Stylemaster	216/6	1942-48	£8,000	£4,000	£1,000
Fleetmaster	216/6	1942-48	£8,000	£4,000	£1,000
Fleetline	216/6	1942-51	£8,000	£5,000	£2,000
Styleline	216/6	1949-52	£8,000	£6,000	£2,000
Bel Air 4 door	235/6	1953-54	£6,000	£4,000	£3,000
Bel Air sports coupé	235/6	1953-54	£7,000	£4,500	£3,500
Bel Air convertible	235/6	1953-54	£12,500	£9,500	£6,000
Bel Air 4 door	283/8	1955-57	£8,000	£4,000	£3,000
Bel Air sports coupé	283/8	1955-56	£11,000	£7,000	£4,000
Bel Air convertible	283/8	1955-56	£16,000	£11,000	£7,000
Bel Air sports coupé	283/8	1957	£11,000	£7,500	£4,500
Bel Air convertible	283/8	1957	£14,500	£10,500	£8,000
Impala sports sedan	235/6, 348/8	1958	£12,500	£9,000	£5,500
Impala convertible	235/6, 348/8	1958	£14,500	£11,000	£7,500
Impala sports sedan	235/6, 348/8	1959	£8,000	£5,000	£4,000
Impala convertible	235/6, 348/8	1959	£14,000	£10,000	£5,000
Corvette roadster	235/6	1953	£40,000	£30,000	£20,000
Corvette roadster	235/6, 283/8	1954-57	£25,500	£20,000	£15,000
Corvette roadster	283, 327/8	1958-62	£20,000	£15,000	£9,000
Corvette Sting Ray	327, 427/8	1963-67	£18,500	£15,000	£10,000
Corvette Sting Ray DHC	327, 427/8	1963-66	£20,000	£15,000	£8,000
Corvette Sting Ray DHC	427/8	1967	£16,000	£13,000	£10,000

Value will also be regulated by build options, rare coachbuilding options, and de luxe engine
spefications etc.

1987 Corvette Convertible, manual gearbox, low mileage.
£14,000-15,000 *COR*

1990 Corvette ZR-1 Coupé, 32 valve, 4 cam, 375bhp, 6 speed gearbox, low mileage.
£24,500-25,500 *COR*

1967 Chevrolet Camaro Convertible, automatic gearbox, very good condition.
£5,000-5,500 *Cen*

The convertible was produced until 1970 when the second generation of Camaro was introduced as a 2+2, with the convertibles being discontinued.

CHRYSLER

Chrysler, founded by Walter Chrysler, an engineer who had previously worked for both Willys and Buick, started production of the 70 model in 1923. Chrysler acquired Dodge and also manufactured Plymouth and De Soto vehicles. Chrysler moved into Europe after WWII and acquired Simca and the Rootes Group.

1926 Chrysler Series G70 2 Seater Roadster, with dickey seat.
£15,500-16,500 *S*

1938 Chrysler Wimbledon, manual gearbox overdrive.
Est. **£4,500-5,500** *ADT*

This car was one of the few cars to be imported by the Rootes Group in parts and then assembled to avoid import duty.

CITROËN

Citroën was founded by the former gear manufacturer, André Citroën. His first production car was the Citroën Type A, which appeared in 1919. Successive models were notably the 1922 5CV Cloverleaf (so called after the seating arrangement for 3 passengers), the Traction Avante and the ubiquitous 2CV, which first appeared in 1929. These cars, along with the DS series of 1955, have ensured Citroën a place in motoring history.

In 1926 Citroën opened a factory at Slough which manufactured cars until 1966. In 1935 the Company was bought by Michelin.

> **Miller's is a price GUIDE not a price LIST.**

c1929 Citroën C6F 2 Litre 4 Door Saloon, 6 cylinders, 2442cc, 3 speed gearbox, Gleason spiral back axle, Slough built, right hand drive, 6 year rebuild, generally good condition throughout.
£6,000-6,500 *S*

1924 Citroën 5CV 2 Seater,
4 cylinders, 856cc, left hand
drive, partly restored, in storage
for a number of years.
£3,500-4,000 *ADT*

1938 Citroën 7C, Paris built,
low mileage, original condition.
£8,250-8,750 *CR*

CITROËN Model	ENGINE cc/cyl	DATES	CONDITION 1	2	3
A	1300/4	1919	£4,000	£2,000	£1,000
5CV	856/4	1922-26	£7,000	£4,000	£2,000
11	1453/4	1922-28	£4,000	£2,000	£1,000
12/24	1538/4	1927-29	£5,000	£3,000	£1,000
2½litre	2442/6	1929-31	£5,000	£3,000	£1,500
13/30	1628/4	1929-31	£5,000	£3,000	£1,000
Big 12	1767/4	1932-35	£7,000	£5,000	£2,000
Twenty	2650/6	1932-35	£10,000	£5,000	£3,000
Ten CV	1452/4	1933-34	£5,000	£3,000	£1,000
Ten CV	1495/4	1935-36	£6,000	£3,000	£1,000
11B/Light 15/Big 15/7CV	1911/4	1934-57	£6,000	£3,000	£1,000
Twelve	1628/4	1936-39	£5,000	£3,000	£1,000
F	1766/4	1937-38	£4,000	£2,000	£1,000
15/6 and Big Six	2866/6	1938-56	£7,000	£4,000	£2,000

1948 Citroën Light 15, Slough
built, recently restored, excellent
condition.
£7,500-8,500 *CR*

1950 Citroën Light 15, Slough
built, needs complete restoration.
£2,750-3,250 *CR*

1955 Citroën Light 15,
4 cylinders, 1911cc, engine and
gearbox in running order, bare
metal respray.
Est. £6,000-7,000 *HOLL*

1956 Citroën 11B, Paris built,
fully restored.
£8,750-9,250 *CR*

1951 Citroën 11BL, Paris built,
40,000 miles from new, original
condition.
£5,000-6,000 *CR*

1951 Citroën 11B, Paris built,
excellent all-round condition.
£6,750-7,250 *CR*

CITROËN Model	ENGINE cc/cyl	DATES	CONDITION 1	2	3
2CV	375/2	1948-54	£1,000	£500	£250
2CV/Dyane/Bijou	425/2	1954-82	£1,000	£500	£250
DS19/ID19	1911/4	1955-69	£5,000	£3,000	£250
Sahara	900/4	1958-67	£5,000	£4,000	£3,000
2CV6	602/2	1963 on	£750	£500	£250
DS Safari	1985/4	1968-75	£5,000	£3,000	£500
DS21	1985/4	1969-75	£5,000	£3,000	£500
DS23	2347/4	1972-75	£5,000	£3,000	£500
SM	2670/ 2974/6	1970-75	£9,000	£6,000	£4,500

Imported (USA) SM models will be 15% less.

1950 Citroën Big 6, Slough built, mechanics fully overhauled, otherwise original condition.
£14,000-15,000 *CR*

1952 Citroën 11B, 4 cylinders, 1911cc, good original condition.
£3,500-3,750 *COYS*

1957 Citroën 1.9 Litre Light 15 4 Door Saloon, sound example.
£3,800-4,400 *BKS*

1955 Citroën 11B, Paris built, mechanically sound.
£5,250-5,750 *CR*

1972 Citroën D Special 19 Saloon, 4 cylinders, 1975cc engine, 4 speed gearbox, left hand drive, generally good condition, requires some slight cosmetic attention.
Est. £4,000-6,000 *S*

CLEMENT-PANHARD

The Clément-Panhard was designed by Commandant Arthur Constantine Krebs, who succeeded Emile Levassor as Technical and Production Manager of Panhard & Levassor. It was assembled in Levallois (Seine) by Ateliers Clément - Adolphe Clément, king of the French cycle industry, was a Panhard & Levassor board member.

1901 Clément-Panhard 4hp Parisian Phæton, rear mounted not quite vertical one cylinder engine, totally exposed gear transmission and centre pivot steering, familarly known as 'Josephine'.
£14,000-15,000 *BKS*

CORD

Errett Lobban Cord became Vice President of the Auburn Automobile Company in 1925, and within 5 years had transformed Auburn from a loss maker into a very successful concern. By 1929, he had set up the Cord Corporation, which included Auburn and Duesenberg cars, Lycoming engines and Stinson aircraft. The company's first model was the L-29 of 1929.

1937 Cord 812 Supercharged 4.7 Litre Custom Beverley 4 Door Sedan.
Est. £25,000-30,000 *BKS(M)*

An outstanding example of the rare long wheelbase 'Custom' version of the Cord 812. The 1935 Cord 810 was the first mass produced American car to combine front wheel drive with independent front suspension. It also had an electrically controlled transmission with overdrive 4th speed.

Locate the source

The source of each illustration in Miller's can be found by checking the code letters below each caption with the list of contributors.

CONRAD

1903 Conrad Rear Entrance Tonneau, only known one in existence, New York Show car in 1903.   **£26,000-27,000** *FHF*

CROSSLEY

1929 Crossley Model IL 20.9hp 7 Seater Tourer, wire wheels, Rotax lighting, radiator stoneguard, running board mounted Klaxon and tool box, glass ashtrays to front and rear, cocktail cabinet and drinks tray, luggage grid and fishtail, rebuilt with all mechanical aspects thoroughly checked and overhauled.
£27,000-29,000 *S*

1937 Cord 812 Convertible Phæton, V8, 4729cc, right hand drive, very good condition.
Est. £38,000-45,000 *COYS*

This is the actual car that appeared at the 1937 Earls Court Show.

DAF

1975 DAF 44, 37,000 miles, good original condition.
£700-800 *Mot*

DAIMLER

Daimler is still considered to be the oldest UK car company, although the earliest vehicles were direct imports from Germany. The Company was bought by BSA in 1901. By the 1920s these luxury vehicles had become the favoured transport of Royalty and after WWII a more affordable range of motor cars was produced, starting with the Conquest Series.

The introduction of the Majestic range and the SP250 'Dart' sports cars failed to save Daimler and the Company was taken over by Jaguar in the 1960s. The Daimler name still appears on their versions of the Jaguar range and all feature the distinctive fluted radiator cowls. Jaguar also acquired the coach-builders Vanden Plas which enabled Daimler to continue to produce Vanden Plas bodied VIP limousines.

1922 Daimler 20hp Doctor's Coupé, with dickey seat, good overall condition.
Est. £14,000-16,000 *S*

c1919 Daimler Light 30 Replica Bodied Phæton, 6 cylinders, sleeve valve, 5 litre, 60bhp, mechanical brakes on rear wheels and transmission, semi-elliptic leaf springs, rear three-quarter elliptic leaf springs, right hand drive, light alloy 3 door 4 seater sports touring body with double folding windscreen constructed by the Oxford Carriage Company, excellent restored condition
£28,000-30,000 *C*

1923 Daimler TS 6-30 Tourer, coachwork by Maythorn & Son Ltd., Biggleswade, 6 cylinders, 30hp, engine overhauled, coachwork largely original, although it probably started life as a landaulette.
£15,000-17,000 *S*

1925 Daimler, good overall condition.
£7,500-8,500 *CC*

1926 Daimler 25/85 6 Light Saloon, coachwork by Daimler Works, Coventry, 3.6 litre engine totally rebuilt, good restored condition.
Est. £15,000-20,000 *BKS*

The 25/85 model was one of the 3 new designs launched for the 1924 season. Apart from His Majesty King George V, owners of 25/85 Daimlers included the King of Spain, HRH the Duke of Connaught, and the Duke of Northumberland.

1935 Daimler Light 15hp, good overall condition.
£4,000-4,500 *CC*

DAIMLER Model	ENGINE cc/cyl	DATES	CONDITION		
			1	2	3
Veteran (Coventry built)	var/4	1897-1904	£75,000	£60,000	£40,000
Veteran	var/4	1905-19	£35,000	£25,000	£15,000
30hp	4962/6	1919-25	£40,000	£25,000	£18,000
45hp	7413/6	1919-25	£45,000	£30,000	£20,000
Double Six 50	7136/12	1927-34	£40,000	£30,000	£22,000
20	2687/6	1934-35	£18,000	£14,000	£12,000
Straight 8	3421/8	1936-38	£20,000	£15,000	£12,000

Value is dependent on body style, coachbuilder and condition of the sleeve valve engine.

1938 Daimler DB18 2½ Litre Drophead Coupé, coachwork by Tickford, 6 cylinders, 2522cc, very good condition throughout.
£10,000-10,500 *ADT*

Daimler had manufactured a 15 model since 1933 and although this had a 1805cc engine the car was further revised for 1937. The most important innovation was the Girling designed independent front suspension employing large coil springs. In the same year the engine size was increased to 2166cc and the track and wheel base dimensions were modified to 52in and 114in. In 1938 the power unit of the 15 was further enlarged to 2522cc and various chassis in the series were designated first to the DB 17 and then the DB 18.

1948 Daimler Barker DB18 Drophead Coupé.
£9,500-10,500 *Cum*

1950 Daimler DB18 Special Sports Coupé, coachwork by Barker.
£12,000-15,000 *FHF*

1949 Daimler DB18 Drophead Coupé, coachwork by Barker, 6 cylinders, 2522cc, pre-select gearbox, good all-round condition, restored.
Est. £5,400-6,400 *ADT*

1951 Daimler DB18 Drophead Coupé, coachwork by Barker, 6 cylinders, 2500cc, 3 position drophead, 4 seater, needs restoration.
£3,250-3,500 *ADT*

1951 Daimler DB18 Drophead Coupé, coachwork by Barker, 6 cylinders, 2522cc, fully restored and in good condition.
£12,000-13,000 *COYS*

1952 Daimler DE36 7 Seater Limousine, coachwork by Hooper, 8 cylinders, 5500cc, resprayed bodywork, interior has luxurious refurbishment and extensive restoration.
£4,500-5,000 *ADT*

1952 Daimler 2½ Litre Special Sports Drophead Coupé, coachwork by Barker, recently well restored.
Est. £13,000-15,000 *S*

This luxuriously trimmed and equipped Sports Special sold for over £2,000 in 1950.

1954 Daimler Empress 11A 3½ Litre Saloon, coachwork by Hooper, good general condition.
Est. £10,500-12,500 *S*

This car is one of only 24 built.

1957 Daimler Conquest Century 2.6 litre Saloon, automatic gearbox, good condition.
Est. £900-1,500 *ECC*

1952 Daimler DB18 Special Sports 3 Seater Drophead Coupé, coachwork by Barker, 6 cylinders, 2522cc, good all-round condition.
£5,000-5,500 *ADT*

608 Special Sport's chassis were produced although only about 500 were given the Barker body with the remainder having Hooper coachwork.

1952 Daimler DB18 3 Seater Drophead Coupé Special Sports, coachwork by Barker, good condition throughout.
Est. £12,000-14,000 *S*

1953 Daimler Empress, coachwork by Hooper, 6 cylinders, 3500cc, restored to a good standard.
Est. £5,000-6,000 *ADT*

1955 Daimler Conquest Century Saloon, 6 cylinders, 2433cc, pre-selector gearbox, good sound condition.
£1,250-1,500 *ADT*

1961 Daimler Majestic 4 Door Coupé, 6 cylinders, 3794cc, overhead valve, 147bhp at 4400rpm, automatic gearbox, disc brakes all-round, front independent coil suspension, rear semi-elliptic leaf springs, right hand drive, factory reconditioned engine, excellent condition.
£2,250-2,700 *C*

In 1958 the Daimler Majestic was launched with automatic transmission and disc brakes as standard equipment. It was based on the earlier 104 saloon structure of 1955, but with revised full width wing treatment behind the centre pillar.

1961 Daimler SP250 B Series, original wire wheels, full history, in excellent condition.
£13,000-15,000 *CGOC*

1962 Daimler SP250 B Series, hard and soft tops, full history, in superb condition.
£15,000-17,000 *CGOC*

1962 Daimler SP250, 8 cylinders, 2500cc, fully restored 3 years ago.
£10,000-11,000 *ADT*

1962 Daimler SP250 B Series, only 50,000 miles, one owner from new with full history.
£14,000-16,000 *CGOC*

1964 Daimler Dart 250SP C Series, wire wheels, 2 owners from new, very good condition.
£12,000-15,000 *VIC*

1964 Daimler 2.5 Litre V8 250 4 Door Saloon, body restored, very good condition throughout. **£3,500-4,000** *BKS*

The origins of the Daimler 2.5 litre V8 saloon go back to the late 1950s, before Sir William Lyons took over of the Daimler Motor Company. Edward Turner of Daimler, best known as the designer of the Ariel Square Four and the Triumph Speed Twin, evolved a 2.5 litre light alloy V8 engine developing 140bhp at 5800rpm This was installed in the glass fibre bodied Daimler SP250 Dart sports car.

1964 Daimler V8 250 Saloon,
automatic transmission, general
mechanical condition good, one
owner from new.
£4,250-4,750 *S*

1968 Daimler V8 250 Saloon,
automatic transmission, wire
wheels, fibreglass replacement
front wings, mechanically sound.
£1,500-1,700 *CCTC*

**1969 Daimler V8 250 Sports
Saloon,** fair condition and
requires restoration.
£2,250-2,750 *S*

1968 Daimler 420 Sovereign,
6 cylinders, 4233cc, engine
completely rebuilt, otherwise
good original condition.
Est. £4,250-5,250 *ADT*

1969 Daimler V8 250 Saloon,
8 cylinders, 2548cc, very good
original condition.
£5,000-5,500 *ADT*

**1982 Daimler Double 6 Mk III
Vanden Plas HE,** automatic
transmission, right hand drive,
bodywork and mechanics very
good. **£3,000-3,500** *LF*

**1975 Daimler Sovereign 4.2
Litre 2 Door Coupé,** automatic
transmission, mechanically
prepared to the highest standard,
coachwork and leather interior
carefully restored to original
specification.
Est. £5,500-6,000 *S*

*Daimler announced the second
series Sovereign in the Autumn of
1969 and it was basically derived
from the Jaguar XJ6.*

**1978 Daimler Double 6
Vanden Plas,** 12 cylinders,
5343cc, good condition overall.
£1,500-1,800 *ADT*

DAIMLER Model	ENGINE cc/cyl	DATES	CONDITION		
			1	2	3
DB18	2522/6	1946-49	£7,500	£4,000	£1,000
DB18 Cony S/S	2522/6	1948-53	£9,500	£6,000	£2,000
Consort	2522/6	1949-53	£4,000	£2,000	£500
Conquest/Con.Century	2433/6	1953-58	£4,000	£2,000	£500
Conquest Roadster	2433/6	1953-56	£9,000	£6,000	£2,000
Majestic 3.8	3794/6	1958-62	£4,000	£2,000	£450
SP250	2547/8	1959-64	£12,000	£10,000	£4,500
Majestic Major	4561/8	1961-64	£5,000	£3,000	£500
2.5 V8	2547/8	1962-67	£7,000	£5,250	£2,500
V8 250	2547/8	1968-69	£5,000	£3,750	£2,000
Sovereign 420	4235/6	1966-69	£5,000	£3,500	£1,500

DARRACQ

'Genevieve', 1904 Darracq
2.3 Litre 12hp 2 Seater, fully
restored condition.
£143,000-148,000 *BKS*

*This is the original car on which
the comedy film* Genevieve *was
based.*

1979 Datsun 2.6 litre 260Z Sports Coupé, engine
modified by fitting triple Weber carburettors and 5
speed manual transmission, excellent overall
condition. **£6,250-6,750** *BKS*

DATSUN

**1972 Datsun Fair Lady
Roadster,** right hand drive.
£7,000-9,000 *FHF*

1981 Datson 280 ZX Targa,
6 cylinders, 2753cc, alloy wheels,
resprayed.
Est. £1,600-1,800 *ADT*

DATSUN Model	ENGINE cc/cyl	DATES	CONDITION		
			1	2	3
240Z	2393/6	1970-71	£6,000	£4,000	£3,500
240Z	2393/6	1971-74	£4,500	£3,250	£1,500
260Z	2565/6	1974-79	£3,000	£2,250	£1,000
260Z 2+2	2565/6	1974-79	£2,250	£1,500	£350

DE DION BOUTON

1904 De Dion Bouton swing seat Tonneau, single
cylinder engine, 6hp, 3 speed, original body by
Carrosserie Lamplugh & Cie, restored with all
original fittings. **£26,500-28,000** *Mot*

**1903/4 De Dion Bouton Model
V 8hp Wagonette,** much
restored, complete engine rebuild,
but gearbox needs attention.
Est. £11,000-15,000 *S*

**1908 De Dion Bouton Model
BR 12/14hp Double Phæton,**
4 cylinders side valve engine,
1767cc, 3 speed gearbox and
shaft drive, equipped with Lucas
oil sidelamps, a P & H acetylene
headlamp and a Ducellier rear
lamp together with rear view
mirror and bulb horn.
Est. £16,000-20,000 *S*

DELAGE

Louis Delage founded the Company in 1905 and soon earned a reputation for high standards of engineering rivalling Rolls-Royce and Hispan-Suiza as manufacturers of top quality motor vehicles. Delage was bought by Delahaye in 1935. Hotchkiss then acquired the Company in the 1940s and by 1954 production had ceased.

c1910 Delage 10hp 3 Seater Runabout, Ballot 4G 4 cylinder 1.6 litre engine, requires restoration following museum storage. **£13,000-15,000** *S*

1930 Delage 2.5 Litre DR70 Saloon, coachwork by Chapron, re-upholstered, in good original order. **£6,800-7,500** *ADT*

Louis Delage, a former employee of Peugeot, started making cars in 1905. Delage became synonymous with large engined cars and turned to 6 cylinder, 3.2 litre overhead valve and side valve units in 1929.

DE LOREAN

1981 De Lorean DMC, 6 cylinders, 2849cc, left hand drive, the car has travelled just 30kms, brushed stainless steel finish, in perfect condition. **£10,000-11,000** *ADT*

10,000 De Loreans were built, most being left hand drive and destined for the United States. This vehicle does not possess United Kingdom Type Approval and cannot be used on British roads.

DELAHAYE

Emile Delahaye made his first motor vehicle in 1894 and produced an ordinary range of models until he acquired Delage in 1935. They then produced sports cars as well as Grand Prix racing cars. Following a series of mergers and takeovers, production finally ceased in 1956.

1951 Delahaye 135 Drophead Coupé, coachwork by Chapron, 6 cylinder in line monobloc engine, 3557cc, overhead pushrod valves, 84 by 107mm bore and stroke, 130hp, single disc clutch, 4 speed Cotal transmission, Gleason rear axle, IFS front suspension, rear semi-elliptic, 116½in wheelbase, chrome wire wheels, excellent overall condition. **£44,000-46,000** *S(NY)*

DELLOW

1952 Dellow DL Mark II, 4 cylinders, 1172cc, Ford E93A engine, Dellow 4 branch exhaust manifold and aquaplane cylinder head, used in trials and hill climbs recently, in sound condition. **£3,200-3,700** *ADT*

DESANDE

The Desande resembled the American built Clenet, but was made by Desande Automobielen of Hülst in the Netherlands. It was based on Ford mechanical components, with either 5 litre or 5.8 litre V8 engines, in a box section frame with coil suspension. Later examples were Chevrolets powered with a 5.7 litre V8 engine with automatic transmission.

The makers announced that production would be limited to only 250 units, but it seems unlikely that more than 18 were built.

1981 Desande Caprice Roadster, good condition throughout. **£20,000-22,000** *S*
This car apparently cost £150,000 when new and was built for the Sultan of Selangor.

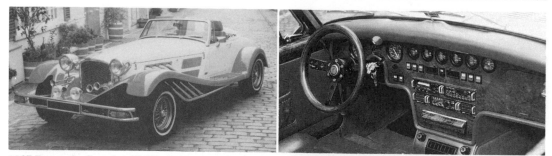

1987 Desande Caprice II, V8, 5300cc, coachwork by Grand Prix Metalcraft, excellent condition.
£23,000-25,000 *C*

DE SOTO

The De Soto marque was introduced as a lower priced range for the Chrysler Group in 1928. The name De Soto comes from the 16thC explorer who discovered the Mississippi River.

c1929 De Soto Roadster, 6 cylinders, 3104cc, complete and total engine overhaul, full body respray and chassis rebuild, uncompleted restoration project as various components are missing.
Est. £5,500-7,500 *ADT*

1929 De Soto 6 Series K Tourer, coachwork probably by Holden in the American phæton style, good overall condition.
Est. £10,000-12,000 *S*

1933 De Soto Custom SD Saloon, 6 cylinders, 3600cc, hydraulic brakes, automatic vacuum clutch, Delco-Remy ignition, twin sun visors, trumpet horns, restored approximately 15 years ago, good condition.
£6,750-7,500 *ADT*

DE TOMASO

1983 De Tomaso Longchamp GTS, 8 cylinders, 5763cc, right hand drive, sound condition.
Est. £12,000-13,000 *ADT*

In late 1972 De Tomaso introduced their Frua inspired Longchamp model. Unlike the Pantera, the Longchamp was a front engined car but still with a Ford V8 engine.

1972 De Tomaso Pantera, engine missing, restoration project, poor general condition.
£5,000-6,000 *COYS*

DIATTO

1922-23 Diatto Tipo 20 Targa Florio Ex-Works Racing 2 seater, 4 cylinders, single overhead camshaft and 'semi-hemi' combustion chambers alloy 2 litre engine, driving via a 4 speed unit gearbox, rebuilt between 1988 and 1992.
£35,000-37,000 *BKS*

Alfieri Maserati began his career as a design engineer by developing Giuseppe Coda's basic production Diatto 20 design, and founded his own Maserati marque in 1926.

CROSS REFERENCE
Racing Cars ——→ p301

DODGE

In 1928 Walter Chrysler paid $175 million for the Dodge Company which had been started by the Dodge Brothers in 1914.

1926 Dodge 5 Seater Tourer, 4 cylinders, 3673cc, 3 speed gearbox, right hand drive, detailed restoration 2 years ago, in good useable condition.
£9,750-10,250 *ADT*

1929 Dodge, right hand drive, very good overall condition.
£9,500-10,500 *CC*

EDSEL

1958 Edsel Citation Convertible, V8 engine, 6790cc, overhead valve, 345bhp at 4600rpm, 3 speed push button gearbox, drum brakes front and rear, left hand drive, total body-off restoration.
£42,000-43,000 *CNY*

ELVA

The Elva name originated from 'elle va', meaning literally 'she goes'. The Bexhill-based company's best remembered model was the Courier, designed by Peter Knott, using a tubular chassis, MGA mechanics and a sleek fibreglass bodyshell. Approximately 600 Elva Couriers were made, of which only 33 were coupés.

1963 Elva 1.8 Litre Courier GT 2 Door Coupé, in good condition throughout. **Est. £4,000-6,000** *BKS*

EMPIRE

1980 Empire Special, based on a 1936 MG.
Est. £3,000-3,500 *ECC*

ENFIELD

The Enfield was a 2 door saloon, powered by a Maudslay 6kw electric motor and 4 x 12 volt heavy duty truck batteries, with a built-in mains charging unit. Bodywork was in rust-free aluminium, with early Mini pattern wheels, tyres and sliding windows, a Hillman Imp steering rack, and the rear axle of Reliant-type. The 6 speed control was by heavy duty solenoid contactors and an accelerator pedal, but without clutch or gears. A simple polarity switch put the car in reverse. Top speed was about 50mph with a 6 hour charge, providing a range of 20-30 miles.

1974 Enfield Electric City Car, original orange paintwork, upholstered in black PVC, good overall condition.
£1,500-2,000 *S*

ERA

English Racing Automobiles of Bourne in Lincolnshire, built 17 single seater A- to D-Type 'old English upright' cars between 1934 and 1939. Only one car has survived to date.

CROSS REFERENCE
Racing Cars ⟶ p301

1934/1988 ERA 1.5 Litre A-Type Racing Voiturette Replica, original 6 cylinder supercharged engine, accepted by the VSCC.
Est. £80,000-120,000 *BKS*

This replica was constructed by Tony Merrick over a number of years with the approval of the VSCC and the members of the ERA Club, who allocated the car its number. The car is made from mainly genuine and original ERA parts, and is virtually new.

FACEL VEGA

1959 Facel Vega HK500, 8 cylinders, 6283cc, push button, pre-select, automatic transmission, right hand drive, roof lining missing, very good overall condition.
£7,750-8,250 *ADT*

1962 Facel Vega Facel II, V8 engine, 6268cc, rare manual gearbox, right hand drive, completely restored, excellent condition.
£32,000-34,000 *COYS*

1960 Facel Vega 6.3 Litre HK500 Coupé, coachwork by Facel Metallon, exhibition car standard.
Est. £20,000-30,000 *BKS*

The HK500 was launched in 1959 with the new 6.3 litre 'wedge-head' unit, developing 350bhp.

FERRARI

Enzo Ferrari joined Alfa Romeo in 1920 as a test driver, and had a successful racing career until illness forced him to retire in 1932. In 1939 he formed his own company, and entered two cars in the 1940 Brescia Grand Prix.

Having suspended car production during WWII, Ferrari started building road and racing cars in 1946, commencing with the 1½ litre V12 125C, first seen at Piacenza in May 1947. This was followed by the bigger engined 159 and 166, which became the basis for their road cars.

In 1954 the 250 Europa committed Ferrari to road car manufacture, and in 1961 the range included the 250GT 2+2, the first of their cars to have more than 2 seats. Ferrari's success in racing continues today, and their cars are among the fastest in the world.

The Prototype1950 Ferrari 166 2 Litre Le Mans Berlinetta, coachwork by Carrozzeria Touring, Milan.
£180,000-220,000 *BKS(M)*

This car has an excellent provenance as the very first Le Mans Berlinetta to have been built by Touring Milan.

Of 165 short wheelbases built at the Maranello factory between 1960 and 1962, only 6 are known to have originated with special bodies, 2 by Bertone and 4 by Pininfarina.

1963 Ferrari 250 GT 3 Litre Short Wheelbase 2 Door Berlinetta Stradale, special coachwork by Carrozzeria Pininfarina, very good overall condition.
Est. £150,000-200,000 *BKS*

1964 Ferrari 275 GTB, Berlinetta coachwork by Pininfarina, V12 engine, 3286cc, 6 carburettors, Borrani wire wheels, complete restoration, mechanical rebuild, superb condition.
Est. £110,000-130,000 *COYS*

1966 Ferrari 275 GTB, Berlinetta aluminium coachwork by Pininfarina, V12 engine, 3285cc, 6 carburettors, useable unrestored condition.
£110,000-115,000 *COYS*

1966 Ferrari 330 GT Mk II Coupé, V12 engine, 3967cc, coachwork by Pininfarina, good overall condition.
£22,000-24,000 *COYS*

Only 36 right hand drive Mk IIs were built.

1971 Ferrari 365 GTC/4, complete body restoration, excellent condition.
£46,000-48,000 *COYS*

1968 Ferrari 365 GTC, V12 engine, 4390cc, single overhead cam, 320bhp at 6600rpm, 5 speed manual gearbox, independent double wishbones and coil springs suspension front and rear, left hand drive, Borrani wheels, factory electric and mechanical fuel pumps, air conditioning, excellent overall condition.
Est. £70,000-80,000 *CNY*

Only just over one hundred 2 seater 365 GTCs were built.

1970 Ferrari 365 GTB/4 Daytona, with immaculate red paintwork.
Est. £75,000-85,000 *COYS*

1966 Ferrari 330 GT 2+2, coachwork by Pininfarina, 78,000 miles, fair to good condition, needs restoration.
£19,000-21,000 *S(Z)*

The 330 GT 2+2 was announced in 1964 and was developed as a replacement for the 250 GTE 2+2. The design was based upon the 4 litre 400 Superamerica engine and Pininfarina's coachwork.

1971 Ferrari 365GT 2+2, Coupé coachwork by Pininfarina, 12 cylinders, 4390cc, right hand drive, optional Borrani wire wheels, restored, excellent condition.
£34,000-36,000 *COYS*

Miller's is a price GUIDE not a price LIST.

1969 Ferrari 365 GTC, V12 engine, 4390cc, coupé coachwork by Pininfarina, right hand drive, one of just 22, optional Borrani wire wheels, excellent condition.
£58,000-60,000 *COYS*

Powered by a 4 litre V12 engine with a 4 speed with overdrive transaxle, later models used a 5 speed gearbox. The 365 GTC, which replaced the 330 GTC in late 1968, was identical in appearance except the relocation of engine cooling vents from the front wings to the bonnet.

1973 Ferrari 365 GTB/4 Daytona 2 seater Berlinetta, coachwork by Pininfarina, 4.4 litres, good condition overall.
Est. £60,000-80,000 *BKS*

The Daytona took its unofficial name from the victories by the 330 P4 in the 1967 Daytona 24-hour race.

1972 Ferrari Dino 246, excellent overall condition.
£35,000-45,000 *FHF*

1972 Ferrari 365 GTC/4, only 14,100 miles, original and excellent condition throughout.
£57,000-65,000 *HWA*

1973 Ferrari 246 GTS Dino, 6 cylinders, 2418cc, no known mechanical faults, in excellent condition.
Est. £35,000-40,000 *ADT*

1974 Ferrari 365 GT4 Berlinetta Boxer, coachwork by Pininfarina, flat-12 alloy longitudinally mounted engine 4390cc, 4 overhead camshafts and 4 triple downdraught Weber carburettors, producing 360bhp at 7,000rpm, 5 speed gearbox, 181mph maximum speed with 0-60mph in 5.3 seconds, full service history, very good condition.
£52,500-55,000 *COYS*

1974 Ferrari 365 GT4 Berlinetta Boxer, 12 cylinders, 4390cc, engine rebuilt, restored to excellent condition.
£47,500-50,000 *COYS*

1974 Ferrari GT4 2+2, with Bertone-designed Scaglietti built coachwork.
£27,000-30,000 *FHF*

1977 Ferrari 308 GTB Berlinetta, coachwork by Pininfarina, V8, 4 cam engine, 2.9 litres, fibreglass body, 46,000 miles, 4 owners from new, good condition throughout.
£21,000-23,000 *BKS*

1977 Ferrari 400 GT Berlina, coachwork by Pininfarina, 4.8 litres, 2 doors, self-levelling rear suspension, standard automatic transmission, good original condition throughout.
Est. £14,000-18,000 *BKS*

Fuel injection was not fitted until late 1979 with the launch of the 400i model. A total of 502 were built.

1978 Ferrari 308 GT4,
8 cylinders, 2926cc, rebuilt engine, new aluminium underplate fitted to the floorplan, interior completely renewed, extensively restored.
Est. £24,000-26,000 *ADT*

1978 Ferrari 308 GTS Sports Spider, 4 carburettors, deep front spoiler, 16in Speedline alloy wheels, stainless steel exhaust, major restoration to excellent condition. **Est. £25,000-28,000** *S*

This model has a 3 litre quad cam V8 engine, a dry sump engine which develops some 255bhp at 7,700rpm, 5 speed manual gearbox, and a top speed of 154mph achieving 0-100mph in just 17 seconds.

1977 Ferrari 512 Boxer Berlinetta, modified Supercar version by Koenig, flat 12, 5 litre engine, modified including addition of the company's full aerodynamic coachwork, fitting of 2 plate heavy duty clutch, high performance free-flow exhaust systems and manifold, race tuned engine, new gearbox, racing specification front brakes, very good overall condition.
Est. £60,000-90,000 *BKS*

1978 Ferrari 400, very good condition. **Est. £15,000-20,000** *Cen*
The first Ferrari to be offered with automatic transmission.

FERRARI Model	ENGINE cc/cyl	DATES	CONDITION 1	2	3
250 GT	2953/12	1959-63	£32,000	£22,000	£20,000
250 GT SWB (steel)	2953/12	1959-62	£235,000	£185,000	-
250 GT Lusso	2953/12	1962-64	£80,000	£65,000	-
250 GT 2+2	2953/12	1961-64	£30,000	£21,000	£18,000
275 GTB	3286/12	1964-66	£95,000	-	-
275 GTS	3286/12	1965-67	£80,000	£60,000	£42,000
275 GTB 4-cam	3286/12	1966-68	£125,000	£95,000	-
330 GT 2+2	3967/12	1964-67	£22,000	£16,000	£11,000
330 GTC	3967/12	1966-68	£55,000	£38,000	£22,000
330 GTS	3967/12	1966-68	£65,000	£60,000	£55,000
365 GT 2+2	4390/12	1967-71	£24,000	£18,000	£11,000
365 GTC	4390/12	1967-70	£40,000	£32,000	£28,000
365 GTS	4390/12	1968-69	£110,000	£75,000	£65,000
365 GTB (Daytona)	4390/12	1968-74	£90,000	£60,000	£42,000
365 GTC4	4390/12	1971-74	£41,000	-	-
365 GT4 2+2/400GT	4390/4823/12	1972-79	£18,000	£12,000	£9,500
365 BB	4390/12	1974-76	£55,000	£38,000	£30,000
512 BB/BBi	4942/12	1976-81	£40,000	£32,000	£28,000
246 GT Dino	2418/6	1969-74	£35,000	£25,000	£15,000
246 GTS Dino	2418/6	1972-74	£42,000	£28,000	£22,000
308 GT4 2+2	2926/8	1973-80	£12,500	£8,000	£7,500
308 GTB (fibreglass)	2926/8	1975-76	£25,000	£18,000	£15,000
308 GTB	2926/8	1977-81	£22,000	£16,000	£9,000
308 GTS	2926/8	1978-81	£26,000	£18,000	£11,000
308 GTBi/GTSi	2926/8	1981-82	£24,000	£17,000	£8,000
308 GTB/GTS QV	2926/6	1983-85	£21,500	£16,500	£9,500
400i manual	4823/12	1981-85	£15,000	£11,000	£7,000
400i auto	4823/12	1981-85	£13,000	£12,000	£8,000

1979 Ferrari 400 Convertible, 12 cylinders, 4823cc, good condition but requires some attention.
£14,500-15,500 *ADT*

Ferrari never actually made a 400 convertible, although quite a number of owners have had their own cars modified from saloon to open top.

Did you know?
MILLER'S Collectors Cars Price Guide *builds up year-by-year to form the most comprehensive photo library system available.*

1980 Ferrari 512BB Boxer, 12 cylinders, 4942cc, Berlinetta coachwork by Pininfarina, less than 50,000 miles from new, very good condtion throughout.
£48,000-50,000 *COYS*

The revised model, called 512BB used an enlarged version of the original Boxer engine bored out to 4.9 litres.

1980 Ferrari 400i Berlina, coachwork by Pininfarina, manual transmission, in good condition.
£18,500-20,000 *BKS*

In 1979, the 6 DCOE Webers of the 400 GT were replaced by a specially developed Bosche K-Jetronic fuel injection installation to create the 400i GT. One of only 24 right hand drive 400i's built.

1981 Ferrari 400i Berlina, coachwork by Pininfarina, 4.8 litres, fitted with optional air conditioning, full service history, fine original example.
Est. 16,000-20,000 *BKS*

1982 Ferrari 308 GTB, only 50,000 miles, full service history, fully restored to high specification.
Est. £25,000-30,000 *ECC*

1983 Ferrari Mondial QV, 8 cylinders, 2926cc, in good condition.
£13,500-14,500 *ADT*

The first road-going model Ferrari to feature 4 valves per cylinder was the Mondial, appropriately named Quattrovalvole.

1984 Ferrari 400i, 12 cylinders, 4823cc, good overall condtion.
£14,500-16,000 *ADT*

1984 Ferrari Mondial QV, 52,000 miles, good example.
£10,000-11,000 *HOLL*

FIAT

Fiat was founded in 1899 in Turin, and started production with the Fiat Tipo A. Exports of their 8 and 12hp cars began in 1901, and by 1904 the factory had trebled in size. During WWI, production grew from staff cars to Italy's first tank and aircraft engines, resulting in quadrupled assets.

With the success in mid-1930s of the Fiat 500 Topolino, expansion continued until well into WWII. Their reputation continues today as a multi-national industrial giant owning both Ferrari and Lancia.

1913 Fiat T52B 12 Seater Shooting Brake, contemporary coachwork, engine removed and dismantled, cylinder block in need of specialist welding, right hand drive.
£5,500-6,000 *C*

1970 Fiat 500L, full sunroof, totally original throughout, exceptionally good condition.
£1,400-1,600 *Cen*

1934 Fiat Balilla Roadster.
£4,800-5,200 *DB*

FIAT Model	ENGINE cc/cyl	DATES	CONDITION		
			1	2	3
501	1460/4	1920-26	£6,000	£3,500	£1,500
519	4767/6	1923-29	£9,000	£7,000	£3,000
503	1473/4	1927-29	£8,000	£4,000	£2,000
507	2297/4	1927-28	£9,000	£5,500	£3,500
522/4	2516/6	1932-34	£10,000	£8,000	£3,500
508	994/4	1934-37	£5,000	£2,500	£1,500
527 Sports	2516/6	1935-36	£14,000	£8,000	£3,500
1.5 litre Balilla	1498/4	1936-39	£10,000	£7,000	£3,000
500	570/4	1937-55	£6,000	£2,500	£1,000
1100 Balilla	1089/4	1938-40	£4,500	£2,000	£1,000

1961 Fiat 600cc Multipla Station Wagon, original trim, good all-round condition.
Est. £4,000-4,200 *S*

Fiat revealed their Multipla model at the Brussels Show in 1956. The model featured 6 seats, 4 of which could fold flat. There was also an optional 4 seater version. The 4 cylinder engine was coupled to a 4 speed gearbox, the front suspension was a new design featuring coil springs and an anti-roll bar, a small radiator in front supplied warm air to the interior from hot water from the engine. The Multipla replaced the Giardinetta 500 station wagon.

1965 Fiat Multipla Station Wagon, 633cc, coachwork in need of restoration, right hand drive, no documents with the car.
Est. £1,000-1,400 *S*

1963 Fiat 600D Saloon, coachwork in good condition, engine recently been rebuilt, good interior.
£1,400-1,600 *S*

1972 Fiat 500L Saloon, original specification, with comprehensive history.
£2,500-3,000 *S*

The Fiat 600D enjoyed a production run from 1960 to 1970 with over 1½ million examples being built primarily in Italy, but also in Germany, Yugoslavia, Argentina and Spain. It featured a 4 cylinder, overhead valve, water-cooled engine of 767cc capacity, developing some 32bhp at 4,800rpm, and a 4 speed synchromesh gearbox.

1966 Fiat Abarth 595 Sports Coupé, 600cc, reconditioned engine, extremely sound condition.
Est. £5,000-7,000 *BKS*

The basic Abarth 595 conversion for the 500 consisted of joined big bore cylinder barrels and pistons, special camshaft, carburettor, exhaust system and deep finned alloy sump, boosting maximum power from 18 to 27bhp.

- **Introduced in 1936, the Fiat 500 was the world's smallest production car.**
- **Quickly nicknamed Topolino (Mickey Mouse) it remained in production until 1948.**
- **Over 122,000 were made.**

1972 Fiat 500 Topolino 2 Door 4 Seater Saloon, rear mounted twin cylinder 499cc engine, 4 speed gearbox, good condition throughout.
£2,250-2,500 *S*

1964 Fiat 1500 Cabriolet, 4 cylinders in line, overhead valve, 1995cc, 2 litres, 120bhp at 5500rpm, 5 speed manual gearbox, disc brakes all round, front suspension independent coil springs, wishbones, anti-roll bar, rear semi-elliptic leaf springs, left-hand drive, totally restored, immaculate example.
£6,250-6,750 *C*

Although resembling the standard 1500 Cabriolet, the original engine has been replaced with a 2 litre Lancia twin overhead camshaft engine with a 5 speed manual gearbox.

1962 Fiat 1600S Roadster, good restored condition.
£1,500-2,500 *ALC*

1967 Fiat 2300S Coupé, panelwork very good, excellent chassis, full repaint, alloy wheels, with spare engine, 2 gearboxes and spares.
£2,500-2,750 *ADT*

1967 Fiat Dino Spyder, 2 litre engine, rebuilt, left hand drive, bare metal respray, re-chromed, major restoration carried out.
£19,000-20,000 *S*

The Fiat Dino used the Ferrari 65° V6 engine of 1,987cc capacity and 160bhp at 7,200rpm, driving through 5 speed gearbox to the rear axle. 2 body styles were offered, the 4 seater coupé by Bertone and the Pininfarina Spyder.

1973 Fiat 130 2 Door Coupé, coachwork by Pininfarina, V6, 3.2 litre engine, 165bhp, automatic transmission, (compulsory with right hand drive), full supporting documentation, very good all-round condition.
£1,800-2,200 *BKS*

1968 Fiat 850 Coupé, 4 cylinders, 843cc, repainted and in excellent condition.
Est. £1,700-2,000 *ADT*

1978 Fiat 124 Spyder, 4 cylinders, 1756cc, reupholstered, good condtion.
£3,500-3,900 *ADT*

1984 Fiat X1/9 VS, good condition.
Est. £1,000-1,500 *Cen*

A Bertone designed mid-engined sports car, the VS edition was introduced in 1983 and was the most luxurious. Standard equipment included leather seats, tinted glass, alloy wheels, electric windows and 2 tone paintwork.

FIAT Model	ENGINE cc/cyl	DATES	CONDITION 1	2	3
500B Topolino	569/4	1945-55	£3,000	£1,500	£750
500C	569/4	1948-54	£4,000	£1,700	£1,000
500 Nuova	479,499/2	1957-75	£3,000	£1,500	£750
600/600D	633, 767/4	1955-70	£4,000	£2,000	£1,000
500F Giardiniera	479, 499/2	1957-75	£3,000	£1,500	£1,000
2300S	2280/6	1961-68	£3,000	£1,700	£1,000
850	843/4	1964-71	£1,000	£750	-
850 Coupé	843, 903/4	1965-73	£1,500	£1,000	-
850 Spyder	843, 903/4	1965-73	£3,000	£2,000	£1,000
128 Sport Coupé 3P	1116/ 1290/4	1971-78	£2,500	£1,800	£1,000
130 Coupé	3235/6	1971-77	£5,500	£4,000	£2,000
131 Mirafiori Sport	1995/4	1974-84	£1,500	£1,000	£500
124 Sport Coupé	1438/ 1608/4	1966-72	£3,000	£2,000	£1,000
124 Sport Spyder	1438/ 1608/4	1966-72	£4,000	£2,500	£1,500
Dino Coupé	1987/ 2418/6	1967-73	£7,500	£5,500	£2,500
Dino Spyder	1987/ 2418/6	1967-73	£9,000	£7,000	£5,000
X1/9	1290/ 1498/4	1972-89	£3,000	£1,500	£750

FORD

Ford, as a company, dates back to almost the turn of the century in the International car market. Henry Ford was born in Springfield, Michigan, into a farming family, but his interest was mechanics and by 1896 had produced his first car. By 1919 Ford was the biggest American producer of tractors.

Factories soon opened in France and Britain, followed by Germany, and sales continued to rise even throughout WWII. The Thunderbird was brought out in the 1950s in answer to the Chevrolet Corvette, and it soon outsold its rival.

The Company enjoys a good reputation, and although the American models have gradually been depleted the British branch is still very successful.

1910 Ford Model T Speedster, 4 cylinders, 2900cc, imported 6 years ago, believed to be one of the oldest of its type in the UK, stored until recently and in very good overall condition. £10,500-11,000 *ADT*

1913 Model T Ford 2 Seater Raceabout, originally built in Canada, restored in Australia as a Speedster, in good condition. £9,000-12,000 *S*

1911 Ford Model T Roadster, with 'mother-in-law' seat, engine reconditioned, transmission overhauled, restored in America and imported, very good condition. Est. £10,000-13,000 *S*

1919 Ford Model T, 4 cylinders, 2890cc, although a Manchester-built car, it was constructed in left hand drive, restored about 20 years ago, very good overall condition. Est. £10,000-12,000 *ADT*

1921 Model T Ford Doctor's Coupé. £5,000-6,000 *HOLL*

- **The Model T Ford sold over 15 million cars between 1909 and 1927.**
- **The engine number on a Model T should be the same as the chassis number.**
- **Basically, the same 2.9 litre engine and 2 speed transmission was used throughout the 18 year production.**

1921 Ford Model T Tudor Saloon. £5,500-6,500 *DB*

1927 Ford Model T 17hp Tourer, 4 doors, sound car requiring little work. £3,500-3,800 *HOLL*

**1925 Ford Model A 24hp
Roadster,** quite sound car, ideal
for restoration.
£3,300-3,500 *HOLL*

1928 Ford Hot Rod, 4 cylinders, Chevrolet II
'Iron Duke' engine, twin Stromberg carburettors,
1939 Ford 3 speed gearbox, 4 wheel hydraulic
brakes, transverse leaf front and rear suspension,
left hand drive, built by Jim Ewing using a genuine
1928 Ford Model A steel body and Model A
frame rails. **Est. £14,000-20,000** *CNY*

**1929 Ford Model A 4 Door
Town Sedan,** 4 cylinders,
3.3 litre side valve engine,
transverse leaf spring
suspension, left hand drive,
imported in 1991, very good all-
round condition.
£4,000-5,000 *ALC*

*Compared to the Model T, the
Model A had a much shorter
production life of about 5 years,
however, they managed to sell
4½ million examples.*

1929 Ford Model A Tourer,
4 door, 4 seater, re-trimmed
interior, generally in very good
overall condition.
£3,800-4,200 *HOLL*

1931 Ford Model A Saloon,
14hp, right hand drive, very good
condition.
£7,750-8,000 *CC*

1929 Ford Model A Tourer,
right hand drive, restored some
years ago, fair condition.
£8,200-8,600 *C*

**1931 Ford Model A Roadster
Pickup,** imported from Canada,
fully restored, excellent condition
throughout.
Est. £5,000-6,000 *ECC*

1931 Ford Model A Saloon,
4 doors, right hand drive, very
good condition throughout.
£8,750-9,000 *CC*

FORD Model	ENGINE cc/cyl	DATES	CONDITION 1	CONDITION 2	CONDITION 3
Model T	2892/4	1908-27	£10,000	£7,000	£4,000
Model A	3285/4	1928-32	£8,500	£6,000	£3,500
Models Y and 8	933/4	1933-40	£4,000	£3,000	£1,500
Model C	1172/4	1933-40	£4,000	£2,000	£1,000
Model AB	3285/4	1933-34	£10,000	£8,000	£4,500
Model ABF	2043/4	1933-34	£9,000	£6,000	£4,000
Model V8	3622/8	1932-40	£8,500	£6,000	£4,500
Model V8-60	2227/8	1936-40	£7,000	£5,000	£2,000
Model AF (UK only)	2033/4	1928-32	£9,000	£6,000	£3,500

A right hand drive vehicle will always command more interest than a left hand drive. Coachbuilt vehicles, and in particular drophead coupés, achieve a premium at auction. Veteran cars (i.e. manufactured before 1919) will often achieve a 20% premium.

1931 Ford Model A Coupé.
£7,750-8,250 *FHF*

1931 Ford Model A Roadster, left hand drive, major restoration to the highest American standards, excellent condition throughout.
£12,000-13,000 *S*

1931 Ford Road Model A Roadster.
£15,000-18,000 *FHF*

1933 Ford V8 4 Door Sedan, rear luggage boot and rear mounted spare wheel, overall original specification, with the exception of GRP front wings, imported from America, very good overall condition.
Est. £9,000-12,000 *S*

1937 Ford V8 Model 78 'Woody' Station Wagon, right hand drive, very good condition.
£10,000-12,000 *S*

The 'Woody' found particular favour on country estates and the most notable owner of a 'Woody' was HM Queen Elizabeth the Queen Mother.

1932 Ford Model B 24hp Tudor Sedan, 2 door coachwork, restored from the chassis up and repainted, in excellent condition.
£6,000-6,500 *S*

1936 Ford 8.
£2,800-3,200 *DB*

1936 Ford 10.
£1,400-1,600 *DB*

1937 Ford Model Y, 4 cylinders,
885cc, in sound condition.
£1,700-1,900 *ADT*

1937 Ford Model Y, 8hp, retrimmed interior,
superb restoration.
£4,700-5,000 *Bro*

1952 Ford Pilot, very good condition.
£4,800-5,000 *CC*

**1938 Ford V8 Model 81A
Saloon,** 8 cylinders, 3622cc, right
hand drive, imported from South
Africa, good sound condition.
£4,250-4,750 *ADT*

**1954 Ford Zephyr Zodiac
Mark 1,** mechanically excellent,
very good body.
Est. £3,000-3,500 *LF*

1955 Ford Consul Mk I,
mechanics excellent, bodywork
good, interior fair condition.
Est. £1,500-2,000 *LF*

*The EOTA Mk I Consul, the
Zephyr and the Zodiac, were the
first post-war designed British
Fords. The Consul was the
smaller 4 cylinder version with its
1508cc overhead valve engine and
3 speed column change and
gearbox. Nearly a quarter of a
million were built.*

1956 Ford Thunderbird Sports Convertible, 2 seater, detachable hard top, good condition throughout. **£14,000-15,000** *S*

1955 Ford Thunderbird Convertible, with removable hardtop, V8 engine, overhead valve, 4785cc, 198bhp at 4400rpm, Fordomatic 3 speed automatic gearbox, 4 wheel brakes, front suspension upper and lower A-arms, coil springs, rear. live axle, semi-elliptic leaf springs, left hand drive, restored some years ago, paintwork is beginning to show its age, interior is original and in good condition, chrome good. **£11,000-12,000** *C*

1956 Ford Thunderbird V8, automatic gearbox, Continental kit, very original, first class condition throughout. **£12,000-15,000** *CGB*

The classic Thunderbird was introduced in 1955, and was Ford's response to the Chevrolet Corvette which appeared in 1953. Although the same wheelbase (102in), the Thunderbird was designed to be more practical and luxurious than General Motors Corvette. The 1955 Thunderbird model outsold the more expensive Corvette by 24:1.

1956 Ford Thunderbird, 6 cylinders, 5112cc, 2 speed automatic gearbox, 50,000 miles from new, totally original including paintwork. **£18,000-19,000** *ADT*

The most desirable Ford Thunderbird model is the 5112cc engined car, with porthole hard top, white coachwork and rear-mounted spare wheel. This vehicle was originally owned by James Stewart.

FORD (American built) Model	ENGINE cc/cyl	DATES	CONDITION		
			1	2	3
Thunderbird	292/ 312/8	1955-57	£18,500	£13,500	£9,000
Edsel Citation	410/8	1958	£9,000	£4,500	£2,500
Edsel Ranger	223/6- 361/8	1959	£6,000	£3,500	£2,000
Edsel Citation convertible	410/8	1958	£12,000	£6,000	£4,000
Edsel Corsair convertible	332/ 361/8	1959	£10,500	£7,000	£4,500
Fairlane 2 door	223/6- 352/8	1957-59	£8,000	£4,500	£3,000
Fairlane 500 Sunliner	223/6- 352/8	1957-59	£12,000	£8,000	£6,500
Fairlane 500 Skyliner	223/6- 352/8	1957-59	£16,000	£10,000	£8,000
Mustang hardtop	170/6- 289/8	1965-66	£8,000	£5,000	£4,000
Mustang fastback	170/6- 289/8	1965-66	£9,000	£6,000	£5,000
Mustang convertible	170/6- 289/8	1965-66	£12,500	£8,500	£6,000
Mustang hardtop	260/6- 428/8	1967-68	£6,000	£4,000	£3,000
Mustang fastback	260/6- 428/8	1967-68	£6,000	£4,000	£3,000
Mustang convertible	260/6- 428/8	1967-68	£10,750	£6,000	£4,000

1957 Ford Ranch Wagon, V8 engine, overhead valve, 302cu in, 137bhp, 1977 Ford C4 automatic 3 speed gearbox, ball joint with coil springs front suspension, rear longitudinal leaf springs, left hand drive, totally mechanically rebuilt and completely restored by Don Edmunds.
£5,000-8,000 *CNY*

This hot-rod was built from a 1957 Ford Ranch Wagon.

1959 Ford Skyliner Retractable, V8, overhead valve engine, 352cu in, 300bhp at 4600rpm, torque 395lbs/ft at 2800rpm, drum brakes front and rear, front suspension independent short and long arms with ball joints and coil springs, left hand drive, air conditioning and fitted luggage, body off restoration to the highest standards, everything in perfect working order.
Est. £30,000-36,000 *CNY*

1955 Ford Anglia 100E 2 Door Saloon, right hand drive, very low mileage, exceptionally original condition, large quantity of spares.
£1,600-1,800 *C*

1959 Ford Prefect 100E, 4 cylinders, 1172cc, side valve engine, 3 speed manual gearbox, original condition.
£800-850 *Cen*

The Prefect 100 enjoyed a production run until 1959, by which time over 100,000 had been produced.

1959 Ford Anglia 2 Door Saloon, engine reconditioned, everything to original specification and in showroom condition.
£1,250-1,450 *S*

1960 Ford Prefect 107E, very good condition.
£900-950 *LF*

1959 Ford Popular 100E, good body with fair mechanics.
£450-500 *LF*

The 2 door Popular was the final 100E produced.

1961 Ford Popular 100E, good
all-round condition.
£800-900 *LF*

1960 Ford Popular, 4 cylinders, 1172cc,
3 forward speed gearbox, with
synchromesh on second and third gears,
independent front suspension, foot
control headlamp dip switch, repainted
and overhauled. **Est. £1,600-1,800** *ADT*

- **The Ford Popular was the cheapest
  4 wheeled/4 seater family car available
  in the early 1950s in the U.K.**
- **1172cc engine produced 30bhp
  through a 3 speed gearbox.**

1959 Ford Anglia 105E,
997cc overhead valve
all square engine,
4 speed gearbox.
Est. £500-800 *LF*

**1961 Ford Anglia 105E De
Luxe Saloon,** 997cc, fully
documented and in superb
original condition.
£1,600-1,800 *BKS*

*The Anglia sold over a million in
its eight year production span.*

FORD (British built) Model	ENGINE cc/cyl	DATES	CONDITION 1	2	3
Anglia E494A	993/4	1948-53	£2,000	£850	£250
Prefect E93A	1172/4	1940-49	£3,500	£1,250	£900
Prefect E493A	1172/4	1948-53	£2,500	£1,000	£300
Popular 103E	1172/4	1953-59	£1,875	£825	£300
Anglia/Prefect 100E	1172/4	1953-59	£1,350	£625	£250
Prefect 107E	997/4	1959-62	£1,150	£600	£200
Escort/Squire 100E	1172/4	1955-61	£1,000	£850	£275
Popular 100E	1172/4	1959-62	£1,250	£600	£180
Anglia 105E	997/4	1959-67	£1,400	£500	£75
Anglia 123E	1198/4	1962-67	£1,550	£575	£150
V8 Pilot	3622/8	1947-51	£7,500	£4,000	£1,500
Consul Mk I	1508/4	1951-56	£2,250	£950	£400
Consul Mk I DHC	1508/4	1953-56	£4,750	£3,000	£1,250
Zephyr Mk I	2262/6	1951-56	£3,000	£1,250	£600
Zephyr Mk I DHC	2262/6	1953-56	£6,800	£3,250	£1,500
Zodiac Mk I	2262/6	1953-56	£3,300	£1,500	£700
Consul Mk II/Deluxe	1703/4	1956-62	£2,900	£1,500	£650
Consul Mk II DHC	1703/4	1956-62	£5,000	£3,300	£1,250
Zephyr Mk II	2553/6	1956-62	£3,800	£1,800	£750
Zephyr Mk II DHC	2553/6	1956-62	£8,000	£4,000	£1,500
Zodiac Mk II	2553/6	1956-62	£4,000	£2,250	£750
Zodiac Mk II DHC	2553/6	1956-62	£8,500	£4,250	£1,800
Zephyr 4 Mk III	1703/4	1962-66	£2,100	£1,200	£400
Zephyr 6 Mk III	2552/6	1962-66	£2,300	£1,300	£450
Zodiac Mk II	2553/6	1962-66	£2,500	£1,500	£500
Zephyr 4 Mk IV	1994/4	1966-72	£1,750	£600	£150
Zephyr 6 Mk IV	2553/6	1966-72	£1,800	£700	£150
Zodiac Mk IV	2994/6	1966-72	£2,000	£800	£150
Zodiac Mk IV Est.	2994/6	1966-72	£2,200	£950	£150
Zodiac Mk IV Exec.	2994/6	1966-72	£2,300	£950	£150
Classic 315	1340/ 1498/4	1961-63	£1,400	£800	£500
Consul Capri	1340/ 1498/4	1961-64	£2,100	£1,350	£400
Consul Capri GT	1498/4	1961-64	£2,600	£1,600	£800

1960 Ford Consul Mark II Saloon,
replacement fibreglass front wings.
£500-1,200 *ALC*

**1963 Ford Anglia 1200 De
Luxe,** 58,000 miles, very
good condition.
£1,400-1,800 *ECC*

1963 Ford Consul Cortina Saloon, good bodywork
and mechanics.
Est. £500-800 *LF*

1961 Ford Consul Convertible,
4 cylinders, 1703cc, very good
overall condition.
£5,500-6,000 *ADT*

**1964 Ford Falcon Sprint
Convertible,** V8 engine,
automatic, left hand drive, new
paintwork, chrome, interior and hood.
£5,000-6,000 *CGB*

**1966 Ford Thunderbird
Landau,** rebuilt 390cu in engine,
new brakes and suspension.
£4,250-4,500 *CCTC*

1965 Ford Mustang GT, V8 engine,
4.7 litres, 289cu in, 4 speed manual floor change
gearbox, front disc brakes and dual exhaust.
£4,000-4,500 *CCTC*

*These cars have a complicated chassis numbering system
and there are many copies and fake GT Mustangs around.
Buyer beware!*

1965 Ford Mustang Coupé,
imported, in good condition.
£3,500-3,750 *Cen*

**1966 Ford Mustang GT 350H
2 Door High Performance
Coupé,** 4.7 litre engine, excellent
condition throughout.
£17,500-18,000 *BKS*

1966 Ford Mustang Convertible,
6 cylinders, 3398cc, automatic
gearbox, left hand drive, rebuilt
engine and transmission.
£6,000-6,500 *C*

1971 Ford Zodiac Mark IV,
6 cylinders, 3000cc, clean and
tidy throughout.
Est. £1,500-2,500 *ADT*

**1973 Ford Granada V8 4 Door
Saloon,** automatic transmission
3 speeds and reverse, very good
condition throughout.
Est. £3,000-4,000 *S*

*Ford have been assembling cars
in Australia since the days of the
Model T Ford in 1925, but in
1960 they opened a new plant at
Broadmeadows, Victoria, initially
to make the Falcon. This
Granada has a 4942cc V8 engine,
of the type which powers the
Mustang, producing 255bhp. The
car accelerates from 0-60mph in
8 seconds, with a maximum speed
of 130mph.*

**1974 Ford Cortina GT 2000
Crayford Convertible
Conversion,** 4 cylinders,
overhead camshaft, genuine and
original conversion.
£900-1,000 *LF*

1967 Ford Cortina De Luxe,
4 cylinders, 1298cc, manual
gearbox, 2 doors, very good
overall condition.
£1,000-1,100 *ADT*

**1975 Ford Cortina Mk III
1300L,** 4 cylinders, 1298cc,
recorded milage of just over
32,000, good condition.
£900-1,000 *ADT*

1975 Ford Fairmont Estate,
V8 engine, 5 litres, 25,000 miles,
excellent condition.
£2,250-2,750 *Mot*

1974 Ford Escort RS 2000 Mk I, excellent condition throughout.
Est. £2,200-2,600 *Cen*

Produced between 1970 and 1974 by AVO at South Ockenden, the RS 2000 was smoother, plusher and a better road car than its sister, the Mexico. It was fitted with a 2 litre overhead cam Pinto engine and German transmission.

1978 Ford Escort RS Mexico Mk II, excellent condition throughout.
£1,500-1,900 *ECC*

1982 Ford Capri 4 Seater Hatchback Coupé, 4 cylinders, 1600cc, overhead camshaft, 4 speed gearbox, 16,040 miles, very good original condition.
£3,300-3,600 *S*

1979 Ford Escort RS 2000 Custom, 3 owners from new, full service history.
£3,300-3,600 *PC*

FORD (British built) Model	ENGINE cc/cyl	DATES	CONDITION 1	2	3
Cortina Mk I	1198/4	1963-66	£1,550	£600	£150
Cortina Crayford Mk I	1198/4	1963-66	£3,500	£1,800	£950
Cortina GT	1498/4	1963-66	£1,800	£1,000	£650
Lotus Cortina Mk I	1558/4	1963-66	£9,000	£7,500	£4,500
Cortina Mk II	1599/4	1966-70	£1,000	£500	£100
Cortina GT Mk II	1599/4	1966-70	£1,200	£650	£150
Cortina Crayford Mk II DHC	1599/4	1966-70	£4,000	£2,000	£1,500
Lotus Cortina Mk II	1558/4	1966-70	£5,500	£3,000	£1,800
Cortina 1600E	1599/4	1967-70	£2,800	£1,000	£450
Consul Corsair	1500/4	1963-65	£1,100	£500	£250
Consul Corsair GT	1500/4	1963-65	£1,200	£600	£250
Corsair V4	1664/4	1965-70	£1,150	£600	£250
Corsair V4 Est.	1664/4	1965-70	£1,400	£600	£250
Corsair V4GT	1994/4	1965-67	£1,300	£700	£250
CorsairV4GT Est.	1994/4	1965-67	£1,400	£700	£350
Corsair Convertible	1664/ 1994/4	1965-70	£4,300	£2,500	£1,000
Corsair 2000	1994/4	1967-70	£1,350	£500	£250
Corsair 2000E	1994/4	1967-70	£1,500	£800	£350
Escort 1300E	1298/4	1973-74	£1,900	£1,000	£250
Escort Twin Cam	1558/4	1968-71	£8,000	£5,000	£2,000
Escort GT	1298/4	1968-73	£3,000	£1,500	£350
Escort Sport	1298/4	1971-75	£1,750	£925	£250
Escort Mexico	1601/4	1970-74	£4,000	£2,000	£750
RS1600	1601/4	1970-74	£5,000	£2,500	£1,500
RS2000	1998/4	1973-74	£4,500	£2,200	£1,000
Escort RS Mexico	1593/4	1976-78	£3,500	£2,000	£850
Escort RS2000 Mk II	1993/4	1976-80	£6,000	£3,500	£2,000
Capri Mk I 1300/ 1600	1298/ 1599/4	1969-72	£1,500	£1,000	£550
Capri 2000/ 3000GT	1996/4 2994/6	1969-72	£2,000	£1,000	£500
Capri 3000E	2994/6	1970-72	£4,000	£2,000	£1,000
Capri RS3100	3093/6	1973-74	£6,500	£3,500	£2,000
Cortina 2000E	1993/4	1973-76	£2,500	£550	£225
Granada Ghia	1993/4 2994/6	1974-77	£4,000	£900	£350

1984 Ford Capri Injection 3 Door Saloon, genuine 29,000 mileage, carefully maintained and in very good condition.
£2,500-3,000 *S*

1986 Ford Granada 2.0i Ghia Saloon.
£2,400-2,800 *C(S)*

FRAZER-NASH

The marque was founded in 1924 by Archie Frazer-Nash and was taken over by H.J. Aldington in 1926, trading as AFN Ltd. In late 1934 AFN began to import BMWs which were marketed as Frazer-Nash-BMWs.

1938 Frazer-Nash-BMW 327 Fast Tourer Convertible Cabriolet, 6 cylinders, 1971cc, 2.0 litre engine, totally refurbished, one of only 20 known survivors.
Est. £24,000-28,000 *BKS*

1924 Frazer-Nash Super Sports, boat-tailed fast tourer coachwork, 4 cylinders, 1496cc, rebuilt engine, first class all-round condition.
£27,000-29,000 *COYS*

1954 Frazer-Nash Sebring, 6 cylinders, 1971cc.
Est. £75,000-100,000 *COYS*
This car was exhibited at the 1954 London Motor Show and raced at Le Mans in 1955 with the works supporting drivers Cecil Ward and K. W. Odium. It retired after 6 hours with engine trouble, perhaps because it had been delivered to its owner only 2 weeks before the race. Frazer-Nash built fewer than 80 cars post-war, which is one reason why they are now so prized. The main reason, however, is that they were superb machines, equally at home on road or track.

1938 Frazer-Nash-BMW 328 2 Seater Sports Racing Car, totally restored, good condition throughout.
£85,000-95,000 *S*
Basically a BMW 328, it is sold as a Frazer-Nash-BMW under an agreement made with the German company.

Don't forget!
If in doubt please refer to the 'How to Use' section at the beginning of this book.

GILBERN

1965 Gilbern 1800 GT, retrimmed, in good overall condition.
£5,750-6,000 *Bro*

Built at Llantwit Fardre in South Wales, the Gilbern Genie was a development of Bernard Frieze and Giles Smith's first model, the Gilbern GT. Constructed of fibreglass, production commenced in 1966.

GINETTA

1971 Ginetta G15, rebuilt 998cc Hillman Imp engine, twin Weber carburettors, race prepared with history.
£4,750-5,500 *KSC*

1972 Ginetta G15, 4 cylinders, 998cc, full respray, good condition. **£4,000-4,500** *ADT*

The Ginetta was manufactured between 1967 and 1973 by the Walklett family. Their original business was building cars for use in British racing classes and it was not until 1967 that they entered road production with the G15 Coupé using the Stiletto 875cc engine.

1969 Gilbern Genie, 3 litre engine, overdrive, Webasto sunroof, full respray, rechromed, new tyres, brakes, wiring loom and front seat coverings.
£4,750-5,000 *Bro*

GLADIATOR

The Company started by manufacturing bicycles under the direction of Alexandre Darracq. Harvey du Cros headed a British company which took over Gladiator in 1896, and following a brief involvement with Adolphe Clément, during which time the cars were variously known as Cléments, Gladiators or Clément Gladiators, the marque was marketed in England as Gladiator by S.F. Edge. The cars used the Aster engine, originally 2½hp and 3½hp. However, by 1901, a more conventional looking car was available with the 6½hp Aster engine. In 1903 the factory was selling 80% of its 1,000 a year production to Britain.

1902 Gladiator Type 3 6½hp Voiturette, original mechanical specification, older restoration, opera style oil sidelights, umbrella basket, De Dion style alligator bonnet. **£15,000-18,000** *S*

This car has not been started or run for a number of years.

1903 Gladiator Rear Entrance Tonneau, 2.4 litre engine, flitch plated wooden chassis and chain final drive, highly presentable overall condition.
Est. £40,000-60,000 *BKS*

This car has been in the same ownership and competing in the Brighton Run for more than 20 years. It is also the oldest 4 cylinder Gladiator to have been officially dated by the Veteran Car Club.

GRAY-DORT

1919 Gray-Dort 4 Door Touring,
4 cylinders, 3150cc, Lycoming
engine, recent major restoration.
£11,000-14,000 *CGB*

*This is a Canadian-built version
of the American Dort and believed
to be the only one outside North
America.*

HEALEY

Donald Healey formed his own car
manufacturing company in Warwick in 1946
and introduced the Silverstone in 1949. With
over 100bhp and relatively low weight, it
could accelerate from 10-107mph in top gear.
Silverstone's won their class in the Alpine
Rally in 1949 and 1951.

**1951 Healey Abbot 2.4 Litre
Drophead Coupé,** coachwork by
Abbott of Farnham, wiring needs
work, excellent condition
throughout.
Est. £9,000-11,000 *S*

CROSS REFERENCE
Austin Healey————▶p49

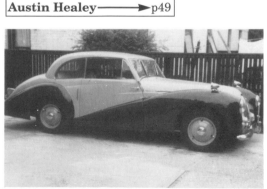

**1951 Healey Tickford 2 Door
Saloon,** 2.4 litre, engine and
other mechanical features good.
Est. £5,000-6,000 *S*

HAYNES-APPERSON

**1902 Haynes-Apperson 12hp 4/6 Seater
Surrey,** 3.9 litre engine, good overall condition.
Est. £25,000-30,000 *BKS*

*Elwood Haynes of Kokomo, Indiana, was one of
the first Americans to build a motor vehicle.
A metallurgist, Haynes invented Stellite
stainless steel, and by the age of 27 he had
already devised a process for producing
tungsten chrome steel. Aided by the Apperson
brothers, he put a Stutz marine engine in a
little 4 wheel buggy, which made its first run on
Independence Day, 1894. Haynes and the
Appersons combined to form the Haynes-
Apperson Company in 1898 and their cars were
among the finest quality American vehicles
of their day. The big 12hp rear-engined
2 cylinder model, of which this car is a rare
survivor, was built during 1902-03, with the
Surrey as their flagship model.*

1950 Healey Silverstone, 6 cylinders, 2443cc,
excellent condition. **£33,000-35,000** *COYS*

1951 Healey Sportsmobile Drophead Coupé, 4 seater
body style, good restored condition. **£6,000-7,000** *CGB*

HEINKEL

The German Heinkel Company, better known for their aircraft, were also responsible for the production of motor scooters. Production was transferred to Ireland in 1958, and in later years was taken over by the English Trojan Company when a 200cc 'bubble car' was built.

1957 Heinkel 175cc Cabin Cruiser, left hand drive, single front door.
Est. £2,000-2,500 *LF*

CROSS REFERENCE	
BMW ⟶	p81
Messerschmitt ⟶	p188

HILLMAN

1964 Hillman Husky Series III Estate Car, original throughout, only 30,000 miles from new.
£1,500-1,700 *S*

Perhaps the most memorable model was the pre- and post-war Minx, truly the company's first mass-produced car. The model name was to exist until 1970 and there were several variations, the Californian and the tough Husky being examples.

1968 Hillman Imp, restored to original condition.
£500-600 *HOLL*

1966 Hillman Super Minx, 4 cylinder, 1725cc, good condition, only 5,800 miles from new.
Est. £2,400-3,400 *ADT*

This Series VI was the last of a long line of Minx starting with the Mark I in 1946. The larger 1725cc engine was only available between 1964 and 1967.

HILLMAN Model	ENGINE cc/cyl	DATES	CONDITION 1	2	3
Minx Mk I-II	1184/4	1946-48	£1,750	£800	£250
Minx Mk I-II DHC	1184/4	1946-48	£3,500	£1,500	£250
Minx Mk III-VIIIA	1184/4	1948-56	£1,750	£700	£350
Minx Mk III-VIIIA DHC	1184/4	1948-56	£3,750	£1,500	£350
Californian	1390/4	1953-56	£2,000	£750	£200
Minx SI/II	1390/4	1956-58	£1,250	£450	£200
Minx SI/II DHC	1390/4	1956-58	£3,500	£1,500	£500
Minx Ser III	1494/4	1958-59	£1,000	£500	£200
Minx Ser III DHC	1494/4	1958-59	£3,750	£1,500	£400
Minx Ser IIIA/B	1494/4	1959-61	£1,250	£500	£200
Minx Ser IIIA/B DHC	1494/4	1959-61	£3,750	£1,250	£500
Minx Ser IIIC	1592/4	1961-62	£900	£500	£200
Minx Ser IIIC DHC	1592/4	1961-62	£3,000	£1,500	£500
Minx Ser V	1592/4	1962-63	£1,250	£350	£150
Minx Ser VI	1725/4	1964-67	£1,500	£375	£100
Husky Mk I	1265/4	1954-57	£1,000	£600	£200
Husky SI/II/III	1390/4	1958-65	£1,000	£550	£150
Super Minx	1592/4	1961-66	£1,500	£500	£100
Super Minx DHC	1592/4	1962-64	£3,500	£1,250	£450
Imp	875/4	1963-73	£800	£300	£70
Husky	875/4	1966-71	£800	£450	£100
Avenger	var/4	1970-76	£550	£250	£60
Avenger GT	1500/4	1971-76	£950	£500	£100
Tiger	1600/4	1972-73	£1,250	£650	£200

1973 Hillman Avenger Tiger Saloon, fitted with a later 1600cc engine.
Est. £1,000-2,000 *ALC*

HISPANPO-SUIZA

1912 Hispano-Suiza 3 Litre Sports Torpedo Tourer, coachwork by Girard et Lacouture of Levallois, 4 cylinder monobloc engine, 85 x 130mm bore and stroke giving a nominal capacity of 2950cc but bored out to 3055cc, complete mechanical restoration to excellent overall condition.
£80,000-100,000 *S*

1922 Hispano-Suiza H6 4 Passenger Touring, coachwork by Brunn and Co., Buffalo, New York, 6 cylinder in line, water-cooled monobloc engine, 100 x 140mm bore and stroke, displacement 6597cc, 120hp at 2000rpm, overhead camshaft, 3 speed transmission, shaft drive, bevel rear axle, semi-elliptic front and rear springs, 4 wheel mechanical brakes with servo, 145in wheelbase, entirely original but in need of total restoration, nearly complete, apparently only missing the front windscreen frame.
£85,000-100,000 *S(NY)*

HOLSMAN

The Holsman Automobile Company of Chicago holds a unique place in automotive history in that they were the first company to adopt the high-wheeler principle. Their commercial success between 1902 and 1910 persuaded other manufacturers to enter the high-wheeler market.

Although a primitive vehicle, even by 1906 standards, the method of transporting power to the rear wheels, via a Manila rope, proved very successful. The primitive brakes, which acted against the solid rubber tyres, were efficient and hand-operated. However, Holsman stayed with the basic high-wheeler principle and as a result went into receivership in 1910.

1906 Holsman 10hp Runabout, believed to be a Model G, 4 seater, 2 cylinder, tiller steering, full elliptic springing, sound wood spoke wheels, side starting handle, leatherette mudguards and Surrey top.
£7,500-8,000 *ADT*

HONDA

1972 Honda 600Z 2 Door Sports Coupé, to original specification, good throughout.
£375-400 *S*

The 600Z coupé followed the Honda 600 saloon and was introduced in 1971, featuring a 2 cylinder, 598cc, overhead camshaft air-cooled engine, 4 speed gearbox, front wheel disc brakes, achieving a top speed of 80mph and 43mpg.

HONDA Model	ENGINE cc/cyl	DATES	CONDITION		
			1	2	3
S800 Mk I Convertible	791/4	1966-69	£7,000	£4,000	£2,500
S800 Mk I Coupé	791/4	1966-69	£6,000	£3,500	£1,000
S800 Mk II Convertible	791/4	1968-69	£7,000	£5,000	£3,000
S800 Mk II Coupé	791/4	1968-69	£6,500	£4,000	£1,200

HORCH

August Horch, one of the pioneers of the German automobile industry, was originally employed as an engineer with Benz from 1896 until 1899, when he started his own company in Cologne. The first car to bear the Horch name left the factory in 1900. August Horch's early cars were built to the highest standards and were ranked highly among German and European motor manufacturers.

The company moved to Zwickau in 1904 and Paul Daimler (son of Gottlieb) joined them in 1923. He instituted a line of straight 8 engined luxury cars for which the company was to become famous, and which endured long after he had left. Horch was one of the companies which formed Auto-Union in 1931.

1932 Horch 780 2 Door Cabriolet, restored coachwork by Le Coq in Paris, rebuilt chassis, engine and gearbox, twin spot lamps/rear view mirrors, twin side-mounted spare wheels, indicators, headlights with Horch motif in the lenses, luggage trunk and rack.
£64,500-70,000 *S*

The 780 featured an 8 cylinder in line engine of 4944cc capacity, 4 speed gearbox and overhead valve engine configuration. Although the cabriolet was only a 2 door model, the wheelbase was 135in.

1935 Horch 853 Sport Cabriolet, restored coachwork by Le Coq of Paris, restored chassis and engine, paintwork and brightwork excellent, twin pillar mounted spotlights with mirrored backs, Bosch main lighting with crowned 'Ht' monogram in the lenses.
£125,000-145,000 *S*

1937 Horch 850 Cabriolet, coachwork by Karosserie Baur of Stuttgart, front screen winds out, black leather-covered trunk by Wilka GmbH of Köln and Berlin, wind-up central division, left hand drive, full ground-up restoration to a very high standard, very good mechanical condition.
£60,000-70,000 *S*

1938 Horch 951 Pullman Limousine, mechanical elements and chassis restored, upholstery, woodwork and panelwork restored by Le Coq, wind-up central glass division, bulkhead supporting 2 occasional folding seats, twin side-mounted spare wheels, fold-down luggage rack to rear, lighting by Bosch, original chassis plate, very good condition throughout.
Est. £40,000-60,000 *S*

HUDSON

**1913 Hudson Model 37
5 Passenger Tourer,** wooden
spoked artillery wheels fitted
with 37 x 4½in tyres, wheelbase
118in, restored to a very high
standard.
£18,000-19,000 *S*

*Introduced in July 1912, just
9,200 Model 37 Hudsons were
made. They superseded the
Model 33 which had included the
famous 'Mile a Minute' Roadster.*

1929 Humber 16/50 Tourer,
imported from Ireland, totally
overhauled.
£7,000-7,500 *LF*

**1965 Humber
Sceptre,** good
condition.
£800-1,200
ECC

HUMBER

1925 Humber 15/25, very good
overall condition.
£15,500-16,500 *CC*

1929 Humber 9, very good
condition throughout.
£5,000-6,000 *CC*

**1939 Humber Pullman
Limousine,** 7 seater with wind-
up central division and
2 occasional folding seats,
powered by Humber's Husky
4086cc engine, total mileage
52,000, only 2,200 miles in the
past 6 years, very good original
condition throughout.
Est. £7,000-10,000 *S*

HUMBER Model	ENGINE cc/cyl	DATES	CONDITION 1	2	3
Veteran	var	1898			
		1918	£25,000	£20,000	£14,000
10	1592/4	1919	£7,000	£5,000	£3,000
14	2474/4	1919	£8,000	£6,000	£4,000
15.9-5/40	2815/4	1920-27	£9,500	£7,000	£4,000
8	985/4	1923-25	£7,000	£5,000	£2,500
9/20-9/28	1057/4	1926	£7,000	£5,000	£4,000
14/40	2050/4	1927-28	£10,000	£8,000	£5,000
Snipe	3498/6	1930-35	£8,000	£6,000	£4,000
Pullman	3498/6	1930-35	£8,000	£6,000	£4,000
16/50	2110/6	1930-32	£9,000	£7,000	£5,000
12	1669/4	1933-37	£7,000	£5,000	£3,000
Snipe/Pullman	4086/6	1936-40	£7,000	£5,000	£3,000
16	2576/6	1938-40	£7,000	£5,000	£3,000

Pre-1905 or Brighton Run cars are very popular.

HUMBER Model	ENGINE cc/cyl	DATES	CONDITION 1	2	3
Hawk Mk I-IV	1944/4	1945-52	£2,750	£1,500	£600
Hawk Mk V-VII	2267/4	1952-57	£2,500	£1,500	£400
Hawk Ser I-IVA	2267/4	1957-67	£2,500	£850	£325
Snipe	2731/6	1945-48	£5,000	£2,600	£850
Super Snipe Mk I-III	4086/6	1948-52	£4,700	£2,400	£600
Super Snipe Mk IV-IVA	4138/6	1952-56	£5,500	£2,300	£550
Super Snipe Ser I-II	2651/6	1958-60	£3,800	£1,800	£475
Super Snipe SIII VA	2965/6	1961-67	£3,500	£1,800	£400
Super Snipe S.III-VA Est.	2965/6	1961-67	£3,950	£1,850	£525
Pullman	4086/6	1946-51	£4,500	£2,350	£800
Pullman Mk IV	4086/6	1952-54	£6,000	£2,850	£1,200
Imperial	2965/6	1965-67	£3,900	£1,600	£450
Sceptre Mk I-II	1592/4	1963-67	£2,050	£900	£300
Sceptre Mk III	1725/4	1967-76	£1,600	£600	£200

INTERMECCANICA

Chemical engineer, Frank Reisner, a Hungarian refugee, returned from the USA to Europe in 1958 where he started designing race car chassis. The following year he set up his own company, Costruzione Automobili Intermeccanica. The first car was the IMP, a rear-engined GT with a 2 cylinder Puch engine.

1969 Intermeccanica Italia Spyder, 5.3 litre Chevrolet V8 engine, 300bhp, 4 speed gearbox, very good condition. **£11,000-12,000** *COYS*

ISO

The Iso company, run by Renzo Rivolto, was probably unique in taking its name from the family refrigerator business 'Isothermo'. The highly successful Isetta bubble car of the 1950s helped finance the supercars like the Rivolta, Grifo and Lele.

1975 Iso Lele 5.8 Litre Sport 2 Door Coupé, by Carrozzeria Bertone, 5.8 litre Ford V8 engine, disc brakes on all 4 wheels, 5 speed manual transmission, limited slip differential, air conditioning, electric windows and aerial.
Est. £14,000-16,000 *BKS*

The Lele was launched in 1969 to succeed the original Iso Rivolta.

INTERNATIONAL

1901 International 5hp Double Phæton, good restored condition. **£19,000-20,000** *Mot*

INVICTA

1930 Invicta 4½ Litre S-Type Low Chassis Tourer, converted to a drophead coupé body, during 1950s 'S26' was fitted with current 1930 style touring coachwork. **£110,000-120,000** *BKS*

- **Only 77 S-Type Invictas were built.**
- **Each individual Invicta S-Type chassis has its own code name, the 'S26' being known as 'Sea Lion'.**

1974 Iso Rivolta Lele, 8 cylinder, 5359cc, 5.4 litre Chevrolet engine, automatic gearbox, right hand drive, paintwork is poor in places. **£2,000-3,000** *ADT*

JAGUAR

Jaguar's history began with the Swallow Sidecar Company in the early 1920s. William Lyons, born in Blackpool in 1901, went into partnership with William Walmsley in 1922, producing streamlined motorcycle sidecars. By 1927 the Swallow Sidecar Company produced their first two seater car bodies for both the Morris Cowley and the Austin 7 chassis.

This was very successful and by 1928 the Swallow Sidecar and Coachbuilding Company had found new premises in Coventry. The sidecar business was sold after WWII, and SS Cars Ltd., the car making side of the business, was renamed Jaguar Cars Ltd.

1937 Jaguar SS100, 6 cylinder, 2663cc, original engine, extensive chassis-up overhaul, repainted in original black, chromium wheels, full set of side screens, plus fold-flat and aero windscreens, excellent condition throughout.
£85,000-95,000 *COYS*

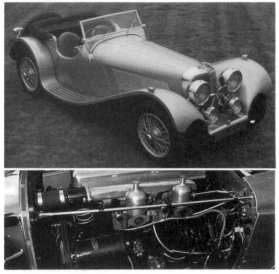

1938 Jaguar Ex-works SS100 3½ Litre, 6 cylinder, 3485cc, excellent condition throughout.
Est. £95,000-120,000 *COYS*

1937 Jaguar SS100 3½ Litre, 6 cylinder, 3486cc, a very well known motor car in superb restored condition.
£100,000-120,000 *COYS*

- **A total of about 310 SS100s were made, of which 195 were the 2.7 litre cars, which sold for £360 in 1937, compared to £222 for the contemporary MG Midget TA and the BMW 328 at £695.**
- **Many successes were achieved in trials and rallies throughout the world.**
- **The name SS was dropped in order to avoid any association with the Nazi organization.**

1938 Jaguar SS100 3½ Litre, restored to excellent overall condition.
£90,000-110,000 *ADT*

1946 Jaguar 2.5 Litre Saloon, 6 cylinder, 2687cc, new headlining, sun roof, resprayed, excellent condition.
£11,000-12,000 *ADT*

1947 Jaguar 2½ Litre, very good all round condition.
£8,500-9,500 *CC*

JAGUAR	ENGINE	DATES	CONDITION		
Model	cc/cyl		1	2	3
SSI	2054/6	1932-33	£20,000	£16,000	£12,000
SSI	2252/6	1932-33	£22,000	£17,000	£13,500
SSII	1052/4	1932-33	£18,000	£15,000	£11,000
SSI	2663/6	1934	£26,000	£22,000	£15,000
SSII	1608/4	1934	£18,000	£15,000	£12,000
SS90	2663/6	1935	£60,000+		
SS100 (3.4)	3485/6	1938-39	£70,000+		
SS100 (2.6)	2663/6	1936-39	£60,000+		

Very dependent on body styles, completeness and originality, particularly original chassis to body.

**1948 Jaguar 3½ Litre
3 Position Drophead Coupé,**
engine overhauled, original
upholstery, left hand drive,
imported to the UK from
California, original specification.
£19,000-22,000 *S*

1947 Jaguar 3½ Litre,
6 cylinders, 3485cc, the chassis
and the body have been stripped
and repainted, the brightwork
re-chromed and the engine
refurbished, dashboard
instrumentation intact but
upholstery needs refurbishment.
£5,750-6,500 *ADT*

1949 Jaguar Mk V, 6 cylinders, 2483cc,
excellent restored condition.
£6,750-7,500 *ADT*

1950 Jaguar XK120, 6 cylinders,
3442cc, left hand drive, one of
240 made with alloy coachwork,
extensive restoration, including
conversion to a similar
specification to 3 works XK120s
prepared for Le Mans 1951,
aluminium passenger side
tonneau, individual seats, C-Type
front disc brakes and wire
wheels, long range fuel tank, aero
screen and ventilated bonnet.
£52,000-54,000 *COYS*

1950 Jaguar XK120 Super Sports Roadster,
steel bodied, excellent general condition.
£25,000-28,000 *S*

1950 Jaguar XK120 Roadster,
6 cylinder in line engine, twin
overhead camshaft, 3442cc,
160bhp at 5200rpm, 4 speed
synchromesh manual gearbox,
4 wheel hydraulic drum brakes,
independent front suspension
with double wishbones,
longitudinal torsion bars, anti-
roll bar, telescopic shock
absorbers, rear by semi-elliptic
leaf springs, left hand drive,
excellent restored condition.
£25,000-30,000 *CNY*

1952 Jaguar XK120 Fixed Head Coupé.
£8,000-10,000   *DB*

1952 Jaguar XK120, 6 cylinders, 3442cc twin overhead camshaft XK engine producing 160bhp, twin SU carburettors, 126mph and 0-60mph in 10 seconds, steel body, excellent condition.
£32,000-35,000   *COYS*

1953 Jaguar XK120 Roadster, left hand drive, in all-round excellent condition.
£33,000-36,000   *S(Z)*

> **Don't forget!**
> *If in doubt please refer to the 'How to Use' section at the beginning of this book.*

1953 Jaguar XK120M 3.4 Litre 2 Seater Sports Roadster, right hand drive, recent comprehensive restoration.
£30,000-33,000   *BKS*

1952 Jaguar XK120 3.4 Litre Competition 2 Seater Roadster, twin SU carburettors, 180bhp+ at 5300rpm, 16in knock-off chromed wire wheels for road use and British Racing Green painted wire wheels for competition work, restoration completed to the very highest standard.
£60,000-64,000   *BKS*

1953 Jaguar XK120M 3.4 Litre 2 Seater Sports Roadster, chrome wire wheels, in very good condition.
Est. £25,000-30,000   *BKS*

Launched in 1951, at the same time as the fixed head coupé version, the 'special equipment' XK120, known in the United States as the XK120M (for 'modified'), was tuned to give a power output of 190bhp. The standard 3.4 litre XK engine developed 160bhp.

1953 Jaguar XK120 SE Drop Head Coupé, 6 cylinders, 3442cc, has been in storage for the last 2 years, in good condition.
£14,500-15,000   *ADT*

1955 Jaguar XK 140 Roadster,
6 cylinders, 3442cc, stainless
exhaust system, right hand drive,
excellent restored condition.
£25,5000-27,500 *ADT*

**1955 Jaguar XK140 3.4 Litre
Drophead Coupé,** right hand
drive, rebuilt engine, gearbox,
front and rear axles and
overdrive, overhauled
suspension, brakes and rack-and-
pinion steering, stainless steel
exhaust system, body completely
rebuilt, brightwork re-chromed,
repainted to show standard,
comprehensive professional
restoration.
£60,000-65,000 *BKS*

1956 Jaguar XK140 Roadster,
6 cylinders, 3442cc, originally
exported to America, restored
and converted to right hand
drive, good condition throughout.
£17,000-18,000 *COYS*

**1957 Jaguar XK150 Fixed
Head Coupé,** 6 cylinders,
3781cc, in very good condition.
£13,500-14,000 *ADT*

**1954/55 Jaguar XK140
3.4 Litre Drophead Coupé,**
thoroughly restored to a high
standard, in excellent condition.
Est. £40,000-50,000 *BKS*

**1956 Jaguar XK140 SE Fixed
Head Coupé,** rust free and in
very good original condition.
£14,200-16,200 *S*

1956 Jaguar XK140 Coupé,
rebuilt C-type engine with racing
camshafts, light flywheel, all
synchromesh gearbox with
overdrive, louvred bonnet, fitted
disc brakes, imported from
California and converted to right
hand drive, rust free.
£14,000-16,000 *CCTC*

**1956 Jaguar XK140 3.4 Litre
2 Seater Roadster,** fitted with a
Jaguar C-type cylinder head,
converted to right hand drive
condition, in excellent mechanical
condition. **Est. £26,000-28,000** *S*

1957 Jaguar XK140 Coupé,
6 cylinder in line engine, 3442cc,
4 speed synchromesh gearbox,
except on first, 4 wheel hydraulic
drum brakes, independent front
suspension with double
wishbones, longitudinal torsion
bars, anti-roll bars, telescopic
shock absorbers, rear semi-
elliptic leaf springs, drives well,
some cosmetic attention required.
£8,500-10,500 *CNY*

**Miller's is a price GUIDE
not a price LIST.**

**1957 Jaguar XK150 Fixed
Head Coupé,** good running
order, requires attention to
interior trim, wheel arches
and sills.
£8,500-9,500 *ALC*

c1958 Jaguar XK150 Roadster,
6 cylinders, 3442cc, converted to
right hand drive, panelwork and
interior in reasonable condition.
£18,000-19,000 *ADT*

**1958 Jaguar XK150 Drophead
Coupé,** 6 cylinders, 3442cc, with
overdrive, engine rebuilt,
renovated body, renewed hood
and interior trim.
£26,000-28,000 *COYS*

**1958 Jaguar XK150 Fixed
Head Coupé,** in excellent
condition.
£19,000-21,000 *FHF*

JAGUAR Model	ENGINE cc/cyl	DATES	CONDITION 1	2	3
XK120 roadster aluminum	3442/6	1948-49	£35,000	£20,000	£15,000
XK120 roadster	3442/6	1949-54	£22,000	£18,000	£13,000
XK120 DHC	3442/6	1953-54	£20,000	£15,000	£11,000
XK120 Coupé	3442/6	1951-55	£16,000	£10,000	£8,000
C-type	3442/6	1951	£110,000	+	
D-type	3442/6	1955-56	£300,000	+	
XKSS (original)	3442/6	1955-57	£320,000	+	
XK140 roadster	3442/6	1955-58	£28,000	£23,000	£15,500
XK140 DHC	3442/6	1955-58	£25,000	£20,500	£15,000
XK140 Coupé	3442/6	1955-58	£14,000	£9,000	£5,500
XK150 roadster	3442/6	1958-60	£24,000	£20,500	£14,000
XK150 DHC	3442/6	1957-61	£22,000	£15,000	£5,000
XK150 Coupé	3442/6	1957-60	£14,000	£9,000	£6,000
XK150S roadster	3442/ 3781/6	1958-60	£35,000	£22,000	£17,000
XK150S DHC	3442/ 3781/6	1958-60	£34,000	£22,000	£16,500
XK150S Coupé	3442/ 3781/6	1958-61	£22,000	£17,000	£11,500

1958 Jaguar XK150 Drophead Coupé, in excellent restored condition.
£22,500-23,500 *BKS*

1958 Jaguar XK150 Fixed Head Coupé, uprated 3.8 litre engine, overdrive not functioning, converted to right hand drive, sound bodywork, non standard vinyl trim, fair paintwork, a project for restoration.
£11,500-12,500 *S*

1958 Jaguar XK150 Drophead Coupé, 6 cylinders, 3781cc, exceptionally fine condition.
£36,000-38,000 *ADT*

1959 Jaguar XK150 'S' Drophead Coupé, 6 cylinders, 3442cc, excellent restored condition.
Est. £33,000-43,000 *ADT*

1959 Jaguar XK150 SE 3.4 Litre Fixed Head Coupé, rebuilt engine, with overdrive, disc wheels, right hand drive, needs some cosmetic attention.
£10,000-12,000 *BKS*

Only 4,400 fixed head coupés were built.

1960 Jaguar XK150 'S' 3.8 Litre, 6 cylinders, 3781cc, overdrive, in excellent and unrestored condition.
£22,000-24,000 *C*

1960 Jaguar XK150 Drophead Coupé, 6 cylinder in line engine, 3442cc, 190bhp at 5500rpm, 3 speed automatic gearbox, 4 wheel Dunlop servo-assisted disc brakes, independent front suspension with double wishbones, longitudinal torsion bars and anti-roll bar, rear semi-elliptic leaf springs, telescopic shock absorbers front and rear, left hand drive, restored and in excellent condition.
£21,000-22,000 *CNY*

1960 Jaguar XK150 'S' Fixed Head Coupé, reconditioned engine, body fully restored.
£42,000-44,000 *BKS*

Only 150 examples of the 3.8 'S' version of the XK150 fixed head coupé with the Weslake developed straight port head were built.

1959 Jaguar Mk IX Saloon,
6 cylinders, 3781cc, requires
some light restoration, good
original condition.
Est. £5,000-6,000 *ADT*

1961 Jaguar Mk IX Saloon,
6 cylinders, 3781cc, refurbished
engine, overdrive and manual
gearbox, original tools, in
excellent condition.
£7,750-8,500 *ADT*

**1958 Jaguar Mk I 3.4 Litre
Saloon,** excellent condition.
£8,000-8,500 *ECC*

**1960 Jaguar Mk II 3.8 Litre
Saloon,** 6 cylinders, 3781cc,
manual gearbox with overdrive
and chrome wire wheels,
repainted panel work, good
brightwork, excellent order
throughout.
Est. £10,000-13,000 *ADT*

**1960 Jaguar Mk II Saloon 2.4
Litre Saloon,** 6 cylinders,
2483cc, very good original
condition.   **£6,000-6,500** *ADT*

**1960 Jaguar Mk II 3.8 Litre
Saloon,** 6 cylinders, 3781cc,
repainted, original interior, an
early model in good unrestored
condition.
£6,500-7,000 *ADT*

*There were many derivatives of
the Jaguar Mk II, but it is the
3.8 litre engined model, fitted
with overdrive, that is arguably
the most desirable. Just over
15,000 right hand drive versions
of the 3.8 litre were built.*

**1963 Jaguar Mk II 3.8 Litre
Saloon,** 6 cylinders, 3781cc,
uprated to resemble one of the
famous Coombs specifications
with louvred bonnet, rear and
narrow rear wheel spats, uprated
Koni suspension, larger profile
tyres.   **Est. £8,000-9,000** *ADT*

**1963 Jaguar Mk II
3.8 Litre Saloon,**
6 cylinders, 3781cc,
imported from
Australia, in good
sound condition.
£8,250-8,750 *ADT*

**1964 Jaguar Mk II 2.4 Litre
Saloon,** rebuilt engine, excellent
restored condition.
£10,000-11,000 *WES*

**1965 Jaguar Mk II 2.4 Litre
Saloon,** right hand drive, owned
by one family from new, 45,000
miles, good condition.
£6,600-7,400 *C*

**1965 Jaguar Mk II 3.8 litre
Saloon,** 6 cylinders, 3781cc,
manual gearbox with overdrive,
bare metal respray, wide
bumpers, non-standard fog
lamps, extensively restored.
Est. £11,000-13,000 *ADT*

Miller's is a price GUIDE
not a price LIST.

**1966 Jaguar Mk II 3.8 Litre
Saloon,** excellent restoration to
original specification throughout.
£13,500-14,500 *S*

**1965 Jaguar Mk II 2.4 Litre
Saloon,** 6 cylinders, 2483cc,
120bhp at 5750rpm, 4 speed
manual gearbox with overdrive,
4 wheel disc brakes, independent
coil front suspension, rear
cantilever, right hand drive,
excellent fully restored condition.
Est. £9,000-12,000 *C*

JAGUAR Model	ENGINE cc/cyl	DATES	CONDITION 1	2	3
1½ Litre	1775/4	1945-49	£8,500	£5,500	£2,000
2½ Litre	2663/6	1946-49	£10,000	£7,500	£2,000
2½ Litre DHC	2663/6	1947-48	£18,500	£11,000	£8,000
3½ Litre	3485/6	1947-49	£12,000	£6,000	£4,000
3½ Litre DHC	3485/6	1947-49	£19,000	£13,500	£5,500
Mk V 2½ Litre	2663/6	1949-51	£8,000	£5,000	£1,500
Mk V 3½ Litre	3485/6	1949-51	£13,000	£7,000	£1,800
Mk V 3½ Litre DHC	3485/6	1949-51	£20,000	£17,000	£8,500
Mk VII	3442/6	1951-57	£10,000	£7,500	£2,500
Mk VIIM	3442/6	1951-57	£12,000	£8,500	£2,500
Mk VIII	3442/6	1956-59	£8,500	£5,500	£2,000
Mk IX	3781/6	1958-61	£9,000	£7,000	£2,500
Mk X 3.8/4.2	3781/6	1961-64	£7,500	£3,500	£1,500
Mk X 420G	4235/6	1964-70	£5,000	£3,000	£1,200
Mk I 2.4	2438/6	1955-59	£7,000	£5,500	£2,000
Mk I 3.4	3442/6	1957-59	£9,000	£6,000	£2,500
Mk II 2.4	2483/6	1959-67	£6,000	£5,000	£2,000
Mk II 3.4	3442/6	1959-67	£9,000	£6,500	£3,000
Mk II 3.8	3781/6	1959-67	£9,850	£9,000	£4,000
S-Type 3.4	3442/6	1963-68	£9,000	£6,500	£2,000
S-Type 3.8	3781/6	1963-68	£11,500	£6,500	£2,000
240	2438/6	1967-68	£8,000	£5,000	£2,500
340	3442/6	1967-68	£9,000	£7,000	£3,000
420	4235/6	1966-68	£6,000	£3,000	£2,000

Manual gearboxes with overdrive are at a premium.

1961 Lincoln Continental Convertible,
V8 overhead valve engine, 3 speed automatic
gearbox, left hand drive, excellent original
condition. £12,000-12,500 *CNY*

1932 Lincoln KB 7 Passenger Sedan,
V12 overhead valve engine, 3 speed manual
gearbox, original interior, repainted, good
condition. £46,000-48,000 *CNY*

1961 Lotus Elite Climax, MGA gearbox,
wire wheels, restored, left hand drive.
£24,000-26,000 *KSC*

1969 Lotus Elan +2 GT Sports Goupé, 1.6 litre
engine, 118bhp twin cam power unit, twin Weber
carburettors, Webasto sunroof, good condition.
£6,000-7,000 *BKS*

1962 Lotus Elite Climax S2, totally
restored to excellent condition.
£29,000-32,000 *KSC*

1974 Lotus Elan +2 130S Sports Coupé, 1.6 litre
engine, 5 speed gearbox, Girling servo-assisted disc
brakes, rebuilt, good condition.
£5,250-5,750 *BKS*

1969 Lotus Elan Drophead Coupé,
Stromberg carburettors, totally original
condition. £8,000-10,000 *KSC*

1967 Lotus Elan S3/SE Fixed Head Coupé,
new chassis, good condition.
£9,000-11,000 *KSC*

**1967 Lotus Elan S3/SE Drophead
Coupé,** original unrestored condition.
£11,000-13,000 *KSC*

1971 Lotus Elan Sprint Fixed Head Coupé,
recently resprayed and retrimmed.
£11,000-13,000 *KSC*

1971 Lotus Europa S2, rebuilt to
Concours standard on Spyder chassis.
£11,000-13,000 *KSC*

1972 Lotus Europa, twin camshafts,
good restored condition.
£6,500-7,500 *KSC*

1972 Lotus Europa, twin camshafts,
4 speed gearbox, 3 owners from new.
£7,500-8,500 *KSC*

1973 Lotus Europa Special, twin camshafts,
5 speed gearbox, full mechanical restoration.
£12,000-13,000 *KSC*

1972 Lotus Europa, twin camshafts,
fully restored on galvanised chassis,
£10,000-11,000 *KSC*

1974 Lotus Europa Special, twin camshafts,
5 speed gearbox, original condition.
£11,000-13,000 *KSC*

1988 Lotus Esprit Turbo, air conditioning,
removable glass sunroof, 48,000 recorded miles.
£14,500-15,500 *KSC*

1987 Lotus Esprit Turbo HC,
air conditioning, 30,000 miles.
£13,000-15,000 *KSC*

1989 Lotus Esprit Turbo SE, air conditioned, glass sunroof, 42,000 miles.
£17,000-19,000 *KSC*

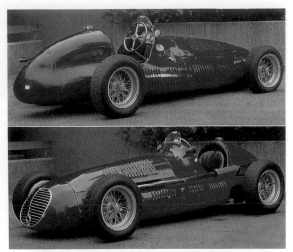

1948 Maserati 4CLT/48 Supercharged 1½ Litre Grand Prix Monoposto Racing Car, ex-Reg Parnell, bodywork by Fantuzzi, 16 valve twin overhead camshaft engine, 260bhp, good condition.
£146,000-148,000 *S(Z)*

1934/35-Type Replica Maserati 6C/34 Grand Prix/Mille Miglia Sport Corsa Single or 2 Seater, 6 cylinder, 3.7 litre supercharged engine.
£175,000-185,000 *BKS*

Only 5 of these cars were produced, and only one with bicycle mudguards.

1968 Maserati Mistral 2 Seater Sports Coupé, 6 cylinder in line engine, 4 litres, engine rebuilt, excellent condition.
£7,500-8,500 *S*

1963 Masterati Tipo 103 5000 GT Sports Coupé, V8 engine, top speed of over 170mph, Borrani wheels, Michelin XWX radial tyres, paintwork and upholstery in fair overall condition.
£42,000-45,000 *S(Z)*

1971 Maserati Tipo 116 Indy 4 Seater Sports Coupé, V8 engine, 4.7 litres, 292bhp at 5500rpm, 160mph, re-upholstered, fully restored, excellent condition.
Est. £14,000-18,000 *BKS*

1907 Mercedes 45/50hp Landaulette, coachwork by H. J. Mulliner, 4 cylinder in line engine, 6785cc, 45hp at 1100rpm, 4 speed gearbox with coil clutch, good overall condition.
£200,000-250,000 *S(NY)*

1955 Maserati A6G/54, 2000 Berlinetta, coachwork by Zagato, 6 cylinder, twin cam 2 litre engine, 160bhp, 117mph, Avon Turbospeed tyres, triple windscreen wipers, only 60 produced, requires restoration.
£85,000-90,000 *S(Z)*

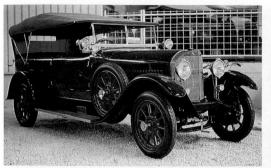

1923 Mercedes 10/40/65 4 Door Torpedo Tourer, coachwork by Drescher of Titisee Neustadt, replica body, 2.6 litres, 4 cylinders, folding screen, right hand drive, fully restored, excellent condition. **Est. £80,000-110,000** *S*

1928 Mercedes-Benz S-Type 26/120/180 Sports Tourer, 6 cylinders, 6.8 litres, Roots type supercharger, Carl Zeiss head and sidelamps, Zeiss windscreen, Bosch horns, unused since restoration. **£335,000-355,000** *S*

1913 Mercedes-Knight 15/20 Ladies' Town Car, 4 cylinder in line engine, 2610cc, 4 speed gearbox. **£32,000-35,000** *S(NY)*

1919 Mercedes-Benz 28/95 Skiff Bodied Tourer, 6 cylinder in line engine, 95hp at 1800rpm, engine replaced, requires complete restoration. **£120,000-125,000** *S(NY)*

1928 Mercedes-Benz 24/110/160 Type 630 Model K Supercharged Sports Tourer, 6 cylinders, single overhead camshaft, single carburettor, adjustable Hartford shock absorbers, complete instrumentation, excellent condition. **Est. £200,000-250,000** *S*

This was one of the fastest touring cars of its time.

1923 Mercedes-Knight 16/45 PS 6 Seater Sports Phæton, 4 speed gearbox, original 3 door bodywork, 2 folding occasional seats, Auster-type screen, detachable sidescreens, mechanically good, older restoration. **£65,000-75,000** *S*

1929 Mercedes-Benz 38/250 SS, 6 cylinders, 7065cc, good condition. **£320-000-340,000** *S(NY)*

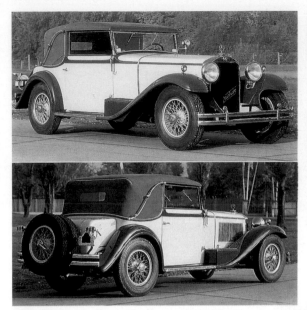

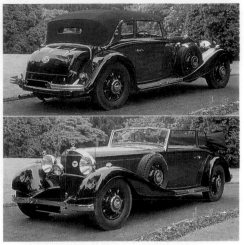

1935 Mercedes-Benz 500K Cabriolet B, 5 litre engine, coachwork fully refurbished to excellent condition after a period of storage. **£150,000-155,000** *S*

1931 Mercedes-Benz Nurburg 460 St Moritz Cabriolet C, 8 cylinder in line engine, 4.6 litres, double rear-mounted spare wheels, running board mounted battery box, excellent condition throughout. **Est. £90,000-120,000** *S*

1930 Mercedes-Benz Nurburg 500 4 Door Open Tourer, coachwork by Drescher of Titisee Neustadt, 5 litre straight 8 engine, detachable sidescreens, left hand drive, chassis totally restored, excellent condition throughout. **£110,000-120,000** *S*

1956 Mercedes-Benz 300S Convertible, 6 cylinder in line, 2996cc engine, 4 speed manual gearbox, hydraulic drum brakes , completely restored. **£95,000-100,000** *CNY*

1935 Mercedes-Benz 540K W24 Supercharged Cabriolet F, 8 cylinders, 115bhp, rebuilt from chassis-up with replacement engine, very good restored condition. **Est. £220,000-250,000** *S*

1953 Mercedes-Benz 300B Convertible, 6 cylinder in line, 2996cc engine, 4 speed manual gearbox, left hand drive, completely restored throughout. **£45,000-50,000** *CNY*

1956 Mercedes-Benz 300SL Gullwing, excellent original condition, a custom-made car. **£120,000-130,000** *PiK*

1956 Mercedes-Benz 300SL Gullwing Coupé, interior replaced to original specification, very good condition. **£120,000-130,000** *S*

1959 Mercedes-Benz 220SE 2 Door Convertible,
fuel injected engine, 120bhp, manual gearbox,
restored by Redfern's, good condition.
Est. £15,000-18,000 *S*

1959 Mercedes-Benz 190SL Convertible,
4 cylinder in line, 1897cc engine, drum brakes all-
round, manual gearbox, right hand drive, very good
condition. **£8,000-8,500** *ADT*

1959 Mercedes-Benz 220S Cabriolet, 6 cylinder
overhead camshaft, 2195cc engine, independent
suspension, servo-assisted drum brakes front and rear,
4 speed synchromesh gearbox, 100bhp at 4800rpm,
totally restored. **£32,000-34,000** *COYS*

1961 Mercedes-Benz 190SL Sports Roadster,
1.8 litres, with 3rd seat, bodywork rebuilt,
118mph, fully restored, right hand drive.
£21,000-22,000 *BKS*

**1960 Mercedes-Benz 300SL 2 Seater
Roadster,** 3 litre, 6 cylinder engine,
restored, good condition.
£67,000-69,000 *BKS(M)*

1968 Mercedes-Benz 280SL 4 Seater, 6 cylinder
overhead camshaft, 2746cc engine, repainted, engine
overhauled, excellent condition.
£14,500-15,500 *ADT*

1969 Mercedes-Benz 280SE 2 Door Coupé,
2.8 litres, replacement automatic gearbox, power
steering, low mileage, good condition.
£7,000-8,000 *BKS*

1963 Mercedes-Benz 300SL Roadster,
6 cylinder, 2996cc aluminium engine,
215bhp, Dunlop disc brakes all-round,
excellent condition.
Est. £90,000-115,000 *COYS*

l. **1969 Mercedes-Benz 280SE Convertible,**
6 cylinders, 2778cc, new automatic gearbox,
steering box, suspension, rear discs and
callipers, resprayed, good condition.
£12,500-13,500 *ADT*

1972 Mercedes-Benz 350SL Sports, good condition.
£10,500-11,500 *SJR*

1975 Mercedes-Benz 350SL Sports, good condition.
£11,750-12,500 *SJR*

1959 Messerschmitt KR200 Sports Tandem 2 Seater, 3 wheeler, 191cc, 60mph top speed, rear mounted Sachs engine, direct geared handlebar steering, restored throughout.
£4,500-5,500 *BKS*

1960 MGA Roadster 1600 Mk I, steel wheels, left hand drive, original body, good condition.
£7,000-9,000 *MSN*

1933 MG Midget J2 Open Sports, 4 cylinders, 847cc, 36bhp at 5500rpm, over 75mph top speed, 4 speed gearbox, rear mounted slab fuel tank with quick action filler cap, fold flat screen, good condition. **Est. £12,000-16,000** *COYS*

1934 MG K3 Supercharged Sports Racing Car, 1100cc, modified lowered bodywork, converted to single seater, restored, good condition.
£60,000-65,000 *S(Z)*

1968 MGB Roadster, 1950cc, with Aldon Automotive 'big bore' conversion, fully restored condition.
£9,000-10,000 *ADT*

1946 MG TC, 1250cc, stored for 30 years in a barn, no rust, engine rebuilt, resprayed, low mileage, superb condition.
Est. £12,000-15,000 *LF*

l. **1971 MGB Roadster,** wire wheels, good restored condition throughout.
£5,000-5,500 *CCTC*

1946 MG TC, 4 cylinder, overhead valve TR4 engine, 109bhp at 4700rpm, 3 speed manual gearbox, Brooklands windscreen, right hand drive, good condition.
£16,500-17,000 *CNY*

1953 MG TF 1.3 Litre Sports 2 Seater, 1250cc XPAG engine bored out to 1292cc, optional chromed centre-lock wire wheels with extra spokes, good condition.
£13,000-14,000 *BKS*

1972 MGB GT, good restored condition.
Est. £3,500-4,500 *ECC*

1972 MGB Roadster, right hand drive, overdrive, Rostyle wheels, very good restored condition throughout.
£7,000-7,500 *MSN*

1937 Morgan 4-4 2 Seater Roadster, 4 cylinder Coventry Climax engine, 1122cc, 34bhp at 4500rpm, 4 speed manual gearbox, 4 wheel drum brakes, very good original condition.
Est. £9,0000-12,000 *C*

1935 Morris 18/6 2.3 Litre 4 Door Saloon, twin wipers mounted at the base of the windscreen, built-in Jackall hydraulic jacks, excellent condition throughout.
Est. £6,000-7,000 *BKS*

l. **1953 Morris Minor Convertible,** 803cc, overhead valve engine, 4 speed gearbox, original condition.
£3,500-3,850 *ESM*

1952 Morris Minor 2 Door Saloon, 803cc, overhead valve engine, 50,000 recorded miles, very original condition.
£3,250-3,650 *ESM*

1957 Morris Minor Convertible, 1098cc engine, very good condition throughout.
£4,250-4,750 *CCon*

1963 Morris Minor Convertible, 1098cc
engine, good condition.
£7,250-7,750 *CCon*

1971 Morris Traveller, 1098cc,
original ash frame with laminated rear
posts, extra gauges fitted including
tachometer and oil pressure gauge,
low mileage.
£4,250-4,650 *ESM*

1960 Porsche 365B Roadster, coachwork by
Drauz, Heilbronn, fully restored, many extras,
excellent condition. **£27,000-29,000** *BKS*

**1931 Packard Model 840 Custom 8 Dual Cowl
Sports Phæton,** 8 cylinders, 4 speed gearbox,
expertly restored, excellent condition.
£70,000-72,000 *S*

1922 Peugeot 175 Open Sports, 4 cylinders, 2951cc,
original engine, chassis, running gear and electrics
retained, 40 gallon brass fuel tank, excellent restored
condition. **£26,000-28,000** *COYS*

1974 Porsche Carrera 3.0 RS Coupé, 6 cylinders,
2992cc, 230bhp at 6200rpm, top speed of 152mph, one
of only 6 right hand drive models made, excellent
condition. **Est. £50,000-70,000** *COYS*

**1973 Porsche TYP 911 Carrera 2.2 Litre RS
Touring 2 Door Sports Coupé,** mechanics and
coachwork in very good condition.
Est. £18,000-24,000 *BKS(M)*

1973 Porsche 911 Carrera 2.7 RS Coupé,
6 cylinders, 2687cc, 210bhp at 6300rpm, 158mph,
all-round disc brakes, good condition.
£28,000-29,000 *COYS*

1902 Renault Rear Entrance Tonneau, 6hp,
4 seater, Jones speedometer, Lanternes Ducellier oil
sidelights, brass double twist bulb horn, sprung live
rear axle, original condition. **£28,000-30,000** *S*

1986 Porsche Ruf 911 Turbo Flat Nose, 3.4
litres, 420bhp at 6800rpm, Ruf 5 speed gearbox,
4 pipe stainless steel exhaust, excellent condition.
Est. £30,000-40,000 *S(Z)*

**1908 Renault 20/30 Type V-I Three-Quarter
Landaulette,** coachwork by Stareys & Wooleys
of Nottingham, 4 cylinders, 4398cc, good
restored condition. **£35,000-37,000** *BKS*

**1908 Rolls-Royce Silver
Ghost 40/50 Roi des Belges
Tourer,** coachwork by
Wilkinsons of Derby, gearbox
replaced, chassis and engine
restored, good condition.
£330,000-350,000 *S*

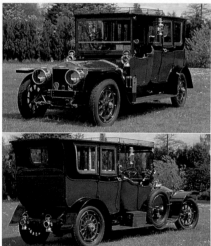

**1911 Rolls-Royce Silver Ghost 40/50
Tulip Backed Semi-Open Drive Pullman
Limousine,** extensively overhaulled, good
condition. **Est. £180,000-220,000** *S*

1912 Renault AX 2 Seater, twin cylinder
engine, 3 speed gearbox, Rotax headlights, Lucas
rear lights and mirrors, double twist bulb horn,
excellent condition. **£12,000-14,000** *S*

**1912 Rolls-Royce Silver Ghost London
Edinburgh-Tourer,** coachwork by Labourdette,
Paris, 6 cylinder in line, 7428cc engine, 3 speed
gearbox, excellent condition.
£1,000,000+ *S(NY)*

1914 Rolls-Royce Silver Ghost 40/50 Sedan, coachwork by Locke, New York, 6 cylinder in line engine, 48hp at 1250rpm, 4 speed gearbox, low mileage, requires restoration. **£105,000-110,000** *S(NY)*

1912 Rolls-Royce Silver Ghost 40/50 Sedan, coachwork by Locke, New York, 6 cylinder in line engine, requires restoration. **£65,000-70,000** *S(NY)*

1923 Rolls-Royce 20hp 2 Door Coupé with Dickey, coachwork by Johnson & Smith, 6 cylinder engine, 3 speed gearbox, Marchal headlamps, running board mounted tool box, Concours condition. **£32,000-34,000** *S*

1914 Rolls-Royce Silver Ghost 40/50 Open Drive Limousine, coachwork by Barker, 6 cylinder in line engine, 2 cylinder blocks with 3 cylinders each, non-detachable heads, side valves operated by a single camshaft, 7 bearing crankshaft, 7428cc, 2 independent ignition systems, separate spark plugs for each system, 48bhp at 1250rpm, pressure lubrication, cone clutch, 4 speed transmission, brakes on rear wheel drums, original condition. **£90,000-100,000** *S(NY)*

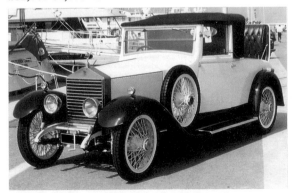

1924 Rolls-Royce Silver Ghost, coachwork by Belvalette of Paris. **£68,000-72,000** *BLE*

1923 Rolls-Royce 20hp Drophead Coupé, replacement coachwork by Park Ward, 3.1 litres, extremely good overall condition. **£20,000-25,000** *BKS(M)*

r. **1921 Rolls-Royce Silver Ghost 40/50 Pickwick Limousine,** coachwork by Brewster & Co., New York, twin mounted spare wheels with barrel style lamps, running board tool box, petrol, oil can and spout holder, luggage rack and trunk to the rear, wind-up division and secret compartments, very original condition throughout. **Est. £55,000-65,000** *S*

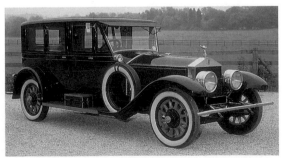

1926 Rolls-Royce 20hp Sedanca Coupé, coachwork by Salmons & Sons, 6 cylinders, 4 speed gearbox, engine rebuilt, fully restored. **£36,000-38,000** *S*
This car was once owned by Sir Edwin Lutyens.

1924 Rolls-Royce Silver Ghost Mayfair Formal Town Car, 6 cylinders 7428cc, 85bhp, 4 speed gearbox, fully restored, excellent condition. **£50,000-55,000** *S(NY)*

1925 Rolls-Royce 20hp 4 Door Saloon, coachwork by Bradburn & Wedge, 6 cylinders, 3103cc, split rim wheels, fitted tool box on either side of the sideskirts, optional spare wheel, externally fitted bulb horn, excellent original condition. **£22,000-24,000** *ADT*

1925 Rolls-Royce Silver Ghost Le Baron Prince of Wales Saloon, fully restored. **£64,000-66,000** *PiK*

1926 Rolls-Royce 20hp Limousine, coachwork by Penman of Dumfries, 6 cylinders, 3257cc, 4 speed gearbox, front wheel brakes, original beaded edge tyre rims, folding rear luggage rack, bulb and electric horns, engine rebuilt, excellent condition. **£27,000-29,000** *ADT*

1926 Rolls-Royce Silver Ghost 40/50 Tilbury Sedan, 6 cylinder in line engine, 7428cc, non-detachable cylinder heads, side valves operated by a single camshaft, 85bhp, 3 speed gearbox, rear wheel drum brakes, left hand drive, excellent condition. **£35,000-37,000** *S(NY)*

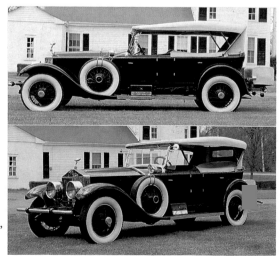

r. **1927 Rolls-Royce Phantom I Pall Mall Phæton,** 6 cylinder in line engine, 7668cc, 113bhp, 3 speed gearbox, 4 wheel drum brakes, 144in wheelbase, restored, excellent condition. **£55,000-57,000** *S(NY)*

1929 Rolls-Royce 20hp Enclosed Limousine, coachwork by J. Cockshoot & Co., Manchester, engine rebuilt in 1987 with replacement cylinder head, re-wired, new radiator and tyres. **£22,000-25,000** *S*

1931 Rolls-Royce Phantom II Doctor's Coupé. £44,000-46,000 *BLE*

1937 Rolls-Royce 25/30 3 Position Drophead Coupé, coachwork by Mulliner, radiator, steering and cylinder head were amongst items improved for 1937, side-mounted spare wheel, excellent overall condition throughout. **£36,000-38,000** *COYS*

1937 Rolls-Royce 25/30 Sedanca De Ville, coachwork by Barker, 6 cylinder, 4257cc refurbished engine, new clutch, Stromberg carburettor, SU fuel pumps, Lucas electrics, Borg & Beck clutch and Marles steering, bare metal respray, totally restored throughout. **Est. £19,000-24,000** *ADT*

1930 Rolls-Royce Phantom II 40/50 Sedanca De Ville, coachwork by Hooper & Co., engine and gearbox rebuilt in 1972, repainted and upholstered in 1980s, twin side-mounted spare wheels, swivel spotlight, wheel discs all-round, Spirit of Ecstasy mascot, imported to U.K., further restoration required. **£25,000-27,000** *S*

1938 Rolls-Royce Wraith Estate Car, original H.J. Mulliner bodywork has been altered to utility style, incorporating 2 side facing bench seats, good running order and to correct mechanical specification. **£11,000-12,000** *RCC*

1934 Rolls-Royce 20/25 Fixed Head Coupé With Dickey, coachwork by P.W. Watson of Lowestoft, twin side-mounted spare wheels, interior refurbished, very good overall condition throughout. **£26,000-28,000** *S*

1930 Rolls-Royce Phantom II Four Seater Open Tourer, coachwork by Brockman of Reading, originally fitted with a closed body by Windover, long wheelbase, engine rebuilt, very good condition throughout. **£30,000-32,000** *COYS*

1937 Rolls-Royce 25/30 Parallel Opening 2 Door Coupé, coachwork by James Young, 4¼ litre engine, 80mph top speed, Lucas short trumpet horns, opening windscreen, good all-round condition.
£30,000-32,000 *S*

1957 Rolls-Royce, Freestone & Webb aluminium ALC10 body on Cloud I chassis, good condition.
£16,000-18,000 *Cum*

This car was shown at the Earls Court Motor Show in 1957.

1954 Rolls-Royce Silver Dawn Standard Steel Saloon, 6 cylinders, 4.5 litres, 4 speed automatic gearbox, hydro-mechanical brake system, good overall condition.
£19,000-20,000 *BKS*

1958 Rolls-Royce Silver Cloud I 4 Door Standard Steel Saloon, good condition.
£9,500-10,500 *BA*

1964 Rolls-Royce Phantom V Limousine, V8 engine, 6230cc, 200bhp at 4000rpm, 4 speed automatic gearbox, drum brakes all-round, left hand drive, Sony television, stereo cassette players in front and rear, telephones, coachwork repainted, very good overall condition.
£39,000-41,000 *CNY*

1961 Rolls-Royce Silver Cloud II 4 Door Saloon, good overall condition.
£10,000-18,000 *BA*

1964 Rolls-Royce Series F Silver Cloud III Flying Spur, coachwork by H. J. Mulliner, V8 engine, 117mph, power steering, dual headlamps, air conditioning, good condition.
£40,000-42,000 *S(Z)*

l. **1965 Rolls-Royce Silver Cloud III Coupé,** coachwork by Mulliner Park Ward, V8 engine, 6230cc, 220bhp, top speed of 115mph, excellent restored condition.
£18,500-19,500 *COYS*

1975 Rolls-Royce Corniche Coupé, magnolia Everflex top and leather trim, needs slight restoration to coachwork, good overall condition.
£12,000-13,000 *RCC*

1965 Rolls-Royce Silver Cloud III Drophead Coupé, coachwork by Mulliner Park Ward, V8 engine, 6230cc, body resprayed, fully restored, excellent condition.
Est. £33,000-38,000 *COYS*

1971 Rolls-Royce Phantom VI Limousine, coachwork by H. J. Mulliner Park Ward, 2 square footrests to the rear, blinds to 4 rear windows, cocktail cabinet under electric division, radio controls in offside rear armrest, low mileage, excellent condition.
£43,000-45,000 *S*

1977 Rolls-Royce Silver Shadow, 8 cylinders, 6750cc, new disc brakes, green upholstery and trim, 117,000 recorded miles, good condition.
£7,500-8,000 *ADT*

1982 Rolls-Royce Spirit, very good overall condition.
£14,000-14,500 *Cum*

1966 Rover 3 Litre, original paintwork, low mileage, very good leather interior, good overall condition.
£2,500-3,000 *CCTC*

1936 Rover 12hp 4 Seater Tourer, 4 cylinders, 1465cc, Luvax Bijur auto chassis lubrication system, ignition-lead cover, free wheel system, automatic restart system and full complement of instruments, folding windscreen, tonneau cover replaced, spare engine and gearbox, requires restoration.
£6,000-7,000 *ADT*

**1966 Jaguar Mk II 3.4 Litre
4 Door Saloon,** substantial
restoration.
£8,000-10,000 *BKS*

**1967 Jaguar Mk II 3.4 Litre
Saloon,** very good overall
condition.
£8,000-8,500 *ADT*

**1967 Jaguar Mk II 3.4 Litre
Saloon,** manual gearbox with
overdrive, low mileage, many
service records, very original car.
£5,000-5,500 *CCTC*

**1968 Jaguar 240 2.4 Litre
4 Door Saloon,** generally good
condition but some cosmetic
attention required.
Est. £4,000-6,000 *BKS*

1968 Jaguar 240 Saloon,
overhauled engine, bare metal
repaint, excellent condition
throughout.
£7,500-8,000 *S*

*Fitted with a 2483cc version of
Jaguar's 6 cylinder overhead
camshaft engine, the 240 model
was basically a continuation of
the 2.4 litre Mk II saloon.*

1969 Jaguar 420G, 6 cylinders,
4228cc, excellent order
throughout.
£4,500-5,500 *ADT*

1967 Jaguar 420G Saloon,
6 cylinders, 4235cc, excellent
restored condition.
Est. £5,000-6,000 *ADT*

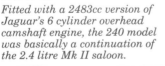

1967 Jaguar 420 Saloon,
6 cylinders, double overhead
camshaft, 4235cc, 245bhp at
5500rpm, 4 speed manual
gearbox with overdrive, servo-
assisted 4 wheel disc brakes,
independent front and rear
suspension, right hand drive,
good overall condition.
£6,500-7,500 *C*

**1970 Jaguar 420G
4 Door Saloon,**
fully restored,
in good general
condition.
Est. £6,500-7,000 *S*

1970 Jaguar XJ6, 6 cylinders, 4235cc, stainless steel exhaust, resprayed, in very good condition. **Est. £2,750-3,750** *ADT*

1961 Jaguar E-Type 3.8 litre Series I 'Flat Floor' Roadster, excellent restoration, components renovated to a very high standard, very original car. **£35,000-38,000** *BKS*

Right hand drive Series I E-Types were always rare and sought after, with only 942 of all types having been built between 1961-64. The highly desirable 'flat floor' models, with the external bonnet release handles, were only available during the short 1961 season.

1963 Jaguar E-Type 3.8 Litre Fixed Head Coupé, 6 cylinders, 3781cc, rebuilt to an excellent standard. **£20,000-22,000** *ADT*

1962 Jaguar E-Type 3.8 Litre Roadster, 6 cylinders, 3781cc, overhauled engine and gearbox, an excellent overall ground-up restoration. **£33,000-36,000** *COYS*

1964 Jaguar E-Type 3.8 Litre Coupé, 6 cylinders, 3781cc, extensively restored. **£44,000-46,000** *COYS*

This well-known car has won several major 'Concours' events.

1963 Jaguar E-Type Coupé, 6 cylinders, 3781cc, totally rebuilt, excellent condition throughout. **£18,000-20,000** *COYS*

**1964 Jaguar E-Type Series I
3.8 Litre Roadster,** in good
condition throughout.
£16,000-18,000 *S*

**1964 Jaguar E-Type Series I
3.8 Litre coupé,** 6 cylinders,
3781cc, bare metal respray and
total mechanical rebuild,
extensive ground-up restoration,
in excellent condition.
£21,000-23,000 *COYS*

**1965 Jaguar E-Type 4.2 Litre
Fixed Head Coupé,** 6 cylinders,
4235cc, re-imported into the UK,
sound condition but requires
some attention.
£8,000-9,000 *ADT*

**1965 Jaguar E-Type 4.2 Litre
Roadster,** stainless steel
exhaust, restored in the early
1980s, in good condition.
£19,000-21,000 *ADT*

**1965 Jaguar E-Type 4.2 Litre
Fixed Head Coupé,** 6 cylinders,
4228cc, converted to right hand
drive, has been in dry storage,
some refurbishment but requires
further attention.
£11,000-12,000 *ADT*

**1965 Jaguar E-Type 4.2 Litre
Fixed Head Coupé,** 6 cylinders,
4220cc, manual gearbox, left
hand drive, good overall
condition.
£9,000-10,000 *ADT*

*This car was probably used for
development work, testing the
manual overdrive and Stromberg
carburettors which were to be
introduced on the Series II E-
Types intended for export to the
USA to meet their emission
controls.*

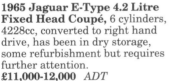

**1967 Jaguar E-Type Series I
2+2 4.2 Litre Coupé,**
6 cylinders in line, double
overhead camshaft, 4235cc
engine, 265bhp at 5400rpm,
4 speed manual gearbox with
overdrive, Dunlop servo-assisted
disc brakes all-round,
independent suspension, right
hand drive, restored to good
overall condition.
£9,000-9,500 *C*

**1965 Jaguar E-Type
Series I 4.2 Litre
2 Seater Roadster,**
fully restored to the
highest standard.
£24,000-25,000 *BKS*

**1967 Jaguar E-Type 4.2 Litre
Fixed Head Coupé,** 6 cylinders,
4235cc, manual gearbox, original
right hand drive, very good
overall condition.
Est. £17,000-19,000 *ADT*

1968 Jaguar E-Type 2+2,
6 cylinders, 4235cc, manual
gearbox, right hand drive, 30,000
miles, good all round condition.
Est. £10,000-11,000 *ADT*

**1970 Jaguar E-Type Series II
4.2 Litre 2 Seater Roadster,**
excellent condition throughout.
£25,000-27,000 *BKS*

**1968 Jaguar E-Type Series II
Roadster,** 6 cylinders in line,
double overhead camshaft,
4235cc, 171bhp at 5400 rpm,
4 speed manual gearbox, front
suspension independent torsion
bar, rear independent coil, left
hand drive, very good restored
condition throughout.
£18,000-20,000 *CNY*

**1970 Jaguar E-Type 4.2 Litre
Roadster,** 6 cylinders, 4235cc,
has been completely dismantled
and rebuilt, resprayed, right
hand drive, good overall
condition.
£19,000-20,000 *ADT*

JAGUAR Model	ENGINE cc/cyl	DATES	CONDITION		
			1	2	3
E-type 3.8 flat floor roadster (RHD)		1961	£40,000	£30,000	£21,500
E-type S1 3.8 roadster	3781/6	1961-64	£28,000	£18,000	£13,000
E-type 3.8 FHC	3781/6	1961-64	£18,000	£13,000	£9,000
E-type S1 4.2 roadster	4235/6	1964-67	£22,000	£18,000	£12,000
E-type 2+2 manual FHC	4235/6	1966-67	£15,000	£10,000	£8,000
E-type S.1 2+2 auto FHC	4235/6	1966-68	£13,000	£9,000	£7,000
E-type S.II roadster	4235/6	1968-70	£22,000	£18,000	£12,000
E-type S.II FHC	4235/6	1968-70	£18,000	£12,000	£8,000
E-type S.II 2+2 manual FHC	4235/6	1968-70	£15,000	£10,000	£8,000
E-type S.III roadster	5343/12	1971-75	£35,000	£24,000	£15,000
E-type S.III 2+2 manual FHC	5343/12	1971-75	£19,000	£14,000	£10,000
E-type S.III 2+2 auto FHC	5343/12	1971-75	£17,000	£12,000	£9,000
XJ6 2.8 Ser I	2793/6	1968-73	£2,600	£1,500	£1,000
XJ6 4.2 Ser I	4235/6	1968-73	£3,000	£2,000	£1,000
XJ6 Coupé	4235/6	1974-78	£7,000	£3,000	£2,000
XJ6 Ser II	4235/6	1973-79	£3,500	£2,000	£750
XJ12 Ser I	5343/12	1972-73	£3,500	£2,250	£1,500
XJ12 Coupé	5343/12	1973-77	£8,000	£4,000	£2,000
XJ12 Ser II	5343/12	1973-79	£2,000	£1,500	-
XJS manual	5343/12	1975-78	£6,000	£4,500	£2,500
XJS auto	5343/12	1975-81	£4,000	£2,200	£1,500

1969 Jaguar E-Type Series II Roadster, 6 cylinders, 4235cc, suspension and brakes overhauled, body restored, left hand drive, very good condition. **£20,000-22,000** *COYS*

1972 Jaguar E-Type Series III Fixed Head Coupé, 12 cylinders, 5343cc, 48,000 miles, in excellent condition. **Est. £15,000-16,000** *ADT*

1971 Jaguar E-Type Series III Fixed Head Coupé, manual gearbox, right hand drive, good overall condition. **£9,000-10,000** *ADT*

1970 Jaguar E-Type 4.2 Litre Fixed Head Coupé, 6 cylinders, 4235cc, good overall condition. **£17,000-18,000** *ADT*

1973 Jaguar E-Type 2+2 V12 Coupé, 12 cylinders, 5343cc, 3 speed automatic transmission, 12,200 recorded mileage, chrome wire wheels, unrestored and original car. **£19,000-20,000** *ADT*

1971 Jaguar E-Type Series III 2+2 Coupé, manual gearbox, engine and suspension rebuilt, gearbox reconditioned and braking system overhauled, stainless steel exhaust, bare metal respray, original right hand drive. **Est. £13,000-14,000** *S*

1973 Jaguar E-Type V12 Roadster, manual gearbox, chrome wire wheels, hard top, 38,000 miles, with history. **£24,000-26,000** *VIC*

1973 Jaguar E-Type Series III V12 Roadster, 5343cc, automatic transmission, good condition throughout. **£17,000-18,000** *COYS*

1973 Jaguar E-Type V12, manual gearbox, wire wheels, in good restored condition. **£13,500-14,000** *Mot*

1974 Jaguar E-Type Series III Roadster, 5343cc, 4,400 recorded miles, restored to excellent condition throughout. **£21,000-22,000** *COYS*

1973 Jaguar E-Type V12 Roadster, mechanical restoration, excellent condition.
£27,000-29,000 *PiK*

1974 Jaguar E-Type Series III V12 Roadster, 60° overhead cam engine, 5343cc, 241bhp at 4750rpm, 4 speed manual gearbox, front and rear disc brakes, front suspension wishbone, torsion bars and anti-roll bar, rear independent suspension with lower wishbones, radius arms, coil springs and anti-roll bar, low mileage, body and chassis restoration, excellent condition.
£28,000-32,000 *CNY*

1974 Jaguar E-Type Series II V12 2 Seater Roadster, 5.3 litre engine, automatic transmission, right hand drive, very good condition throughout.
£22,000-24,000 *BKS*

1974 Jaguar E-Type Series III Roadster, 12 cylinders, 5343cc, manual gearbox, original right hand drive, Ziebarted from new, free of corrosion.
Est. £32,000-35,000 *ADT*

1972 Jaguar XJ6 Coupé, ex-Coumbs demonstrator.
£9,500-10,000 *FHF*

1976 Jaguar XJ6 4.2 Litre Coupé, automatic gearbox.
£3,500-4,000 *CCTC*

1972 Jaguar XJ6 Series I Saloon, left hand drive, good condition.
£3,000-5,000 *BA*

1981 Jaguar XJ6 5 Seater Estate, original coachwork conversion by Avon, good all round condition.
Est. £5,000-6,000 *S*

1982 Jaguar XJS Lynx Convertible V12 HE, electric hood, 46,000 miles, completely restored.
£10,000-12,000 *VIC*

JENSEN

Jensen Motors Ltd., was only formed in 1934, although Alan and Richard Jensen, the Company's founders, had produced coachbuilt car bodies for a number of years prior to this date. Jensen favoured large, powerful engines, such as the Ford V8, the Lincoln V12, and later the Chrysler V8, 7.2 litre engine, used in the Interceptor Mk III.

1937 Jensen H Series, Nash 4.2 litre straight 8 engine.
£18,000-19,000 *CBG*

1939 Jensen S-Type Sports Saloon, 8 cylinders, 3622cc, very good overall condition.
£16,500-17,500 *ADT*

Only 3 pre-war saloons are known to the Jensen Owners Club.

1948 Jensen PW Sportsman's Saloon, 6 cylinders, 3993cc, good overall condition.
£9,000-9,500 *ADT*

1956 Jensen 541, 6 cylinders, 3993cc, triple carburettor, manual gearbox, restored in 1992 to a very high standard.
£5,500-6,000 *ADT*

1957 Jensen 541 Coupé, 6 cylinders, 3993cc, restored to Concours standard.
£12,000-13,000 *COYS*

1959 Jensen 541R, 4 litre Austin straight 6 engine.
£11,500-12,500 *CBG*

1958 Jensen 541R, manual gearbox with overdrive, restored.
£10,500-11,500 *Mot*

1965 Jensen CV8 Mk III Coupé, V8 engine, 6276cc, fully restored, in excellent condition.
£7,500-8,500 *COYS*

Launched in 1953, the 541 was the first ever production 4 seater to use a fibreglass body. For its new CV8, Jensen continued with this design, substituting the 541's 4 litre Austin engine for a Chrysler V8 while restyling the front and rear of the body.

JENSEN Model	ENGINE cc/cyl	DATES	CONDITION		
			1	2	3
541/541R/541S	3993/6	1954-63	£8,000	£5,000	£3,500
CV8 Mk I-III	5916/				
	6276/8	1962-66	£10,000	£6,000	£4,000
Interceptor SI-SIII	6276/8	1967-76	£8,000	£5,000	£4,500
Interceptor DHC	6276/8	1973-76	£20,000	£12,000	£9,000
Interceptor SP	7212/8	1971-76	£10,000	£8,000	£6,500
FF	6766/8	1967-71	£13,000	£10,000	£9,000
Healey	1973/4	1972-76	£5,000	£3,000	£1,500
Healey GT	1973/4	1975-76	£6,000	£3,000	£2,000

Jensen CV8 Mk II, Chrysler
383cu in engine, 6376cc.
£9,000-10,000 *CBG*

1966 Jensen CV8, 8 cylinders,
6276cc, stainless steel exhaust
system, with original wheels and
interior, in good overall condition.
£7,500-8,500 *ADT*

c1970 Jensen FF II, Chrysler
V8 383cu in, 6376cc engine.
£15,000-16,000 *CBG*

**1973 Jensen Interceptor
Mk III,** 50,000 miles, in excellent
condition.
£10,500-11,500 *Mot*

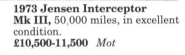

**1973 Jensen Interceptor
Series IV EFi Convertible,**
completely rebuilt by the factory
for their own use in 1991, 5,200
miles, a superb example.
£38,000-40,000 *S*

**1973 Jensen Interceptor
Mk III SP,** coachwork by
Vignale, V8, 7212cc engine,
excellent overall condition.
£8,500-9,500 *COYS*

**1975 Jensen Interceptor
Special Coupé,** 6 cylinders,
7212cc, engine and gearbox in
good condition, refurbished with
all original Jensen parts.
£13,000-14,000 *ADT*

*The last derivative of the
Interceptor, called the coupé, was
created out of Jensen's own
successful re-design of the rear
panelwork for the convertible to
produce a very new stylish fixed
head saloon.*

1974 Jensen Interceptor Convertible, mechanically excellent.
£22,000-24,000 *HWA*

1976 Jensen Interceptor Mk III, Chrysler V8 engine, 440cu in, 7212cc engine.
£16,000-17,000 *CBG*

1976 Jensen Interceptor Convertible, 7.2 litre, excellent condition.
£12,000-15,000 *ECC*

1974 Jensen Healey Mk II, 1973cc, Lotus engine, 4 speed gearbox, rubber bumper.
£5,000-6,000 *CBG*

1972 Jensen Healey Mk I, 1973cc, Lotus engine.
£4,750-5,000 *CBG*

1974 Jensen Interceptor Mk III Convertible, coachwork by Vignale, V8, 7212cc engine, very good condition.
£21,000-23,000 *COYS*

One of only 267 convertibles produced.

JOWETT

1952 Jowett Jupiter 2 Seater Sports, left hand drive, mechanics and engine rebuilt, extensively restored to highest standard.
Est. £14,000-16,000 *S*

KAISER

1953 Kaiser Manhatten 4 Door Sedan, left hand drive, excellent condition throughout.
£7,000-9,000 *CGB*

LAGONDA

Lagonda has always been a British built motor car, despite its American founder, Wilbur Gunn. Lagonda was the local Indian name for the river in Gunn's home town in Ohio. The factory in Staines, Middlesex, produced a range of magnificent vehicles including sports cars which, although somewhat under-powered, managed to win the Le Mans 24 hour race before the war.

David Brown, the tractor manufacturer acquired Lagonda in 1947. The marque continues to feature on several Aston Martin products.

1927 Lagonda 16/65 Open Tourer, 6 cylinders, 2931cc, twin SU carburettors, restored. **Est. £35,000-40,000** *COYS*

1927 Lagonda 2 Litre High Chassis Tourer, excellent restored condition. **£38,000-40,000** *Pik*

1930 Lagonda 2 Litre 4 Seater Low Chassis Tourer,
4 cylinders, 1954cc, overhead valve with twin high mounted camshafts, 60bhp at 3500rpm, 4 speed sliding mesh gearbox, 4 wheel mechanical drum brakes, semi-elliptic leaf springs with friction dampers suspension, right hand drive, paintwork in fine condition, clock and fuel gauge not working, includes hood cover, tonneau and side screens, electric fuel pump, modern electric fan and 4 indicators.
£27,000-29,000 *C*

1931 Lagonda 2 Litre 4 Seater Tourer, coachwork by Lagonda Ltd., of Staines, major restoration and rebuild, in excellent condition. **£33,000-35,000** *S*

LAGONDA Model	ENGINE cc/cyl	DATES	CONDITION		
			1	2	3
12/24	1421/4	1923-26	£14,000	£10,000	£8,000
2 litre	1954/4	1928-32	£28,000	£25,000	£19,000
3 litre	2931/6	1928-34	£35,000	£30,000	£22,000
M45	4429/6	1934-36	£35,000	£26,000	£18,000
LG45	4429/6	1936-37	£40,000	£30,000	£20,000
LG6	4453/6	1937-39	£35,000	£28,000	£20,000
V12	4480/V12	1937-39	£65,000	£50,000	£40,000

Prices are very dependent upon body type, originality and competition history.

1935 Lagonda M35R 4 Seater Tourer, in excellent restored condition. **Est. £30,000-40,000** *S*

The Lagonda 3½ litre (M35R) was an interim model, built for 1935 only. It used the Rapide chassis designed for the 4½ litre (M45R) but was fitted with a re-cast, big bore Lagonda 3 litre engine.

Don't forget!
If in doubt please refer to the 'How to Use' section at the beginning of this book.

1936 Lagonda LG45, 6 cylinders, 4453cc, in good condition. **£37,000-40,000** *COYS*

Originally supplied with saloon coachwork, it now has tourer bodywork believed to have been fitted during a complete restoration.

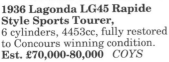

1938 Lagonda V12 Saloon,
very good restored condition.
£10,000-12,000 *ADT*

**1936 Lagonda LG45 Rapide
Style Sports Tourer,**
6 cylinders, 4453cc, fully restored
to Concours winning condition.
Est. £70,000-80,000 *COYS*

**1938 Lagonda LG6 Drop Head
Coupé,** 6 cylinders, 4453cc, very
good condition throughout.
Est. £65,000-70,000 *COYS*

1939 Lagonda V12 De Ville,
coachwork by Lagonda,
12 cylinders, 4479cc, original
upholstery, in very good
condition.
Est. £20,000-24,000 *ADT*

*3 chassis lengths were available
and these were 124in, 132in and
138in, and this example is one of
the few 132in chassis built.*

**1950 Lagonda DB 2.6 Litre
Drophead Coupé,** 6 cylinders,
2580cc, very good overall
condition.
Est. £12,000-14,000 *ADT*

CROSS REFERENCE
**Restoration
Projects** ⟶ p305

**1950 Lagonda 2.6 Litre
Convertible,** suitable for
restoration.
£5,800-6,200 *DB*

LAGONDA (post-war) Model	ENGINE cc/cyl	DATES	CONDITION		
			1	2	3
3 litre	2922/6	1953-58	£10,500	£7,000	£4,500
3 litre DHC	2922/6	1953-56	£14,000	£10,000	£8,500
Rapide	3995/6	1961-64	£11,000	£7,000	£4,500

LAMBORGHINI

1967 Lamborghini 400GT Coupé, V12, 3929cc engine, from a private collection, entirely original, in good all-round condition.
£30,000-34,000 *COYS*

1972 Lamborghini Islero 'S' Coupé, coachwork by Marazzi, V12 engine, 3929cc, from a private collection, completely original, in good all-round condition.
£19,000-22,000 *COYS*

1974 Lamborghini Espada Mk III Sports Coupé, major engine rebuild, original interior upholstery, in good overall condition.
£16,000-18,000 *S*

The P250 was powered by a 2463cc engine producing 220bhp which gave a top speed of 140mph. Only 520 P250s were built during its production run to 1979.

1974 Lamborghini Urraco P250, only 9480 miles, very good original condition.
Est. £9,000-11,000 *Cen*

LANCHESTER

1902 Lanchester Rear Entrance Tonneau, original condition.
£28,000-32,000 *FHF*

1913 Lanchester 38hp Torpedo Tourer, dated by the Veteran Car Club of Great Britain, repainted and in excellent condition.
£40,000-42,000 *S*

1927 Lanchester Landaulette, 1913 coachwork by Hooper, fitted to original owners specification.
£24,000-26,000 *FHF*

1921 Lanchester 40hp Limousine, 6178cc, single overhead camshaft engine, glass division to the rear compartment, occasional seats, blinds to the rear windows, interior reading lights and running board courtesy lights, twin side mounted spare wheels, rear luggage carrier and running board tool box, original interior trim, coachwork recently painted to the highest standard.
£23,000-25,000 *S*

1932 Lanchester 30 Straight 8 Sports Tourer, coachwork by Jarvis, 8 cylinders, 4437cc, 82bhp at 2800rpm, hemispherical combustion chamber straight 8 engine with dual ignition and overhead camshaft, 4 speed manual gearbox, 4 wheel drum brakes, semi-elliptic springs front suspension, rear cantilever springs, right hand drive, engine rebuilt.
Est. £25,000-30,000 *C*

1953 Lanchester 14hp 4 Door Saloon, fluid flywheel and pre-selector gearbox, has been stored for many years, in sound order but in need of complete overhaul.
£900-1,000 *S*

LANCHESTER Model	ENGINE cc/cyl	DATES	CONDITION 1	2	3
LD10	1287/4	1946-49	£2,500	£1,500	£750
LD10 (Barker bodies)	1287/4	1950-51	£2,800	£1,500	£700

LANCIA

Vicenzo Lancia, the son of a soup manufacturer, was born in 1881. His first car was produced in 1906 in Turin.

Lancia have produced several innovative models, notably the Lambda, the Aprilia, the Aurelia and, more recently, the Stratos. Lancia found it hard to compete with Alfa Romeo and Fiat and were subsequently taken over by Fiat in 1969.

1947 Lancia Aprilia Saloon, 4 cylinders, 1488cc, pillarless fastback, 4 door coachwork, independent suspension, cloth interior, in excellent condition.
£12,000-14,000 *COYS*

1955 Lancia Aurelia B20 (2500GT) Series IV Berlinetta, coachwork by Pininfarina, V6 engine, 2451cc, interior in excellent condition, Nardi steering wheel, floor gear shift, tinted glass, very rare optional Borrani wire wheels, excellent paintwork, one owner, 26,000 miles.
£65,000-70,000 *COYS*

Few Series IV cars were made in 1955 with the 118bhp 2½ litre engine (the works B20s had 97bhp) and a de Dion rear axle. Aurelia B20s, and their 2½ litre successor, were built from 1951-58 and a total of just 2,568 were made.

1956 Lancia Aurelia 2.4 Litre B20 Series V Coupé, coachwork by Pininfarina, Nardi floor change and steering wheel, electrics, cylinder head and camshaft overhauled, full body and interior renovation, right hand drive, excellent condition.
£27,000-29,000 *BKS*

LANCIA Model	ENGINE cc/cyl	DATES	CONDITION 1	2	3
Theta	4940/4	1913-19	£24,000	£16,500	£8,000
Kappa	4940/4	1919-22	£24,000	£16,000	£8,000
Dikappa	4940/4	1921-22	£24,000	£16,000	£8,000
Trikappa	4590/4	1922-26	£25,000	£18,000	£10,000
Lambda	2120/4	1923-28	£28,000	£20,000	£10,000
Dilambda	3960/8	1928-32	£24,000	£16,000	£8,000
Astura	2604/8	1931-39	£25,000	£18,000	£9,000
Artena	1925/4	1931-36	£9,000	£5,000	£2,000
Augusta	1196/4	1933-36	£9,000	£4,000	£2,000
Aprilia 238	1352/4	1937-39	£10,000	£5,000	£3,000

1959 Lancia Aurelia B24S Convertible, coachwork by Farina, V6 engine, overhead valves activated by pushrod, bore and stroke 78 x 86mm, displacement 2451cc, 118hp at 5000rpm, 4 speed transaxle with bevel gear drive, 4 wheel hydraulic drum brakes, 98in wheelbase, 59,000 miles, original leather upholstery, fair condition. **£23,000-25,000** *S(NY)*

1959 Lancia Aurelia B24S Convertible, coachwork by Farina, complete engine overhaul and extensively restored. **£26,000-28,000** *S(NY)*

1967 Lancia Flavia Sports Coupé, resprayed, rust free, original specification. **Est. £3,000-5,000** *S*

1960 Lancia Flaminia Coupé, V6 engine, 2458cc, Solex carburettor, left hand drive, well maintained original car. **Est. £6,500-7,500** *ADT*

1976 Lancia Fulvia Series II Door Coupé, 1.3 litre twin overhead camshaft engine, 90bhp, reconditioned bodywork, low mileage, in good condition. **£3,500-4,000** *BKS*

Miller's is a price GUIDE not a price LIST.

1968 Lancia Flaminia GT Sports Coupé, coachwork by Touring of Milan, 6 cylinders, 2458cc, 60°V, triple Weber carburettors, 140bhp at 5600rpm, 4 speed manual gearbox, disc brakes all round, independent quadrilateral transverse link coil springs front suspension, rear tubular axle, stabilizer bar, leaf springs, left hand drive, poor paintwork, original car in need of restoration. **£4,200-5,000** *C*

LANCIA Model	ENGINE cc/cyl	DATES	CONDITION		
			1	2	3
Aprilia 438	1486/4	1939-50	£11,000	£6,000	£3,000
Ardea	903/4	1939-53	£10,000	£5,000	£3,000
Aurelia B10	1754/6	1950-53	£7,000	£5,000	£2,000
Aurelia B15-20-22	1991/6	1951-53	£10,000	£5,000	£2,500
Aurelia B24-B24S	2451/6	1955	£20,000	£15,000	£10,000
Aurelia GT	2451/6	1953-59	£15,000	£10,000	£7,000
Appia C10-C105	1090/4	1953-62	£5,000	£3,000	£2,000
Aurelia Ser II	2266/6	1954-59	£10,000	£5,000	£3,000
Flaminia Zagato	2458/6	1957-63	£15,000	£10,000	£7,000
Flaminia Ser	2458/6	1957-63	£12,000	£7,000	£5,000
Flavia 1500	1500/4	1960-75	£6,000	£4,000	£2,000
Fulvia	1091/4	1963-70	£3,000	£2,000	£1,000
Fulvia S	1216/4	1964-70	£3,500	£2,500	£1,500
Fulvia 1.3	1298/4	1967-75	£3,000	£2,000	£1,000
Stratos	2418/6	1969-71	£25,000	£18,000	£10,000
Flavia 2000	1991/6	1969-75	£2,500	£1,500	£500
Fulvia HF/1.6	1584/4	1969-75	£4,000	£2,000	£1,000
Beta HPE	1585/4	1976-82	£2,500	£1,500	£500
Beta Spyder	1995/4	1977-82	£2,000	£1,000	£500
Monte Carlo	1995/4	1976-81	£4,000	£2,000	£1,000

1981 Lancia Beta Coupé, 4 cylinders, 1301cc, 5 speed gearbox, all round disc brakes, good panelwork, right hand drive. **£1,000-1,500** *ADT*

1982 Lancia Gamma 2500 Coupé FI, automatic gearbox, in good condition. **£4,250-4,750** *S*

LAND ROVER

1950 Land Rover 4 x 4 Short Wheelbase, recently restored, all round very good condition. **£2,250-2,750** *S*

c1950 Land Rover Series I, 4 cylinders, 1595cc, fully reconditioned engine, very good restored condition throughout. **Est. £5,000-6,000** *ADT*

1968 Land Rover 101in Forward Control Pilot Vehicle, 6 cylinder, 3 litre petrol engine, multi-leaf springs, rear take off for power driven trailer. **£7,750-8,250** *LRT*

One of the 20 pilot models made for testing.

CROSS REFERENCE
Military Vehicles ⟶ p90

1963 Land Rover 109in Forward Control, 4 cylinder petrol engine, non-dropside body, original paintwork. **£3,800-4,200** *LRT*

LAND ROVER Model	ENGINE cc/cyl	DATES	CONDITION		
			1	2	3
Ser 1	1595/4	1948-51	£2,200	£1,000	£500
Ser 1	1995/4	1951-53	£2,000	£1,000	£300
Ser 1	1995/4	1953-58	£2,000	£1,000	£300
Ser 1	1995/4	1953-58	£2,800	£1,500	£750
Ser 2	1995/4	1958-59	£2,000	£950	£500
Ser 2	1995/4	1958-59	£2,800	£1,200	£500
Ser 2	2286/4	1959-71	£2,000	£950	£500
Ser 2	2286/4	1959-71	£2,500	£1,200	£500
Range Rover	3528/V8	1970-	£2,200	£1,200	£600

LA SALLE

1934 La Salle Convertible Coupé, straight 8 engine, 240cu in, 95hp at 3700rpm, 3 speed manual gearbox, front and rear drum brakes, left hand drive, in excellent overall condition.
£36,000-38,000 *CNY*

1931 La Salle 345A 2 Door Coupé with 1926 Eccles Caravan, Cadillac V8 engine, 5997cc, 95bhp at 3000rpm, 3 speed synchromesh gearbox, 4 wheel mechanical drum brakes, leaf springs front and rear suspension, left hand drive, excellent overall condition.
£17,000-19,000 *C*

The name La Salle came from an early French explorer from Illinois.

LEA-FRANCIS

1937 Lea-Francis 14hp Doctor's Coupé, fitted tool box, restored body with fabric covering.
£8,750-9,000 *Bro*

1951 Lea-Francis 14hp 4 Door Saloon, in sound condition, in need of restoration.
£4,500-5,000 *S*

1954 Lea-Francis 14hp, right hand drive, imported from California, in running order, needs restoring.
£1,500-1,750 *C*

1947 Lea-Francis 14hp, 4 cylinders, 1767cc, totally rebuilt as a 2 door coupé during the 1980s.
£7,000-7,500 *ADT*

Lea-Francis launched their post-war company early in 1946, using a similar engine to the pre-war models, but using bodies manufactured by A. P. Aircraft Ltd. The 14hp 1629cc engine was replaced by a 1.8 litre 4 cylinder unit.

LEA-FRANCIS Model	ENGINE cc/cyl	DATES	CONDITION		
			1	2	3
12HP	1944/4	1923-24	£10,000	£5,000	£3,000
14HP	2297/4	1923-24	£10,000	£5,000	£3,000
9HP	1074/4	1923-24	£7,000	£4,000	£2,000
10HP	1247/4	1947-54	£10,000	£5,500	£3,000
12HP	1496/4	1926-34	£11,000	£6,000	£4,000
Various 6 cylinder models	1696/6	1927-29	£13,500	£9,500	£5,000
Various 6 cylinder models	1991/6	1928-36	£10,500	£8,750	£5,000
14HP	1767/4	1946-54	£6,000	£4,000	£2,000
1.5 litre	1499/4	1949-51	£9,000	£5,000	£2,500
2.5 litre	2496/4	1950-52	£10,000	£8,000	£4,000

LINCOLN

1931 Lincoln Model K Convertible Coupé, coachwork by Le Baron, well equipped and sympathetically restored.
£28,000-36,000 *S*

Henry Leland left Cadillac in 1917 to form his own company which he named after Abraham Lincoln. The company ran into financial troubles and was rescued by Henry Ford in 1922.

1939 Lincoln Zephyr 8/73 Sedan, 12 cylinders, 4700cc, original interior, in good all-round condition.
£6,500-7,000 *ADT*

1957 Lincoln Premiere 4 Door Hard Top, 22,500 miles, repainted, in excellent original condition.
£4,000-5,000 *CGB*

1956 Lincoln Continental Mk II, 7.2 litre engine, in Concours winning condition.
£7,750-8,000 *Bro*

1962 Lincoln Continental 4 Door Sedan, V8 overhead valve engine, 430cu in, 300bhp at 4100rpm, 3 speed automatic gearbox, left hand drive, excellent original condition.
£5,000-7,000 *CNY*

LINCOLN Model	ENGINE cc/cyl	DATES	CONDITION 1	2	3
Première Coupé	368/8	1956-57	£6,000	£4,000	£2,000
Première Convertible	368/8	1956-57	£14,000	£8,000	£5,000
Continental Mk II	368/8	1956-57	£10,000	£6,000	£4,000
Continental 2 door	430/8	1958-60	£6,000	£4,000	£2,000
Continental Convertible	430/8	1958-60	£18,000	£10,000	£6,000

1974 Lincoln Continental V8 4 Door Saloon, automatic gearbox, electric windows, 6-way power seat, tinted glass, remote control outside mirror and automatic parking brake release, original paintwork, in good overall condition.
Est. £8,000-10,000 *S(Z)*

1979 Lincoln Continental Mk V Coupé, generally in good condition.
£2,500-3,000 *S*

LOCOMOBILE

1901 Locomobile Steamer 5½hp Spindle Seat Runabout, excellent restored condition. **£14,000-18,000** *S*

1902 Locomobile Steam Car, in Concours condition. **£24,000-26,000** *FHF*

1915 Locomobile 48 Open Drive Limousine, coachwork by Brewster, New York, 6 cylinder T-head, needs restoration. **£38,000-45,000** *FHF*

1915 Locomobile Model 48 Touring Car, 6 cylinder T-head, 529cu in, 4 speed gearbox, rear drum brakes, semi-elliptic spring suspension front and rear, left hand drive, restored to a high standard. **£61,000-71,000** *CNY*

LOTUS

Lotus Engineering was founded by Colin Chapman whose first production car was the Mk 6 Chapman Sports Car. The Mk 7 (Lotus 7) is still made today under licence by Caterham Cars and is one of the longest lived cars ever produced. The Lotus Elite, or Mk 14 Coupé, was the first production car in Britain to feature a glass reinforced plastic body.

Lotus racing cars have won several world championships, but sadly Colin Chapman died suddenly in 1982.

1963 Lotus Elite Series II Coupé, 4 cylinders, 1216cc, originally exported to the USA, very good restored condition. **£14,000-15,000** *COYS*

1966 Lotus Elan S3 Roadster, 4 cylinders, 1558cc, very good overall condition. **£15,000-16,000** *ADT*

This car was formerly the property of the late Mr. Peter Sellers.

1970 Lotus Elan S4, 4 cylinders, 1558cc, stored for many years, resprayed, in good condition. **£6,500-7,000** *ADT*

1970 Lotus Elan 1.6 Litre SE4 Sports 2 Seater, new backbone chassis, engine rebuilt, 'Gold Leaf' red, white and gold colour scheme, in good condition throughout.
Est. £8,000-10,000 *BKS*

1970 Lotus Elan S4 Drophead Coupé, 4 cylinders, 1600cc, repainted, in very good condition throughout.
£8,400-8,800 *ADT*

1972 Lotus Elan +2S 130/4, completely restored.
£9,500-10,500 *KSC*

1970 Lotus Europa S2, 4 cylinders, 1565cc, excellent restored condition.
£5,000-5,500 *ADT*

The Europa was first launched for the French market with a 1470cc Renault engine. Production began in earnest in early 1967 with cars becoming available in the UK by 1969.

1973 Lotus Elan Sprint Drophead Coupé, 13,000 miles, original car throughout.
£24,000-26,000 *KSC*

1972 Lotus Elan 2+2 130S Coupé.
£3,500-3,750 *H&H*

1971 Lotus Europa S2, original Renault engine, mechanically sound.
£4,750-5,250 *KSC*

**1974 Lotus Europa Twin Cam
Special,** 5 speed gearbox,
extensively restored.
£12,000-13,000 *KSC*

1979 Lotus Elite, 4 cylinders,
1973cc, good panelwork, interior
leather trim in original condition,
mechanically sound.
£1,800-2,200 *ADT*

1976 Lotus Elite 501, 2 litre
engine, twin overhead camshaft,
5 speed gearbox, rebuilt cylinder
head, in good condition.
£1,400-1,600 *CCTC*

1983 Lotus Excel, air
conditioning, in excellent
condition throughout.
£4,750-5,250 *Bro*

1989 Lotus Esprit, with
removable roof, 35,000 miles.
£14,000-16,000 *KSC*

CROSS REFERENCE
Ford ──────────▶ p119

1968 Lotus Cortina Mk II,
original interior.
£4,000-6,000 *VIC*

LOTUS Model	ENGINE cc/cyl	DATES	CONDITION 1	2	3
Six		1953-56	£9,000	£7,000	£4,500
Seven S1 Sports	1172/4	1957-64	£12,000	£9,000	£4,000
Seven S2 Sports	1498/4	1961-66	£9,000	£7,000	£4,000
Seven S3 Sports	1558/4	1961-66	£9,000	£7,000	£4,000
Seven S4	1598/4	1969-72	£6,000	£4,500	£2,500
Elan S1 Convertible	1558/4	1962-64	£12,000	£8,000	£4,500
Elan S2 Convertible	1558/4	1964-66	£9,000	£6,500	£4,000
Elan S3 Convertible	1558/4	1966-69	£11,000	£7,250	£5,000
Elan S3 FHC	1558/4	1966-69	£11,000	£6,000	£4,000
Elan S4 Convertible	1558/4	1968-71	£12,500	£8,000	£5,000
Elan S4 FHC	1558/4	1968-71	£9,000	£6,250	£4,150
Elan Sprint Convertible	1558/4	1971-73	£11,000	£7,500	£5,000
Elan Sprint FHC	1558/4	1971-73	£9,000	£6,250	£4,500
Europa S1 FHC	1470/4	1966-69	£3,500	£2,000	£1,500
Europa S2 FHC	1470/4	1969-71	£4,000	£2,500	£1,500
Europa Twin Cam	1558/4	1971-75	£7,000	£5,000	£3,250
Elan +2S 130	1558/4	1971-74	£7,000	£4,500	£3,000
Elite S1 FHC	1261/4	1974-80	£3,000	£2,500	£1,500
Eclat S1		1975-80	£3,500	£3,000	£1,500
Esprit 1		1976-81	£6,500	£5,000	£3,000
Esprit 2		1976-81	£7,000	£5,000	£3,000
Esprit Turbo		1980-81	£8,000	£5,500	£3,500

MARMON

1932 Marmon V16 Club Sedan, Type 149, V16 cast aluminium block engine, steel sleeved cylinders, bore and stroke 3⅛ x 4in, displacement 490.8cu in, 200bhp at 3400rpm, dry double disc clutch, 3 speed synchromesh gearbox, rear semi-floating Spicer rear axle, bevel gear differential, semi-elliptical front and rear springs, Bendix 4 wheel mechanical brakes, wheelbase 144in, in original condition.
£48,000-50,000   *S(NY)*

MASERATI

All six Maserati brothers were involved in motor sport or vehicle building in some way. They produced magnificent racing and sports cars before the war, winning the Mille Miglia, Grand Prix and the Indianapolis 500.

In 1938 the company was acquired by the Orsi Group who did not produce their first road-going vehicle until 1947. Citroën became involved with the ailing Maserati company in 1968 but withdrew in 1985. DeTomaso, in conjunction with GEPI, took over and Maserati still survives today.

1965 Maserati Sebring, with Borrani alloy rim wire wheels, rare right hand drive, very original unrestored car.
£19,000-21,000   *CCTC*

1967 Maserati Ghibli 4.7 Litre Coupé, coachwork by Ghia, left hand drive, good paintwork, brightwork and interior trim.
£15,000-17,000   *S(Z)*

Only 1,149 examples of the coupé were constructed.

1962 Maserati 3500GTi Vignale Spyder, drophead coupé coachwork by Vignale, 6 cylinders, 3485cc, right hand drive, with photographic record of complete restoration.
£44,000-48,000   *COYS*

1970 Maserati Tipo 116 Indy 4.2 Litre Coupé, coachwork by Vignale, in good and original condition. **Est. £14,000-16,000**   *S(Z)*

1972 Maserati Mexico 4.7 Litre coupé, coachwork by Vignale, V8 engine, 4719cc, totally restored, in excellent condition.
£15,000-17,000   *COYS*

1971 Maserati Indy, fitted with later 8 cylinder, 4.7 litre engine, 4719cc, manual gearbox, right hand drive.
£12,500-13,500 *ADT*

1982 Maserati Merak SS, 6 cylinders, 2965cc, in very good condition.
£17,000-18,000 *ADT*

MASERATI Model	ENGINE cc/cyl	DATES	CONDITION		
			1	2	3
AG-1500	1488/6	1946-50	£30,000	£20,000	£10,000
A6G	1954/6	1951-53	£50,000	£35,000	£22,000
A6G-2000	1985/6	1954-57	£45,000	£35,000	£20,000
3500GT	3485/6	1957-64	£25,000	£15,000	£9,000
5000GT	4935/8	1960-65	£29,000	£20,000	£10,000
Sebring	3694/6	1962-66	£30,000	£18,000	£10,000
Quattroporte	4136/8	1963-74	£18,000	£15,000	£10,000
Mistral	4014/6	1964-70	£15,000	£10,000	£7,500
Mexico	4719/8	1965-68	£22,000	£15,000	£9,000
Ghibli	4719/8	1967-73	£30,000	£22,000	£12,000
Ghibli-spyder	4136/8	1969-74	£60,000	£45,000	£25,000
Indy	4136/8	1969-74	£18,000	£14,000	£9,000
Bora	4719/8	1971-80	£30,000	£21,000	£11,000
Merak	2965/6	1972-81	£18,000	£14,000	£9,000
Khamsin	4930/8	1974-81	£16,000	£10,000	£8,000

1963 Maserati Bi-Turbo, 6 cylinders, 2500cc, standard 5 speed dog leg manual gearbox, very good overall condition.
£4,000-4,500 *ADT*

1983 Maserati Kyalami, coupé coachwork by Frua, V8 engine, 4930cc, stored for the past 2 years, in fair condition.
£7,000-7,500 *COYS*

MATRA

1981 Matra Murena, 4 cylinders, 1600cc, ex-Simca 1.6 litre engine, 5 speed gearbox, standard interior with 3 abreast seating, good all-round condition.
£4,000-4,500 *ADT*

The French based Matra company built the Murena as a replacement for the Bagheera Coupé. Both cars had a mid-engine power unit.

MERCEDES-BENZ

Emil Jellinek was a wealthy Austrian who lived in France. He was a very keen Daimler enthusiast. Jellinek became the Daimler representative in France and used his daughter's name, Mercedes, to market the vehicles. By 1901 Mercedes was the accepted name for German Daimlers, although the formal amalgamation of Daimler and Benz was not until 1926.

1935 Mercedes-Benz 130 Cabriolet, 4 cylinders, 1318cc, in original condition, some mechanical and body restoration required.
£8,000-8,500 *COYS*

1936 Mercedes-Benz Type 290 Cabriolet B, recently discovered in remarkably good original condition, but requires restoration.
£13,000-14,000 *S*

1957 Mercedes-Benz 220 Saloon, right hand drive, 4 doors, good original condition.
Est. £6,000-7,000 *S*

The 220, introduced in 1951, was the first of a new generation of Mercedes-Benz cars, which returned them to the forefront of luxury car production.

1958 Mercedes-Benz 180A Saloon, 4 cylinders, 1897cc, imported from South Africa, engine, panel work, floor pan, chassis all in good condition.
Est. £3,000-3,500 *ADT*

1961 Mercedes-Benz 180B, original right hand drive, recorded mileage 46,500, excellent condition throughout.
£5,500-6,000 *LF*

1962 Mercedes-Benz 220SE Cabriolet, 6 cylinders, 2200cc.
£12,000-13,000 *COYS*

1961 Mercedes-Benz 220SE, right hand drive, 32,000 recorded miles, in good overall condition.
£6,000-6,500 *LF*

1964 Mercedes-Benz 190C Fin Tail Saloon, 4 cylinders, 1897cc, single carburettor.
£5,000-6,000 *PC*

1963 Mercedes-Benz 220SE Convertible, in very good overall condition.
£15,000-16,000 *S*

Only 3,755 of both the Coupé and Convertible examples were produced in 1963.

1965 Mercedes-Benz 300SE Convertible, 6 cylinders, 2996cc, good overall condition, very slight cosmetic attention required.
£16,500-17,500 *ADT*

The 2996cc light aluminium engine with fuel injection developed 160hp at 5000rpm and from January 1964 power was increased by raising the compression ratio.

1965 Mercedes-Benz 220Sb, automatic gearbox, in sound condition.
£3,200-3,600 *C*

The Mercedes-Benz 220Sb was introduced in 1959 and produced until 1965. It was the last generation of the 220 series and was only available as a much modernised fin back 4 door saloon. It used a 6 cylinder overhead camshaft engine of 2195cc which gave 95bhp at 4800rpm.

1967 Mercedes-Benz 300SEL, 8 cylinders, 3500cc, automatic gearbox, very good condition throughout.
Est. £6,500-7,500 *ADT*

1968 Mercedes-Benz 280S, 6 cylinders, 2897cc, automatic gearbox, in good condition.
Est. £2,500-3,000 *ADT*

1966 Mercedes-Benz 220SE Cabriolet, 6 cylinders, 2496cc, very good condition.
£10,000-11,000 *COYS*

1970 Mercedes-Benz 280SE, 6 cylinders, 2778cc, engine in excellent original condition, bodywork restored to a very high standard. **Est. £4,000-4,500** *ADT*

1972 Mercedes-Benz 280CE
4 Seater Coupé, in very good
condition.
£5,300-5,800 *S*

1971 Mercedes-Benz 280SE 3.5
Litre 2 Door Coupé, repainted,
in very good condition.
Est. £8,000-12,000 *BKS*

Just 4,502 280SE 3.5 Coupés and
Convertibles were built between
1969-71. All had floor mounted
automatic transmissions, power
steering and right hand drive.

1972 Mercedes-Benz 280CE
4 Seater Coupé, in very good
condition throughout.
£5,500-6,000 *S*

1973 Mercedes-Benz 280CE
2.8 Litre 2 Door Coupé, in good
overall condition.
£4,000-4,500 *BKS*

1973 Mercedes-Benz 280CE
2 Door Coupé, automatic
4 speed gearbox, in excellent
overall condition.
Est. £6,500-7,500 *S*

1974 Mercedes-Benz 280CE,
6 cylinders, 2778cc, in very good
condition.
£4,500-5,000 *ADT*

1976 Mercedes-Benz 450 SEL,
V8 engine, 6843cc, right hand
drive, in good overall condition.
£8,250-8,750 *C*

1977 Mercedes-Benz 450SEL,
V8 engine, 6834cc, right hand
drive, completely renovated,
exceptional order throughout.
£11,000-12,000 *COYS*

1976 Mercedes-Benz 280SE
Automatic, 6 cylinders, 2746cc,
in good condition throughout,
some restoration completed.
£4,000-4,500 *ADT*

MERCEDES-BENZ Model	ENGINE cc/cyl	DATES	CONDITION		
			1	2	3
300AD	2996/6	1951-62	£12,000	£10,000	£8,000
220A/S/SE Ponton	2195/6	1952-60	£7,500	£3,500	£1,800
220S/SEB Coupé	2915/6	1956-59	£9,000	£5,000	£3,500
220S/SEB Cabriolet	2195/6	1958-59	£22,000	£18,000	£7,000
190SL	1897/4	1955-63	£15,000	£12,000	£9,000
300SL 'Gullwing'	2996/6	1954-57	£120,000	£100,000	£70,000
300SL Roadster	2996/6	1957-63	£110,000	£90,000	£70,000
230/250SL	2306/ 2496/6	1963-68	£13,000	£9,000	£7,000
280SL	2778/6	1961-71	£14,000	£10,000	£8,000
220/250SE	2195/ 2496/6	1960-68	£8,000	£6,000	£3,000
300SE	2996/6	1961-65	£10,000	£8,000	£5,000
280SE Convertible	2778/6	1965-69	£20,000	£16,000	£12,000
280SE V8 Convertible	3499/8	1969-71	£25,000	£18,000	£15,000
280SE Coupé	2496/6	1965-72	£7,000	£4,000	£3,000
300SEL 6.3	6330/8	1968-72	£12,000	£7,000	£3,500
600 & 600 Pullman	6332/8	1964-81	£20,000	£10,000	£8,000

1979 Mercedes-Benz 450SEL 4 Door Saloon, mechanically excellent, bodywork in good condition.
Est. £3,500-4,500 *S*

1980 Mercedes-Benz 280CE Sports Coupé, 6 cylinders, double overhead camshaft, full factory specification, automatic gearbox, alloy wheels, headlamp wash-wipe, electric sunroof, self-levelling suspension, central locking and electric windows, cruise control, leather interior, head restraints, in very good condition throughout.
£3,200-3,600 *S*

1978 Mercedes-Benz 280CE 2 Door Coupé, automatic gearbox, factory air conditioning, self-levelling suspension, electric sunroof, electric windows, central locking and cruise control, in very good overall condition.
£8,000-8,500 *S*

Did you know?
MILLER'S Collectors Cars Price Guide *builds up year-by-year to form the most comprehensive photo library system available.*

1979 Mercedes-Benz 450SEL 6.9 Litre Saloon, good overall condition.
£2,400-2,800 *S*

Using the same body chassis as the 'S' class it featured hydro-pneumatic suspension with self-levelling, a V8 engine also used in the 600 Pullmans, electric windows, head restraints, central self-locking, disc brakes all-round and Bosch K-Jetronic fuel injection. Produced between 1975 and 1980, less than 7,500 models of this type were produced.

1957 Mercedes-Benz 190SL Roadster, a period conversion to twin Weber carburettors, stainless steel exhaust system, left hand drive, in good condition throughout.
£15,000-16,000 *S*

1961 Mercedes-Benz 190SL Convertible, 3 owners from new, in very good condition.
Est. £14,000-18,000 *S*

1964 Mercedes-Benz 230SL, 6 cylinders, 2306cc, 4 speed manual gearbox, in very good original condition.
Est. £15,500-16,500 *ADT*

The 230SL was the first of a new series of models for Mercedes-Benz. Although the cars relied on existing production car componentry, the elegant styling characterised the range. With a dished hard top they are referred to as the 'Pagoda roof' models.

1967 Mercedes-Benz 250SL, fully restored condition.
£11,500-12,500 *COYS*

1965 Mercedes-Benz 230SL, manual gearbox converted to right hand drive, in good overall condition.
£12,000-13,000 *Cen*

1970 Mercedes-Benz 280SL Sports 2 Seater, 6 cylinder in line engine, 2800cc, automatic transmission, original specification and in good condition throughout.
Est. £10,000-11,000 *S*

1972 Mercedes-Benz 350SLC, alloy wheels, repainted, overall good condition.
£7,000-7,500 *ADT*

1972 Mercedes-Benz 350SL Sports, with hard and soft tops.
£10,500-11,500 *SJR*

1978 Mercedes-Benz 450SLC 4.5 Litre 2 Door 4 Seater Coupé, automatic transmission, bodywork in generally good condition, good upholstery.
Est. £5,000-7,000 *BKS*

**1977 Mercedes-Benz 450SEL
6.9 Litre 4 Door Saloon,**
repainted and restored, rare right
hand drive.
Est. £7,000-10,000 *BKS*

1979 Mercedes-Benz 350SL Sports, alloy wheels,
matching trim. **£11,500-12,500** *SJR*

**1981 Mercedes-Benz 280SL
Sports,** alloy wheels.
£12,500-13,500 *SJR*

MERCER

The American automobile company Mercer
derived its name from Mercer County in
New Jersey. The factory was based in the
town of Trenton and the company was owned
by the Roebling family who were famous for
steel rope making and building the Brooklyn
Bridge.

**c1923 Mercer 2 Seater
Raceabout,** 6 cylinders, 5500cc,
overhead valve, 84bhp at 2550rpm,
3 speed manual gearbox, floor
operated transmission brake and
handbrake operating rear wheel
drum only, semi-elliptic leaf
springs, left hand drive, engine
rebuilt, restored in the USA,
painted in Mercer yellow.
Est. £40,000-45,000 *C*

*This particular raceabout is a
Series Six and dates from around
1923, although it is thought the
chassis may date from around
1916. Only about a dozen of the
last Series Six cars exist in
complete form and only 2 are the
raceabout models.*

MESSERSCHMITT

**1958 Messerschmitt KR200
Sport Replica,** 191cc, rear
mounted Sachs engine, direct
geared handlebar steering,
converted 2 years ago to Sports
Replica, bodywork rebuilt.
Est. £3,000-4,000 *BKS*

CROSS REFERENCE	
Heinkel	→ p132
BMW Isetta	→ p84
Trojan	→ p264

**1960 Messerschmitt KR200
Cabriolet,** single cylinder,
2 stroke, original specification, in
good condition throughout.
£3,400-3,800 *S*

MG

Tuned versions of the Morris Cowley were produced at William Morris's garage at Longwell Street, Oxford before 1913. This retail business was managed by Cecil Kimber who, more than anyone, was responsible for the MG marque. MG have always produced a fine range of affordable sports cars and have survived through difficult times.

1930 MG C-Type Replica, with competition engine, in excellent condition.
£21,000-23,000 *PiK*

1938 MG TA Midget 2 Seater Sports, knock-on wire wheels, restored, in excellent condition.
£15,000-15,500 *S*

1939 MG TA Midget 2 Seater Sports, with new black mohair hood, restored to a good standard 5,000 miles ago.
Est. £12,000-14,000 *S*

1939 MG TA 2 Seater Drophead Coupé, original Tickford coachwork by Salmons of Newport Pagnell, original rebuilt engine, professionally restored, bodywork excellent.
£16,000-16,500 *S*

1946 MG TC, 4 cylinders, 1250cc, factory replacement EXPEG/SE engine, bodywork in excellent condition.
£16,000-16,500 *ADT*

1949 MG TC, totally restored.
£16,000-16,500 *GML*

MG Model	ENGINE cc/cyl	DATES	CONDITION 1	2	3
14/28	1802/4	1924-27	£26,000	£18,000	£10,000
14/40	1802/4	1927-29	£25,000	£18,000	£10,000
18/80 Mk I/Mk II/Mk III	2468/6	1927-33	£40,000	£28,000	£20,000
M-Type Midget	847/4	1928-32	£11,000	£9,000	£7,000
J-Type Midget	847/4	1932-34	£14,000	£12,000	£10,000
J3 Midget	847/4	1932-33	£18,000	£14,000	£12,000
PA Midget	847/4	1934-36	£13,000	£10,000	£8,000
PB Midget	936/4	1935-36	£14,000	£10,000	£8,000
F-Type Magna	1271/6	1931-33	£22,000	£18,000	£12,000
L-Type Magna	1087/6	1933-34	£22,000	£16,000	£12,000
K1/K2 Magnette	1087/6	1932-33	£45,000	£40,000	£35,000
N Series Magnette	1271/6	1934-36	£35,000	£30,000	£20,000
TA Midget	1292/4	1936-39	£15,000	£12,000	£9,000
SA 2 litre	2288/6	1936-39	£22,000	£18,000	£15,000
VA	1548/4	1936-39	£12,000	£8,000	£5,000
TB	1250/1	1939-40	£15,000	£11,000	£9,000

Value will depend on body style, history, completeness, racing history, the addition of a supercharger and originality.

1951 MG TD, 4 cylinders, 1250cc, with canvas hood, extensive restoration.
Est. £11,000-13,000 *ADT*

1951 MG TD 2 Seater Sports, 1250cc, in good overall condition.
Est. £12,000-15,000 *S*

This car was purchased new by the American actor James Cagney. An original car with interesting provenance.

1951 MG TD 2 Seater Sports, 4 cylinders, 1250cc, originally exported to the USA, left hand drive, restored.
£6,000-6,500 *COYS*

1952 MG TD Open Sports, left hand drive, a well maintained example.
£10,000-11,000 *COYS*

1954 MG TF 1.25 Litre 2 Seater Sports, subject of a ground-up restoration.
£17,000-18,000 *BKS*

1954 MG Midget TF Open Sports, left hand drive, originally exported to California, restored.
£12,000-13,000 *COYS*

1952 MG TD Open Sports, in excellent condition throughout.
£14,500-16,000 *GML*

1954 MG TF Open Sports, wire wheels, in excellent condition.
£15,000-16,000 *SJR*

1952 MG YA 4 Door Saloon, in reasonable condition throughout.
£5,000-5,500 *S*

The YA saloon was introduced by the MG factory in 1948 with a 1¼ litre engine and featured a rigid box frame chassis of welded form, rack-and-pinion steering and a main bodyshell which it shared with the Morris Series E and Wolseley 8 models.

1952 MG YA Saloon, in very good condition.
£5,000-6,000 *CC*

1957 MG ZB Magnette Saloon, engine and clutch overhauled, same ownership for 31 years and one previous owner, very original car. £1,200-1,500 *C*

1963 MG Magnette Mk IV Saloon, to factory specification in all major respects, good original condition. £900-1,000 *S*

1958 MGA Roadster, 4 cylinders, 1489cc, rebuilt engine, very good restored condition.
Est. £11,500-12,500 *ADT*

1956 MGA Roadster, high standard refurbished engine and gearbox, good condition.
Est. £9,500-11,000 *ADT*

1958 MGA Roadster, 1500cc, wire wheels, luggage rack, badge bar. **£10,000-11,000** *SJR*

1959 MGA 1500cc Roadster, imported from the USA, left hand drive, bodywork in good condition. **£4,000-4,500** *CCTC*

1960 MGA Fixed Head Coupé, 4 cylinders, 1588cc, restored to good overall condition. **£5,500-6,000** *ADT*

1960 MGA Roadster, 1622cc, original Weber carburettor, wire wheels, stainless steel exhaust system, converted to right hand drive, restored. **£9,000-11,000** *ADT*

1958 MGA Roadster, 4 cylinders, 1489cc, imported from the USA in 1989, fully restored, in excellent condition. **£7,000-8,000** *COYS*

1959 MGA 1600 Roadster, 4 cylinders, 1622cc, engine in good condition, cooling system needs attention, repainted, bodywork in good condition. **Est. £5,500-6,500** *ADT*

1960 MGA Roadster, original right hand drive, in excellent rebuilt condition. **£10,000-12,000** *VIC*

1960 MGA Roadster, 4 cylinders, 1588cc, UK car, body-off restoration, in excellent condition. **£11,000-12,000** *COYS*

1924 Sunbeam 24/70 4-5 Seater Tourer, rebuilt 4½ litre engine, left hand drive, body-off restoration, excellent condition. **£46,000-48,000** *BKS*

r. **1961 Sunbeam Alpine,** 4 cylinders, 1500cc, rebuilt engine and gearbox, suspension and braking system restored, new stainless steel exhaust, stripped to bare metal and repainted, left hand drive, excellent restored condition. **£9,000-10,000** *ADT*

1949 Triumph 2000 Roadster With Dickey, right hand column 3 speed gear change, completely renovated, excellent condition throughout. **Est. £15,000-20,000** *LF*

1955 Triumph TR2, with overdrive, original right hand drive, restored. **£12,000-13,000** *NTC*

1949 Triumph 2000 Roadster, 4 cylinders, 2088cc, 3 speed gearbox, completely restored to Concours condition. **£16,500-18,000** *COYS*

1955 Triumph TR2, 4 cylinders, 1991cc, engine overhauled, new exhaust, bare metal respray with many replacement body parts, good restored condition. **£9,200-9,600** *ADT*

1946 Triumph 1800 Roadster, mechanically sound, repainted and rechromed, good original interior, good overall condition. **£8,500-9,000** *Mot*

1966 Triumph TR4A, independent rear suspension, bodywork in excellent condition, left hand drive. **£4,750-5,250** *CCTC*

1960 Triumph TR3A, 4 cylinders, 1991cc, complete mechanical overhaul and body-off restoration, chassis refurbished, new chromework, trim and glass, in excellent condition. **£10,000-11,000** *COYS*

1960 Triumph TR3A Open Sports, 4 cylinders, 1991cc, independent wishbone/coil spring front suspension, semi-elliptally sprung rear axle, all-round drum brakes, complete body-off restoration, in Concours condition. **£15,000-17,000** *COYS*

1964 Triumph 2000 Italia 2 + 2 Sports, coachwork by Vignale, engine rebuilt, imported and unregistered, excellent condition throughout. **Est. £14,000-15,000** *S*

1973 Triumph TR6, 6 cylinders, 2498cc, engine in good order, interior restored, excellent condition. **£5,250-5,750** *ADT*

l. **1968 Triumph TR5,** 6 cylinders, 2498cc, mechanics and complete body-off rebuild, original hard and soft Surrey top, excellent condition. **Est. £11,000-12,000** *ADT*

1973 Triumph Stag, 8 cylinders, 2997cc, 67,000 recorded miles, electric windows, replacement steel front wings and boot lid, resprayed, good overall condition.
£4,600-5,000 *ADT*

1975 Triumph Spitfire Sports, 1500cc, 59,000 recorded miles, very good condition throughout.
Est. £1,300-1,800 *ECC*

1980 Triumph TR7/TR8 Convertible, 3900cc, converted to TR8 specifications with Rover V8 engine, modified automatic gearbox, prop shaft and mountings, low mileage, restored, good overall condition.
Est. £5,000-7,000 *ADT*

1980 Triumph Spitfire, 4 cylinders, 1493cc, twin SU carburettors, anti-roll bar, wood veneer dashboard with extra gauges, mechanically good condition, hood in reasonable condition.
£2,400-2,800 *ADT*

1976 Triumph Stag, 8 cylinders, 2998cc, engine rebuilt, manual gearbox with overdrive, resprayed, good restored condition throughout.
Est. £12,000-13,000 *ADT*

1963 Volkswagen Kharmann-Ghia Cabriolet, left hand drive, imported from America, good condition throughout.
£5,500-6,000 *CCTC*

1976 Triumph Stag 2 + 2, 8 cylinders, 2997cc, automatic gearbox, 27,000 recorded miles, fully restored throughout.
Est. £4,000-5,000 *ADT*

1968 Volvo P1800 S, 4 cylinders, 1800cc, fully restored throughout.
Est. £4,800-5,800 *ADT*

1963 Works Mini Cooper Saloon, with full rally equipment, 1.3 litre engine, original works bodyshell, excellent condition.
£16,500-17,500 *BKS(M)*

1964 Austin Mini Cooper S Rally Car, 4 cylinders, 1275cc, rebuilt engine, new brakes and wheel bearings, full roll cage and original rally seats, renovated body, very original car.
Est. £6,500-7,500 *ADT*

1950-1953 AFM-BMW Formula 2 Racing Car, éx-Willi Heeks/Tony Hutchings, fully restored and resumed racing in recent years, very good condition. **Est. £35,000-45,000** *BKS*

1935-36 Alfa Romeo Tipo 8C-35, ex-Scuderia Ferrari/Hans Ruesch/ Dennis Poore, 3.8 litres, museum stored, excellent original condition.
£6,000-8,000 *BKS*

1965-66 Alfa Romeo 1600GTA 2 Door Competition Saloon, 1.6 litre twin plug race modified engine, very good condition.
Est. £18,000-25,000 *BKS*

1959 Alfa Romeo Giuletta Sprint Coupé, coachwork by Bertone, 4 cylinder, 1290cc engine, 5 speed gearbox.
£15,500-16,500 *COYS*

l. **1963 Alfa Romeo Giulia TZI,** Berlinetta coachwork by Zagato, 4 cylinders, 1570cc, twin overhead camshaft, 112bhp, 5 speed gearbox, excellent condition.
Est. £90,000-110,000 *COYS*

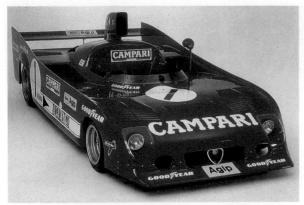

1974/75 Alfa Romeo Tipo 33 TT-12, 12 cylinders at 180°, 2995cc, 500bhp at 11000rpm, 5 speed gearbox, completely rebuilt, mechanics to full racing specification, excellent condition.
£150,000-160,000 *CNY*

1982 Alfa Romeo F1 182 Racing Car, V12 engine, 520hp at 12500rpm, restored.
£100,000-120,000 *S(Z)*

1952 Bandini Open Sports Racer, 4 cylinder in line engine, 750cc, 4 speed manual gearbox, drum brakes all-round, independent front suspension, left hand drive, many spare parts, eligible for vintage racing, excellent condition.
Est. £24,000-28,000 *CNY*

1953 Aston Martin Sigma 2 Seater Sports Touring Special, ex-Paul Jackman, 2 litre DB1 series engine, Triumph Gloria rear axle.
£24,000-25,000 *BKS*

1962 Austin Healey 3000 2 Seater Competition Grand Touring Coupé, ex-works rally team car, 3 litre engine, excellent condition.
Est. £50,000-80,000 *BKS*

1991 BMW M3 Group N Race Car, 4 cylinders, standard 5 speed gearbox, Specfab cage welded into the bodyshell, BMW Motorsport suspension, Recaro racing seat with Sabelts.
£10,000-11,000 *ADT*

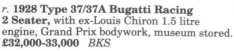

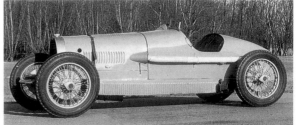

r. **1928 Type 37/37A Bugatti Racing 2 Seater,** with ex-Louis Chiron 1.5 litre engine, Grand Prix bodywork, museum stored.
£32,000-33,000 *BKS*

1972-81 Datsun 240Z 2 Door Circuit Racing Coupé, 2.4 litre, very good original condition.
Est. £25,000-35,000 *BKS*

This ex-works Samuri Motor Company car was known as Big Sam.

1961 Cooper T53 F1 Single Seater Racing Car, Coventry Climax FPF engine, 4 cylinders, 1496cc, excellent condition throughout.
£64,000-68,000 *COYS*

1947 Ferrari Tipo 166 Spyder Corsa, dual-purpose 2 seater Formula 2 Sports Racer, ex-Prince Igor Troubetskoy, Dudley Folland, 2 litres, good condition.
£220,000-230,000 *BKS*

1934 ERA R1A Single Seater Racing Car, 1500cc Riley unit, Wilson 4 speed pre-selector gearbox, original livery, imported to the UK from Switzerland.
£250,000-260,000 *S*

r. **1950 Ferrari-Jaguar Spyder Corsa,** Jaguar XK120 6 cylinders, 3442cc engine, Ferrari 166 chassis and cycle winged body.
£46,000-48,000 *COYS*

l. **1954 Frazer-Nash Le Mans Coupé 2 seater Grand Tourer,** Bristol 6 cylinder, 2 litre engine, remote control gear change, Delaney Gallay heater and Alfin high performance brake drums, original specification except addition of period overdrive, completely rebuilt.
£54,000-56,000 *BKS*

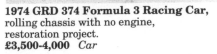

1974 GRD 374 Formula 3 Racing Car,
rolling chassis with no engine,
restoration project.
£3,500-4,000 *Car*

1966 Ford GT40 Mk I Road Car, Ford 7 litre engine,
4 speed gearbox, chromed Borrani spoke wheels, Plexiglass
side windows, interior in good condition.
£190,000-200,000 *S(Z)*

1955 Frazer Nash Le Mans Coupé, 6 cylinders,
1971cc Bristol engine, triple Solex carburettor,
requires major restoration throughout.
£28,000-30,000 *BKS*

**1948 Iota-Jap Air-Cooled Single Cylinder
Formula 3 Single Seater Racing Car,** 500cc,
rebuilt, overhauled mechanically, new body,
excellent restored condition. **£8,000-9,000** *BKS*

1963 Ginetta G4, 1600cc, 175bhp, twin
cam engine, fully race prepared, restored.
£25,000-30,000 *Car*

1951 HAR Jaguar Formula 2 Monoposto Racing Car,
Jaguar 3.8 litre engine, completely restored, excellent
condition throughout.
Est. £55,000-60,000 *S*

**1976 Image Formula Ford Club
Racing Car.**
£2,400-2,600 *Car*

1953 Jaguar C-Type Open Sports Racing Car, 6 cylinders, 3781cc, modified 3.8 litre engine, wishbone front suspension, drum brakes, original frame, body repainted, in excellent condition, with spare 3.4 litre engine and gearbox. Est. £280,000-320,000 *COYS*

l. **1962 Jaguar E-Type 3.8 Litre Competition Coupé,** 6 cylinders, 3781cc, excellent restored condition. £29,000-30,000 *COYS*

1962 Jaguar E-Type Racing Car, 6 cylinders, 3.8 litre twin cam engine, 6 branch exhaust, good condition. £24,000-26,000 *CCTC*

1928 Lea-Francis Hyper Ex-Works 2 Seater Sports, 1.5 litre supercharged engine, garage stored, requires extensive restoration. £28,000-29,000 *BKS*

1975 Lancia Stratos HF Coupé, V6, 2.4 litre Ferrari Dino engine, twin overhead camshafts, rose jointed wishbone kit, in good condition throughout. £45,000-47,000 *S*

1955 Lotus-Climax Mk IX 2 Seater Sports Racing Car, ex-Tony Page/Paul Emery, 1100cc, completely restored, race prepared, excellent condition throughout. Est. £35,000-45,000 *BKS*

1956/57 Lotus 11 Climax Le Mans Series I Sports Racing Car. £23,000-25,000 *BKS*

1986 Lamborghini QVX Group C Sports Racing Coupé, V12, 5700cc engine, coachwork, museum stored, in excellent condition. £66,000-68,000 *COYS*

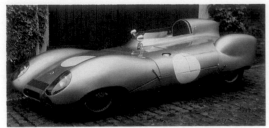

1957 Lotus 11 Le Mans Mk 2 Racing Car,
full history and in race condition.
£38,000-40,000 *PiK*

**1960 Lotus 20 Formula Junior Single Seater
Racing Car,** Cosworth 4 cylinder, 1100cc engine,
Renault 4 speed manual gearbox, 4 wheel disc
brakes, Armstrong shock absorbers, recent
professional ground-up restoration, good condition.
£30,000-35,000 *CNY*

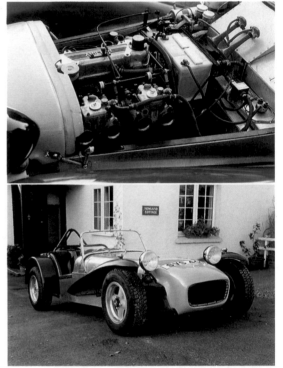

1962 Lotus 24 Climax Formula 1 Racing Car,
ex-Jim Clark/Trevor Taylor/Peter Arundell/Jo
Siffert, 4 cylinders, 1.5 litre Coventry Climax
FPF engine, fully restored.
£95,000-105,000 *Car*

1962 Lotus Super 7 Series II, Holbay Ford
1500cc engine.
£14,500-15,500 *Car*

1959 Lotus 7 Series I, BMC 998cc engine,
completely restored.
£14,500-15,500 *Car*

**1960-61 Lotus Coventry Climax FPF Type 18
Formula 1 Grand Prix Single Seater,** 4 cylinders,
2.5 litre engine, in need of rebuild, in good condition.
£37,000-39,000 *BKS*

1965 Lotus 31 Racing Car, Formula Ford specification, fully restored.
£14,000-16,000   *Car*

1967 Lotus 47A Sports Racing Coupé, 4 cylinders, 1594cc, engine rebuilt, repainted bodywork, some components missing.
£30,000-32,000   *COYS*

1969 Lotus 61 Formula Ford, excellent restored condition.
£14,000-16,000   *Car*

1968 Mallock U2 Mk 8, Ford 1600cc, updated to 1975 Mk 12 specification.
£3,750-4,250   *Car*

1932 Maserati 4CM 1½ Litre Supercharged Grand Prix Monoposto Racing Car, 193bhp at 6700rpm, chassis rebuilt, excellent condition.
£170,000-180,000   *S*

1964 Marcos GT Racing Car, Volvo 1800cc engine, race prepared, completely restored.
£20,000-21,000   *Car*

r. **1955-58 Maserati Tipo 300S Sports Racing 2 Seater,** ex-Antonio Mendes de Barros, 3 litre engine, Fantuzzi coachwork, Concours condition.
Est. £400,000-500,000   *BKS*

1969 Merlyn Mk 11A, Scholar engine, restored, excellent condition.
£17,000-18,000 *Car*

1969 Merlyn Mk 12 Formula B, Lotus 1600cc twin camshaft engine, restored, in race ready condition.
£19,500-20,500 *Car*

1971 Palliser F 5000, Rover 3.9 litre engine, 310bhp, restored, in excellent condition.
£30,000-32,000 *Car*

1962 Merlyn Mk 4 Sports Racing Car, 175bhp, twin camshaft engine, alloy body, restored.
£24,000-26,000 *Car*

1963 Merlyn Mk 6 Sports Racing Car, 185bhp, twin camshaft engine, excellent condition.
£34,000-36,000 *Car*

1986 MG Metro 6R4 2 seater Coupé, V6, turbocharged 2.6 litre twin camshaft engine, complete factory rebuild, low mileage, excellent condition.
£20,000-22,000 *COYS*

1971 Merlyn Mk 20 Formula Ford, completely restored.
£14,500-15,500 *Car*

1954 Porsche 550RS Spyder Sports Racer,
4 cylinders, 1480cc twin overhead camshaft engine,
excellent condition.
Est. £110,000-140,000 *COYS*

1973 Porsche 911RS Carrera Lightweight, flat 6
cylinder, 2687cc engine, 210bhp at 6300rpm, 5 speed
manual gearbox, ventilated disc brakes all-round, left
hand drive, competition suspension and racing seats,
exceptionally good condition.
Est. £30,000-40,000 *C*

1960 Rejo Mk III Sports Racing Car,
Ford 1200cc racing engine, restored.
£24,000-26,000 *Car*

1967 Milmor GT Racing Car, Lotus 1600cc twin
camshaft engine, the only known surviving car
from 5 models made.
£24,000-26,000 *Car*

1954 Siata 208CS Mexico Coupé,
coachwork by Balbo, V8, 1996cc engine,
complete rebuild of transmission,
suspension, brakes and carburettors,
for vintage racing.
Est. £115,000-130,000 *CNY*

l. **1973 Porsche 911 Carrera 2.7 RS
Lightweight Coupé,** 6 cylinders,
2687cc, 210bhp at 6300rpm, restored
and in excellent condition.
£35,000-36,000 *COYS*

1948 Leyland Beaver LWB Flatbed Truck, 6 cylinders, 6000cc, manual gearbox, rear axle steering and suspension, good condition. **Est. £4,000-5,000** *ADT*

1930 Dennis 30cwt Lorry, canvas tilt, engine overhauled, original maker's plate in cab, generally in good condition. **£3,300-3,500** *S*

1949 Ford F1 Stepside Truck, V8 side valve engine, 6 volt electrics, left hand drive, good condition throughout. **£4,100-4,400** *CCTC*

1958 Ford Thames Dropside Truck, 4 cylinders, engine in good condition, restored to a very high standard. **Est. £4,000-5,000** *ADT*

c1967 Bedford Tipper Truck, restored to a high standard, excellent condition throughout. **£2,600-2,700** *HOLL*

1964 Ford Thames Trader, engine in good condition, restored tipper body, interior refurbished, completely repainted. **Est. £4,000-5,000** *ADT*

r. **1947 Fordson Model 7V Tipper,** 8 cylinders, 3500cc, mechanically in good condition, steering needs attention, tipping body rebuilt to original design. **Est. £6,500-8,500** *ADT*

1942 Austin K2 2 Ton 4 x 2 Auxiliary Towing Vehicle, with Gwynne Trailer Pump, 6 cylinders, 63bhp petrol engine, complete with roof mounted ladder, bell, double rear wheels and hose reel, good condition, pump not operational. **Est. £4,000-5,500** *S*

1961 Commer Fire Appliance, 6 cylinders, with 2 side folding doors, wooden extending ladder, hose fittings and controls, dry stored, in good condition. **£1,300-1,400** *ADT*

c1951 Austin Fire Engine, 6 cylinders, mechanically sound, turntable with metal ladder, stablising arms and manual ladder erector, spare wheel, some hoses and general fittings. **£2,750-3,000** *ADT*

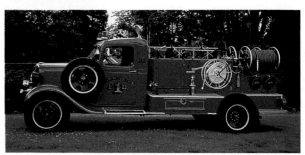

1935 Chevrolet Pumper Fire Truck, 6 cylinder in line engine, left hand drive, 2 doors, pumps and hoses removed, dry stored since full restoration. **£7,000-9,000** *CNY*

1949 Merryweather 100 TTL Fire Engine, Leyland 6 cylinder diesel engine, 6538cc, manual gearbox, mechanically sound, very good condition throughout. **£2,600-2,800** *ADT*

1936 Dennis Ace Fire Engine, complete with ladders, hoses, nozzles and fire fighting equipment, brass searchlight and chrome fire bell. **£7,000-7,500** *S*

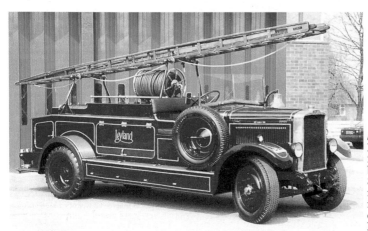

l. **1933 Leyland FK1 Cub Fire Engine,** 6 cylinder petrol engine, 27.3hp, hydraulic 4 wheel brakes, chassis-up restoration, 35ft Ajax ladder stripped and restored, Leyland Gwynne pump in full working order, excellent overall condition. **Est. £15,000-20,000** *S*

1943 Austin K2/Y 2 Ton 4 x 2 Military Mobile Canteen, 6 cylinders, 4 speed gearbox, good overall condition.
Est. £3,000-4,000 *S*

Citroën T23R 2 Ton Series U Dropside Flatbed Truck, 1911cc, twin rear wheels for greater carrying capacity, restored but still requiring further attention.
£2,500-2,750 *S*

1943 Dodge T214 ¾ Ton Command Reconnaissance Car, 6 cylinder engine, overhauled gearbox, new clutch, body-off restoration, complete with jerry cans, pick, shovel, axe and new canvas.
£5,500-6,000 *S*

c1951 Daimler Mk I Ferret Scout Car, Rolls-Royce B60 6 cylinder engine, 2.26 litres, 129bhp, 45mph,5 speed pre-selector gearbox with reverse.
£2,200-2,400 *ADT*

1940 Morris Commercial 4 x 2 15cwt Mk II GS Truck, 6 cylinder, side valve 3½ litre engine, 4 speed gearbox.
£2,250-2,500 *S*

1920 Rolls-Royce 40/50 Silver Ghost 12 Seater Omnibus, mahogany mouldings, aluminium panelling, good condition.
£27,000-29,000 *S*

1918 FWD Model B 3 Ton Truck, 4 cylinder side valve T-head engine, 3 speed gearbox, good restored overall condition.
Est. £9,000-12,000 *S*

Austin A40 Pick-Up, manual gearbox, fair condition.
£1,400-1,500 *HOLL*

1937 Commer Type N1 Delivery Van,
4 cylinders, 13.95hp, 25cwt, shelving in body,
steel artillery wheels, bulb horn, good condition.
£4,250-4,500 *S*

1967 Morris Minor 1000 Pick-Up, with canvas
tilt, 1098cc, 48bhp, torsion bar independent front
suspension, rack and pinion steering, excellent
condition.
£5,250-5,750 *BKS*

1926 Austin 7 Type AD
2½cwt Van, 4 cylinders, 747cc,
gate change gearbox, excellent
condition throughout.
Est. £5,000-6,000 *ADT*

1936 Austin 7 Van, restored to
a 1928-style with 'C' cab using
bonnet and doors from a 1928
Chummy, 4 speed crash
gearbox, period CAV ignition,
and PA speedo.
Est. £3,300-3,600 *LF*

1955 Morris J-Type Van, 4 cylinders, 1499cc,
completely restored, all original components
are intact and serviceable.
Est. £4,000-6,000 *ADT*

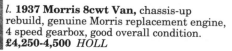

l. **1937 Morris 8cwt Van,** chassis-up
rebuild, genuine Morris replacement engine,
4 speed gearbox, good overall condition.
£4,250-4,500 *HOLL*

1962 MGA Mk II 1600cc Roadster, wire wheels, luggage rack and leather trim.
£14,000-15,000 *SJR*

1962 MGA Mk II Roadster, 1600cc, wire wheels.
£12,750-13,500 *SJR*

1963 MG Midget Mk II, right hand drive, in very good original condition.
£1,700-1,900 *C*

The MG Midget was introduced in 1961 as an MG version of the Austin Healey Sprite Mk II. The 1963 Midget was fitted with an enlarged 1098cc engine giving 56bhp at 5750rpm. Disc brakes were fitted on the front wheels.

1966 MG Midget Mk II, totally original panels and interior, 25,000 miles from new.
£7,750-8,250 *KSC*

1974 MG Midget, 4 cylinders, 1275cc, reconditioned engine, reconditioned roller bearing gearbox, resprayed after comprehensive preparation.
£3,000-3,500 *ADT*

1971 MG Midget, 1500cc.
£2,500-4,000 *Cum*

1978 MG Midget 2 Seater Sports, 1500cc, mechanically sound, bodywork in good condition.
£1,750-2,000 *S*

1972 MG Midget, 4 cylinders, 1275cc, engine and suspension rebuilt, wire wheels, left hand drive, in very good condition.
Est. £3,500-4,500 *ADT*

1978 MG Midget, 4 cylinders, 1491cc, Minilite wheels, restored 4 years ago, in good condition throughout.
£5,250-5,750 *ADT*

1978 MG Midget, 1500cc, engine rebuilt in 1989, leather interior.
Est. £3,000-4,000 *WBH*

1980 MG Midget, 4 cylinders, 1491cc, low mileage, good original condition.
£3,600-3,800 *ADT*

1965 MGB Roadster, 4 cylinders, 1798cc, original style wheels, restored, in very good condition.
£6,500-7,000 *ADT*

MG Model	ENGINE cc/cyl	DATES	CONDITION 1	2	3
TC	1250/4	1946-49	£15,000	£11,000	£7,000
TD	1250/4	1950-52	£13,000	£9,000	£5,000
TF	1250/4	1953-55	£16,000	£13,000	£8,000
TF 1500	1466/4	1954-55	£18,000	£14,000	£9,000
YA/YB	1250/4	1947-53	£5,500	£2,750	£1,500
Magnette ZA/ZB	1489/4	1953-58	£3,000	£2,000	£500
Magnette Mk III/IV	1489/4	1958-68	£2,500	£850	£350
MGA 1500	1489/4	1955-59	£9,000	£6,500	£3,500
MGA 1500 FHC	1489/4	1956-59	£7,000	£5,000	£3,000
MGA 1600	1588/4	1959-61	£11,000	£9,000	£4,500
MGA 1600 FHC	1588/4	1959-61	£7,000	£5,000	£3,000
MGA Twin Cam	1588/4	1958-60	£17,000	£12,000	£9,000
MGA Twin Cam FHC	1588/4	1958-60	£14,000	£9,000	£7,000
MGA 1600 Mk II	1622/4	1961-62	£12,000	£10,000	£4,000
MGA 1600 Mk II FHC	1622/4	1961-62	£9,000	£7,000	£3,000
MGB Mk I	1798/4	1962-67	£7,000	£4,000	£1,200
MGB GT Mk I	1798/4	1965-67	£5,000	£3,500	£1,000
MGB Mk II	1798/4	1967-69	£7,500	£4,000	£1,500
MGB GT Mk II	1798/4	1969	£4,500	£2,500	£850
MGB Mk III	1798/4	1969-74	£6,500	£4,000	£1,100
MGB GT Mk III	1798/4	1969-74	£4,500	£2,500	£1,000
MGB Roadster (rubber bumper)	1798/4	1975-80	£6,000	£4,500	£1,200
MGB GT	1798/4	1975-80	£4,000	£3,000	£1,000
MGB Jubilee	1798/4	1975	£6,000	£3,000	£1,200
MGB LE	1798/4	1980	£8,500	£4,750	£2,250
MGB GT LE	1798/4	1980	£6,000	£3,750	£2,000
MGC	2912/6	1967-69	£8,000	£6,500	£4,000
MGC GT	2912/6	1967-69	£6,000	£4,500	£2,000
MGB GT V8	3528/8	1973-76	£8,250	£6,000	£3,000
Midget Mk I	948/4	1961-62	£4,000	£2,000	£850
Midget Mk II	1098/4	1962-66	£3,000	£2,000	£850
Midget Mk III	1275/4	1966-74	£3,200	£2,000	£850
Midget 1500	1491/4	1975-79	£3,000	£2,000	£850

All prices are for British right hand drive cars. Deduct 10-15% for left hand drive varieties, even if converted to right hand drive.

1966 MGB GT, wire wheels, recent restoration, very good condition.
£8,500-9,000 *MSN*

1967 MGB Roadster, totally restored.
£7,000-7,500 *GML*

1967 MGB 2 Seater Sports Roadster, 4 speed gearbox fitted with overdrive, factory option oil cooler, repainted, in good overall condition.
Est. £7,000-9,000 *S*

1967 MGB GT, 4 cylinders, 1798cc, engine in good working order, resprayed.
£2,500-2,800 *ADT*

1968 MGB GT, fitted with overdrive, wire wheels, Webasto roof, completely restored.
£5,000-6,000 *VIC*

1969 MGB Roadster, 4 cylinders, 1795cc, wire wheels, professionally restored.
Est. £9,000-10,000 *ADT*

1970 MGB Roadster, 1800cc, in good condition throughout.
£4,000-4,500 *S*

1973 MGB Roadster, 4 cylinders, 1792cc, in very good overall condition.
£4,250-4,750 *ADT*

1974 MGB GT, 4 cylinders, 1798cc, fair to good condition.
£1,200-1,400 *ADT*

1975 MGB GT, 4 cylinders,
1798cc, fair to good condition.
£1,700-2,000 *ADT*

1974 MGB 1800cc Roadster,
wire wheels, wooden steering
wheel, leather trim.
£8,750-9,250 *SJR*

1975 MGB Anniversary GT,
4 cylinders, 1798cc, 36,015
recorded mileage, very good
original condition.
Est. £5,500-6,500 *ADT*

*To celebrate their Golden Jubilee
year in 1975, British Leyland
announced a limited production
run of the MGB GT which was
sold and badged as the
Anniversary GT.*

1977 MGB GT, mechanically
excellent, bodywork and interior
in good condition.
£2,500-2,800 *LF*

1978 MGB GT, in sound and
good condition.
Est. £5,000-5,500 *S*

1978 MGB GT, gearbox fitted
with overdrive, only 25,300 miles,
with full service history.
Est. £4,500-5,500 *S*

1981 MGB GT Limited Edition,
4 cylinders, 1798cc, in very good
overall condition.
Est. £5,000-6,000 *ADT*

*The Limited Edition MGs mark
the end marque before the badged
saloon series appeared.
Distinguished by their colour
scheme, the GTs, of which only
580 were made, came in pewter
metallic paint with side stripes,
as well as with alloy wheels and
a black front air spoiler.*

1979 MGB GT, 8 cylinders,
3499cc, subsequently fitted with
a Rover V8 engine and 5 speed
gearbox.
£3,250-3,750 *ADT*

**Miller's is a price GUIDE
not a price LIST.**

1979 MGB Roadster, UK car,
right hand drive, overdrive,
Rostyle wheels, clean and
original car.
£7,750-8,250 *MSN*

1980 MGB GT, 1.8 litre engine,
4 speed manual gearbox with
overdrive, 30 delivery miles on
the clock, dry stored, full Ziebart
rust proofing, bodywork in perfect
condition.
£12,000-12,500 *BKS*

1980 MGB Roadster, US specification limited edition,
left hand drive, new wheels, tyres and stainless steel
exhaust, mechanically overhauled.
£8,750-9,250 *MSN*

1969 MGC Roadster, in good
condition throughout.
£6,000-6,500 *LF*

*Originally designed to be the
Austin Healey 3000 Mk IV, it had
a completely reworked C series
3 litre engine derived from the
earlier Austin Healey 3000. This
model was produced between
1967 and 1969.*

1981 MGB GT Limited Edition,
very good original condition.
Est. £6,000-6,500 *S*

1969 MGC GT, 6 cylinders,
2912cc, good overall condition.
Est. £4,000-5,000 *ADT*

1969 MGC GT, 6 cylinders,
2992cc, engine fully rebuilt,
manual gearbox with overdrive,
leather interior.
£6,500-7,000 *ADT*

1969 MGC GT, standard 4 speed
manual gearbox fitted with
electrically engaged overdrive,
original specification, fully
restored.
Est. £7,000-9,000 *BKS*

1974 MGB GT, V8 engine, very good condition throughout.
Est. £7,000-8,000 *S*

1979 MGB GT V8 EFi, 8 cylinders, 3500cc, comprehensively restored.
Est. £8,000-9,000 *ADT*

MILWAUKEE

1901 Milwaukee Steam Car, a rare car in excellent original condition.
£20,000-26,000 *FHF*

MINI

1959 Morris Mini, 4 cylinders, 850cc, one owner from new, original bill of sale, 25,000 miles, good original condition.
£1,200-1,500 *ADT*

1976 MGB GT V8, 8 cylinders, 3500cc, very good restored condition.
Est. £5,500-6,500 *ADT*

MINERVA

Sylvain de Jong had produced bicycles at his Antwerp factory since 1897 and produced his first motorcycle and car in 1900. The Minervette, his first car to go into series production, appeared in 1904, but the most notable step forward was in 1908 when de Jong was granted a license to produce Knight sleeve valve engines.

His products were superbly engineered and offered electric lighting in 1912 and electric starting in 1914. By the outbreak of war the Minerva factory was operating on a massive scale employing almost 2,000 people.

1921 Minerva Type NN 20hp Open Drive Limousine, coachwork by Rothschild, in good sound condition but some restoration required.
Est. £15,000-20,000 *S*

1961 Austin 7 Mini 2 Door Saloon, totally standard and to maker's original specification, low mileage, good condition throughout.
£3,000-3,500 *S*

**1966 Morris Mini Cooper 'S'
Mk I Saloon**, new Cooper
gearbox, no synchromesh on first
gear, fully rebuilt to 1310cc
specification, comprehensively
restored.
Est. £3,000-3,200 *S*

**1962 Morris Mini Minor
2 Door Saloon,** 848cc, original
sliding windows, wire door pulls,
low mileage, good original
condition. **£900-1,100** *BKS*

**1967 Morris Mini Minor
Saloon,** engine and gearbox
rebuilt, complete body rebuild
and respray, very good condition.
£500-700 *C*

**1966 Morris Mini Cooper 'S'
Competition Saloon,** 1275cc,
rebuilt by John Cooper Garages
Limited. **Est. £4,800-5,500** *S*

1968 Morris Mini Cooper,
4 cylinders, 998cc, good overall
condition.
£4,500-5,000 *ADT*

**1969 Austin Mini Cooper
Mk II,** full length sunroof, very
good overall condition.
£1,100-1,300 *COYS*

MINI Model	ENGINE cc/cyl	DATES	CONDITION 1	2	3
Mini	848/4	1959-67	£2,000	£900	-
Mini Countryman	848/4	1961-67	£1,800	£900	-
Cooper Mk I	997/4	1961-67	£5,000	£3,000	£1,500
Cooper Mk II	998/4	1967-69	£3,500	£3,000	£1,500
Cooper S Mk I	var/4	1963-67	£6,000	£4,000	£2,000
Cooper S Mk II	1275/4	1967-71	£5,000	£4,000	£2,000
Innocenti Mini Cooper	998/4	1966-75	£3,000	£1,500	-

1969 Mini Cooper, 4 cylinders,
998cc, excellent restored condition.
£4,000-4,500 *ADT*

**1972 Morris Mini 1000
Automatic,** only 50,000 miles,
very good condition throughout.
£1,800-2,200 *Bro*

1972 Austin Mini Clubman,
4 cylinders, 998cc, 3,303 recorded
miles, in very good condition.
£2,300-2,600 *ADT*

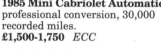

1985 Mini Cabriolet Automatic,
professional conversion, 30,000
recorded miles.
£1,500-1,750 *ECC*

1987 Austin Mini City E,
4 cylinders, 998cc, 1,660
recorded miles.
Est. £3,000-4,000 *ADT*

*The Austin Mini City Series E
dates from 1987.*

**1988 Austin Mini 'Jet Black'
Saloon,** 1000cc, delivery mileage
only recorded.
Est. £5,000-5,400 *S*

*This limited edition 'Jet Black'
example has never been registered.*

**1991 Mini Cooper Limited
Edition,** leather seats, sunroof,
stereo, alloy wheels, twin spot
lamps, John Cooper signed
bonnet. **£3,000-3,500** *CCTC*

1968 Austin Mini Moke,
4 cylinders, 1098cc, restored,
very good condition.
Est. £3,000-4,000 *ADT*

MITSUBISHI

**1982 Mitsubishi Colt Lancer
Turbo Works World
Championship Rally Car,**
2 litre engine, large turbo and
intercooler developing 380bhp,
twin plate paddle clutch, 5 speed
close ratio dog box, 4-6 LSD
differential, special strengthened
axle, vented discs with large pot
calipers, forest suspension,
Recaro seats, full aero equipment
navigation computer, totally rebuilt.
Est. £16,000-20,000 *S*

*This historic rally car was built
for the 1982 World Rally
Championship driven by Pentti
Arikalla and Anders Kulang.*

CROSS REFERENCE
Racing Cars ———→ p301

MORGAN

1957 Morgan Plus 4, imported
from California, left hand drive,
some chassis and bodywork
restoration required, complete car.
£5,250-5,500 *CCTC*

*Morgan project cars always sell
very well and are in great
demand.*

CROSS REFERENCE
**Restoration
   Projects** ———→ p305

MOON

Joseph Moon set up business in St. Louis,
Missouri. He produced his first car in 1905
with 4 cylinders, 30-35hp with a Rutenber
engine, 3 speed gears and shaft drive.
Moon's first 6 cylinder car arrived with the
Model 65 in 1913 and from 1916 onwards
only 6 cylinder cars were produced.

CROSS REFERENCE
**Restoration
   Projects** ———→ p305

**1920 Moon Model 642
5 Passenger Touring Car,**
chassis-up restoration, re-
upholstered, right hand drive.
£14,000-16,000 *S*

1930 Moon Straight Eight,
body by Brainsby, possibly
unique.
£7,000-8,000 *DB*

**1929 Morgan 3 Wheeler The Family Model.
£11,000-13,000** *FHD*
This model cost £85 new in 1931.

**1931 Morgan 3 Wheeler
Super Aero.
£13,000-15,000** *FHD*

*The last 3 wheelers were made
in the early 1950s.*

MORGAN Model	ENGINE cc/cyl	DATES	CONDITION		
			1	2	3
4/4 Series I	1098/4	1936-50	£9,000	£7,000	£6,000
Plus 4	2088/4	1950-53	£12,000	£9,000	£7,000
Plus 4	1991/4	1954-68	£11,000	£9,000	£7,000
4/4 Series II/III/IV	997/4	1954-68	£8,000	£6,000	£3,000
4/4 1600	1599/4	1960 on	£11,000	£9,000	£6,000
Plus 8	3528/8	1969 on	£17,000	£13,500	£10,000

1933 Morgan 3 Wheeler Runabout, 1100cc watercooled Jap V-twin engine, with hood, side screens and tonneau, fully restored. **£8,500-9,500** *RJ*

1936 Morgan 4/4 Flat Radiator, 1122cc engine. **£12,000-14,000** *FHD*

Morgan's first production 4 wheeler car with 1122cc engine. This car is one of the first ever made.

1948 Morgan 4/4, in very good condition. **£10,000-12,000** *CC*

c1936 Morgan 4/4, 4 cylinders, 1122cc, engine and gearbox fully refurbished, new hood, re-registered and imported in early 1950s. **£8,500-9,500** *ADT*

1951 Morgan Plus 4 Flat Radiator 2 Seater. **£18,500-21,500** *FHD*

This model was also made as a 4 seater from 1951-54.

1952 Morgan 4/4 Roadster, original car. **£14,500-15,500** *FHF*

1962 Morgan Plus 4 Drophead Coupé. **£32,000-40,000** *FHD*

This model was built from 1952 to 1969 and is now very collectable.

Miller's is a price GUIDE not a price LIST.

1987 Morgan Plus 8 3.5Litre, with fuel injection engine.
£20,000-23,000 *FHD*

1985 Morgan Plus 8 3.5 Litre.
£16,750-18,250 *FHD*

This model was made with carburettors from 1968-1985, then replaced with a fuel injection engine.

1962 Morgan 2 Seater Series IV, 1340cc engine.
£8,000-10,000 *FHD*

This model was made between 1961-62.

1978 Morgan 4/4 2 Seater.
£8,000-10,000 *FHD*

Also available in 4 seater format, introduced with a Ford engine in 1968-1981, and thereafter made with a Ford CVH engine.

1985 Morgan 4/4 4 Seater, with CVH engine.
£12,000-14,000 *FHD*

MORRIS

William Morris's philosophy was to buy good components at competitive prices and create a straightforward vehicle at an affordable price. Morris, later Lord Nuffield, had created the largest motor manufacturer in the UK by the 1920s, and started to acquire his competitors, notably Wolseley (1927) and Riley (1938). Despite producing two of the most notable British motor cars, the Morris Minor and the Mini (both designed by Issigonis), in 1952 when the BMC was formed, the Morris name disappeared.

c1924 Morris Bullnose Cowley 2 Seater with Dickey, in good restored condition throughout. **£9,000-12,000** *S*

1923 Morris Cowley Sports, 4 cylinders, 1489cc, re-built from an original chassis, in excellent order. **£7,500-8,500** *ADT*

85 Morris Cowley Sports were manufactured during the early 1920s, and sold at a price of 335 guineas.

1926 Morris Bullnose Cowley 2 seater, 4 cylinders, 1548cc, 3 speed gearbox, wet plate clutch and 3 stud wheels, dickey body, right hand drive, in good condition. **£8,000-8,500** *ADT*

1925 Morris Bullnose Cowley 4 Door Tourer, 4 cylinder side valve engine, 1548cc, 3 speed manual gearbox, rear wheel drum brakes, semi-elliptic leaf spring suspension, right hand drive, museum stored, good overall condition. **£10,500-11,500** *C*

1929 Morris Minor, overhead camshaft, rare original boat-tail sports bodywork. **£5,000-6,000** *FHF*

1930 Morris Minor, overhead camshaft. **£2,750-3,000** *DB*

1929 Morris Cowley Open 2 Seater with Dickey, 1.5 litre, engine rebuilt, chassis reconditioned, bodywork taken back to bare metal before refinishing, totally restored. **£10,500-11,500** *BKS*

c1930-31 Morris Oxford 6, near original condition, wired spoke wheels, running boards with flanged mudguards, leather interior seats, inset sliding Rexine roof, wood veneered fascia panel, interior blinds. **£6,200-6,600** *L&E*

1937 Morris 8 Series II 4 Seat Tourer, very good overall condition. **£4,750-5,250** *CC*

1932 Morris Minor Tourer, originally an open 2 seater, modified by fitting cycle wings and fabric bodywork. **Est. £2,900-3,500** *ALC*

1932 Morris 8 Family Saloon, original car in good running order. **£4,250-4,500** *HOLL*

1933 Morris Minor 2 Seater Tourer, 4 cylinders, 847cc, rebuilt engine and gearbox, very good restored condition. **£6,200-6,600** *ADT*

1936 Morris 8 Saloon, 4 cylinders, 918cc, bodyshell in need of some restoration, good sound example. **£2,250-2,750** *ADT*

1933 Morris 10/6 Saloon, good overall condition. **£4,600-5,000** *S*

1935 Morris 12/4 Saloon, 4 cylinders, 1550cc, largely original, in good condition. **Est. £3,500-4,000** *ADT*

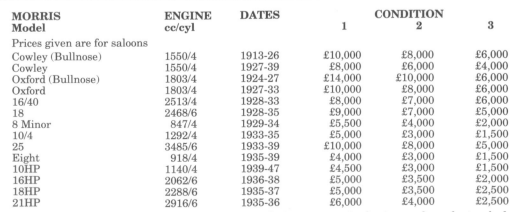

MORRIS Model	ENGINE cc/cyl	DATES	CONDITION 1	2	3
Prices given are for saloons					
Cowley (Bullnose)	1550/4	1913-26	£10,000	£8,000	£6,000
Cowley	1550/4	1927-39	£8,000	£6,000	£4,000
Oxford (Bullnose)	1803/4	1924-27	£14,000	£10,000	£6,000
Oxford	1803/4	1927-33	£10,000	£8,000	£6,000
16/40	2513/4	1928-33	£8,000	£7,000	£6,000
18	2468/6	1928-35	£9,000	£7,000	£5,000
8 Minor	847/4	1929-34	£5,500	£4,000	£2,000
10/4	1292/4	1933-35	£5,000	£3,000	£1,500
25	3485/6	1933-39	£10,000	£8,000	£5,000
Eight	918/4	1935-39	£4,000	£3,000	£1,500
10HP	1140/4	1939-47	£4,500	£3,000	£1,500
16HP	2062/6	1936-38	£5,000	£3,500	£2,000
18HP	2288/6	1935-37	£5,000	£3,500	£2,500
21HP	2916/6	1935-36	£6,000	£4,000	£2,500

A touring version of the above is worth approximately 30% more and value is very dependent on body type and has an increased value if coachbuilt.

**1957 Morris Oxford
Traveller,** mechanically
sound, interior needs attention.
£100-120 *MoT*

CROSS REFERENCE
**Restoration
Projects** ⟶ p305

**1959 Morris Oxford Series V
Saloon,** 4 cylinders, 1489cc,
very good show condition
throughout.
£2,250-2,500 *ADT*

**1953 Morris Minor
Convertible,** 918cc, single
valve engine, genuine 52,000
miles.
£4,750-5,250 *CCon*

1955 Morris Minor Convertible,
4 cylinders, 1098cc, rust free,
generally in good condition.
Est. £2,500-2,800 *ADT*

1954 Morris Minor Saloon,
4 cylinders, original 803cc
overhead valve engine, split
windscreen, 2 doors, old MOT
certificates, good condition
throughout.
£1,800-2,200 *ADT*

**1959 Morris Minor
Convertible,** 1098cc, MOT
certificate, needs restoring.
£1,800-2,200 *CCon*

**1959 Morris Minor 4 Door
Saloon,** 948cc, with original
semaphore indicators, partly
restored.
£1,600-1,800 *ESM*

**1956 Morris Minor Series II
2 Door Saloon,** split windscreen,
stored for 8 years, good condition
throughout.
Est. £3,000-4,000 *S*

1960 Morris Minor, 4 cylinders,
948cc, in very good overall
condition.
Est. £2,500-3,500 *ADT*

**1955 Morris Minor 2 Door
Saloon,** later 1000cc rebuilt
engine, split windscreen,
repainted.
£2,800-3,200 *S*

**1967 Morris Minor 1000
Traveller,** original paintwork
and interior, in good condition
throughout.
Est. £2,500-2,750 *S*

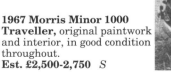

1960 Morris Minor Convertible, 948cc, leather interior, excellent condition throughout.
£6,250-6,750 *CCon*

1962 Morris Minor Convertible, converted from saloon, good overall condition.
£3,250-3,500 *ESM*

1964 Morris Minor 1000 Saloon, 54,000 miles, full service history.
Est. £700-1,000 *ECC*

1969 Morris Minor, 4 cylinders, 1098cc, same family owners from new, well maintained, reasonable condition.
Est. £1,000-1,200 *ADT*

1969 Morris Minor Traveller, good condition.
Est. £1,500-1,800 *ECC*

1962 Morris Minor Convertible, 1098cc, very good overall condition.
£3,800-4,200 *CCon*

1968 Morris Minor 4 Door Saloon, resprayed, in very good condition.
£3,250-3,500 *ESM*

1968 Morris Minor Convertible, 1098cc, very good overall condition.
£4,250-4,750 *CCon*

1968 Morris Minor Convertible, 1098cc, restored.
£3,300-3,600 *ESM*

1969 Morris Minor 2 Door Saloon, 1098cc, with period sunroof, some restoration needed.
£1,500-1,750 *ESM*

MORRIS Model	ENGINE cc/cyl	DATES	CONDITION 1	2	3
Minor Series MM	918/4	1948-52	£1,800	£1,000	£300
Minor Series MM Conv	918/4	1948-52	£3,250	£1,500	£650
Minor Series II	803/4	1953-56	£1,500	£850	£300
Minor Series II Conv	803/4	1953-56	£3,000	£2,000	£650
Minor Series II Est	803/4	1953-56	£2,500	£1,000	£350
Minor 1000	948/4	1956-63	£1,750	£925	£250
Minor 1000 Conv	948/4	1956-63	£3,000	£2,000	£750
Minor 1000 Est	948/4	1956-63	£2,000	£1,200	£350
Minor 1000	1098/4	1963-71	£2,000	£950	£250
Minor 1000 Conv	1098/4	1963-71	£3,500	£2,250	£750
Minor 1000 Est	1098/4	1963-71	£3,000	£1,200	£400
Cowley 1200	1200/4	1954-56	£1,675	£1,000	£300
Cowley 1500	1489/4	1956-59	£1,750	£950	£350
Oxford MO	1476/4	1948-54	£2,000	£850	£250
Oxford MO Est	1476/4	1952-54	£3,000	£1,500	£350
Series II/III	1489/4	1954-59	£2,000	£1,200	£300
Series II/III/IV Est	1489/4	1954-60	£2,250	£1,350	£250
Oxford Series V Farina	1489/4	1959-61	£1,800	£800	£250
Oxford Series VI Farina	1622/4	1961-71	£1,750	£750	£200
Six Series MS	2215/6	1948-54	£2,500	£1,500	£500
Isis Series I/II	2639/6	1955-58	£2,500	£1,300	£450
Isis Series I/II Est	2639/6	1956-57	£2,600	£1,350	£500

1972 Morris Suntour Motor Caravan, 1622cc, good overall condition.
£900-1,000 *ALC*

1970 Morris 1300GT, 1275cc, 43,000 miles from new, original and good condition.
£400-500 *Cen*

1981/83 Morris Hustler Estate, 1400cc, front wheel drive and twin rear axles, handmade mahogany dashboard, 11,000 miles since completion, capable of carrying 9 people, in excellent condition.
£3,000-3,500 *S*

MORS

Mors was one of the pioneering firms of the French motor industry. The company initially made insulated electrical wiring and then moved on the make small boats and oil-fired steam tricycles, producing its first car in 1895. Their large variety of vehicles were popular, selling as far away as the United States. Financial difficulties in 1908 led to André Citroën being brought in to run the company. He immediately sold the electrical side of the company to Emile Mors and concentrated on building motor vehicles and a wide range of cars, buses, taxis and lorries.

1912 Mors Type NX 2 Seater Tourer, 4 cylinders, 12/15hp, Sankey wheels.
Est. £20,000-25,000 *LF*

1914 Mors 12/15hp 2 Seater with Dickey, museum displayed, largely completed restoration. **£11,000-15,000** *S*

MOSQUITO

1903 Mors 2 Seater, 4 cylinder individually cast engine, atmospheric intake valves, displacement 2.2 litres, 15hp, make and break ignition, Mors magneto and surface carburettor, 4 speed gearbox, cone clutch, double chain drive, wheel base 74⅓in, in very good overall condition.
£39,000-43,000 *S(NY)*

Locate the source
The source of each illustration in Miller's can be found by checking the code letters below each caption with the list of contributors.

1978 Mosquito, 4 cylinders, 850cc.
Est. £1,300-1,500 *HOLL*

This is one of about 5 or 6 prototypes built by Robert Moss at Kidlington, Nr. Oxford. His idea was to produce an inexpensive and cheap to run sports car. The 3 wheeler has fibreglass bodywork and Mini running gear.

NASH-HEALEY

1952 Nash-Healey Roadster, comprehensively overhauled and prepared for the Mille Miglia, in excellent condition.
£16,500-17,500 *COYS*

The Nash Motor Company gained a reputation for building individual cars. Healey's contribution was to build the entire car in England using the Silverstone model as its base. Healey designed aluminium roadster coachwork with a distinctive Nash-type grille.

1952 Nash-Healey Roadster, coachwork by Pinin Farina, 6 cylinders, 3827cc, wire wheels, hood and side screens, museum stored, in excellent condition.
£13,000-14,000 *COYS*

1953 Nash-Healey Convertible. 58,812 miles recorded.
£27,000-28,000 *HWA*

Cross Reference	
Healey ⟶	p100
Austin Healey ⟶	p100

NASH

1948 Nash Ambassador, 4500cc, imported from the USA, mechanically restored and rust free. **£2,000-3,000** *HOLL*

NSU

1967 NSU Sport Prinz, twin cylinder, 598cc, overhead camshaft, air-cooled engine, all coil independent suspension, disc front brakes, right hand drive, complete mechanical restoration, interior refurbished.
£2,000-2,500 *PC*

OLDSMOBILE

1903 Oldsmobile 5hp Curved Dash Runabout, very good condition throughout.
Est. £15,000-18,000 *BKS*

1967 Oldsmobile Cutlass 442 Convertible, V8 overhead valve engine, 6580cc, 360bhp at 5000rpm, 4 speed manual gearbox, factory equipped with L69 option replacing the 4 barrels with 3 two-barrel carburettors, power front disc brakes, rear drum, left hand drive, restored and in good condition throughout.
£12,000-14,000 *CNY*

OLDSMOBILE Model	ENGINE cc/cyl	DATES	CONDITION		
			1	2	3
Curved Dash	1600/1	1901-04	£15,000	£13,000	£11,000
30	2771/6	1925-26	£9,000	£7,000	£4,000
Straight Eight	4213/8	1937-38	£12,000	£8,000	£6,000

OVERLAND

The Overland first appeared in 1903. They were manufactured at Terre Haute, Indiana, and designed by Claude Cox. Following a change of location to Indianapolis with new financial backing, the company ran into serious difficulties by 1907. John North Willys, a car dealer from Elmira, New York, took over the company and in 1909 production moved to Toledo, Ohio.

1917 Overland Big 4 Model 85 Tourer, engine in running order, right hand drive, in sound condition, needs restoring.
£7,200-7,800 *C*

1938 Packard S110 Opera Coupé 2+2, 6 cylinders, left hand drive, mechanics and interior in good condition, rust free, needs slight restoration.
£6,000-7,000 *CGB*

PACKARD

1929 Packard 7th Series Standard 8 Victoria Coupé, museum stored original car.
Est. £16,000-20,000 *S*

1952 Packard 200 2 Door Club Sedan, straight 8 engine, 4720cc, 135bhp, 3600rpm, 3 speed manual gearbox with overdrive, 38,000 miles recorded, imported.
£4,500-5,500 *DDM*

1953 Packard Convertible, straight 8 engine, automatic gearbox, left hand drive, restored, excellent condition.
£11,000-12,000 *CGB*

PACKARD Model	ENGINE cc/cyl	DATES	CONDITION		
			1	2	3
Twin Six	6946/12	1916-23	£25,000	£20,000	£13,000
6	3973/6	1921-24	£20,000	£15,000	£12,000
6, 7, 8 Series	5231/8	1929-39	£35,000	£30,000	£22,000
12	7300/12	1936-39	£35,000	£30,000	£18,000

PANHARD

1961 Panhard Dyna PL17 Saloon, original right hand drive import to UK, has been dry stored, recorded mileage 46,000, original car. **£2,400-2,800** *ALC*

1914 Panhard et Levassor Model X22 5 Seater Torpedo Touring, Knight sleeve valve engine, 4899cc, 28hp, good condition throughout. **£24,500-26,500** *S*

The car is believed to have been used by Marshall Foch as a parade car after the Great War.

PEERLESS

1959 Peerless GT Phase II, 4 cylinder, restored 1998cc TR3A engine, standard manual gearbox without overdrive, standard De Dion rear suspension, wire wheels, fully restored. **Est. £6,000-7,000** *ADT*

PANHARD ET LEVASSOR

1898 Panhard et Levassor Type M2F 6 Seater Wagonette, twin cylinder vertical engine with overhead inlet valves and side exhaust, 4 speed gearbox, chain drive to the rear wheels, hot tube ignition, original tiller steering, totally restored. **£36,000-40,000** *S*

1902 Panhard et Levassor Rear Entrance Tonneau, coachwork by Rothschild, owned by one family, original car. **£62,000-67,000** *FHF*

The Peerless was based on the Triumph TR3 engine, transmission and front suspension. The fibreglass 2 door, 4 seater, with the use of TR mechanics, made for effective maintenance.

1960 Peerless 2 Litre GT, rebuilt Triumph TR engine, overdrive gearbox, new clutch, tubular space frame chassis, independent front suspension, rear De Dion, wire wheels, new interior trim. **£3,750-4,000** *CCTC*

PEUGEOT

Peugeot is one of the oldest car firms in the world, second only to Daimler-Benz. Armand Peugeot's car production started in 1890 and by 1899 had built 500 cars. The end of WWI left Peugeot in a strong financial position and continued production with a new 2.8 litre 4 cylinder Type 153 and introduced a diesel engine in 1928. By the 1970s Peugeot offered one of the widest range of vehicles of any car manufacturer.

1904 Peugeot 1.1 litre 9hp Rear Entrance Tonneau, engine, 3 speed quadrant change gearbox, in good all-round condition.
Est. £22,000-28,000 *BKS*

1904 Peugeot Bébé, in good running order, eligible for the Brighton Run.
£24,000-26,000 *PiK*

1913 Peugeot Lyon 4 Seater Tourer, restored, in excellent condition.
£29,000-35,000 *FHF*

1972 Peugeot 304 Cabriolet, 1288cc, good overall condition.
£2,800-3,400 *ALC*

1915 Peugeot Bébé Convertible, in good condition throughout.
£13,000-14,000 *LF*

PEUGEOT Model	ENGINE cc/cyl	DATES	CONDITION 1	2	3
153	2951/4	1913-26	£5,000	£4,000	£2,000
163	1490/4	1920-24	£5,000	£4,000	£2,000
Bebe	676/4	1920-25	£7,000	£6,000	£3,000
156	5700/6	1922-24	£7,000	£5,000	£3,000
174	3828/4	1922-28	£6,000	£4,000	£2,000
172	714/4	1926-28	£4,000	£3,000	£1,500
183	1990/6	1929-30	£4,000	£3,000	£1,500
201	996/4	1930-36	£4,000	£3,000	£1,500
402	2140/4	1938-40	£4,000	£3,000	£1,000

Right hand drive cars will always achieve more interest than left hand drive. Good solid cars.

PIERCE-ARROW

1933 Pierce-Arrow Model 836 2 Door Club Brougham, totally restored, imported from USA, excellent condition.
Est. £20,000-25,000 *S*

Production was never high by American standards, and in 1931 only 2,692 were made.

1933 Pierce-Arrow Model 836 4 Door Sedan, chassis-up restoration in 1988, excellent condition throughout.
Est. £18,000-22,000 *S*

**1935 Pierce-Arrow Model 845
Coupé with Rumble Seat,**
straight 8 engine, 140bhp at
3400rpm, 3 speed gearbox with
freewheel unit, power braking,
airstream headlamps, twin side
mounted spare tyres, twin horns,
auxiliary lights, rear trunk
mounted on luggage grid, left
hand drive.
£36,000-38,000 *S*

> **Miller's is a price GUIDE
> not a price LIST.**

PONTIAC

1954 Pontiac Starchief De Luxe Convertible,
straight 8 engine, partial restoration, left hand
drive. **£9,000-12,000** *CGB*

1988 Pontiac Firebird GTA Transam Targa Coupé,
V8 engine, 4 speed automatic gearbox, Pontiac
Performance suspension WS6, Goodyear Eagle VR50 16in
tyres, pop-up headlamps, digital dashboard, electric
windows, power steering, air conditioning, anti-theft
ignition, stereo radio, imported new to UK, left hand drive.
£5,500-6,000 *S*

PONTIAC Model	ENGINE cc/cyl	DATES	CONDITION 1	2	3
Six-27	3048/6	1926-29	£9,000	£7,000	£4,000
Silver Streak	3654/8	1935-37	£12,000	£9,000	£5,500
6	3638/6	1937-49	£7,000	£4,000	£3,500
8	4078/8	1937-49	£7,000	£4,000	£3,500

PORSCHE

The Porsche family has been responsible for
some of the most famous German motor
vehicles since the early 1900's including the
popular Volkswagen and a series of sports
cars. Today Porsche sports cars continue to
dominate both the race track and road. The
911 Series celebrated its 30th birthday in 1993.

1957 Porsche 356A, 4 cylinders,
original right hand drive, good
overall condition.
£10,000-12,000 *ADT*

1957 Porsche 356A Speedster,
1600cc, restored, good condition.
£32,000-34,000 *DF*

1960 Porsche 356B T-5 Coupé,
1600cc, restored, excellent
condtion. **£13,000-15,000** *DF*

1958 Porsche 356A Coupé,
1600cc, restored, excellent
condition. **£11,000-13,000** *DF*

**1961 Porsche 356 1.6 litre
Super 90 Coupé,** excellent
restoration to competition
winning standard.
£15,000-16,000 *BKS*

1961 Porsche 356B T-5
Roadster, 1600cc, restored,
good condition.
£24,000-26,000 *DF*

1958 Porsche 356 Speedster,
Roadster coachwork by Reutter,
4 cylinders, 1600cc, full weather
equipment, period Nardi steering
wheel, left hand drive, excellent
condition throughout.
Est. £24,000-27,000 *COYS*

1962 Porsche 356B 1600cc
Sports Coupé, good original
condition throughout.
£9,000-9,500 *S*

1962 Porsche 356B T-6 Coupé,
1600cc, restored, good condition.
£12,000-14,000 *DF*

1963 Porsche 356B T-6
Cabriolet, 1600cc, restored,
excellent condition.
£23,000-25,000 *DF*

1964 Porsche 356C Carrera
2 Litre Coupé, 2000cc, restored,
excellent condition.
£58,000-62,000 *DF*

1965 Porsche 356SC
Cabriolet,1600cc, restored,
good condition.
£24,000-26,000 *DF*

1968 Porsche 912, 4 cylinders,
1582cc, rare long wheelbase,
replacement wings and sills,
resprayed, good original condition.
£4,500-5,000 *COYS*

1970 Porsche 911S, 6 cylinders, 2195cc, resprayed,
good overall condition. **Est. £6,500-7,500** *ADT*

**1972 Porsche 914 1.7 Litre
Targa Top Sports 2 Seater,**
engine and transmission fully
rebuilt, 5 speed gearbox, good
condition throughout.
Est. £2,800-3,400 *BKS*

CROSS REFERENCE
Racing Cars ⟶ p301

1972 Porsche 911 RSR Replica,
6 cylinders, 3300cc, regularly
raced in club events, good
condition. **£9,000-9,500** *COYS*

**1974 Porsche 911/935 3 Litre
Sports Coupé,** flat 6 cylinder
engine, 2993cc, 204bhp at
6200rpm, 5 speed manual
gearbox, all-round disc brakes,
independent Macpherson
telescopic damper struts front
suspension, lower wishbones,
longitudinal torsion bars,
independent rear suspension,
trailing radius arms, transverse
torsion bars, telescopic dampers,
right hand drive, new fibreglass
coachwork.
Est. £12,000-15,000 *C*

1981 Porsche 924 Carrera GT,
one of only 75 right hand drive
examples built, very good original
condition throughout.
£16,000-18,000 *S*

1986 Porsche 911 Turbo SC Coupé, US model, all steel
Blackburn and Daley slantnose, 25,700 miles recorded.
£30,000-35,000 *HWA*

PORSCHE Model	ENGINE cc/cyl	DATES	CONDITION 1	2	3
356	var/4	1949-53	£12,000	£8,000	£4,000
356 Cabriolet	var/4	1951-53	£22,000	£14,000	£10,000
356A	1582/4	1955-59	£11,500	£7,000	£3,000
356A Cabriolet	1582/4	1956-59	£15,000	£9,000	£7,000
356A Speedster	1582/4	1955-58	£23,000	£19,000	£14,000
356 Carrera	1582/1966/4	1960-65	£24,000	£20,000	£15,000
356C	1582/4	1963-65	£11,000	£8,000	£4,000
356C Cabriolet	1582/4	1963-64	£15,000	£12,000	£7,000
911/911L/T/E	1991/6	1964-68	£8,500	£5,500	£3,500
912	1582/4	1965-68	£6,500	£5,000	£2,000
911S	1991/6	1966-69	£11,000	£8,000	£5,500
911S	2195/6	1969-71	£11,000	£8,000	£6,000
911T	2341/6	1971-73	£8,000	£6,000	£4,000
911E	2341/6	1971-73	£9,000	£7,000	£5,000
914/4	1679/4	1969-75	£4,000	£3,000	£1,000
914/6	1991/6	1969-71	£5,000	£3,500	£1,500
911S	2341/6	1971-73	£14,000	£9,000	£7,500
Carrera RS lightweight	2687/6	1973	£32,000	£28,000	£16,000
Carrera RS Touring	2687/6	1973	£30,000	£26,000	£18,000
Carrera 3	2994/6	1976-77	£14,000	£9,000	£7,000
924 Turbo	1984/4	1978-83	£4,500	£3,000	£1,500

Sportmatic cars are less desirable.

PLYMOUTH

The Chrysler Corporation's new car for 1928 was called the Plymouth in recognition of the strength and endurance of the first American colonists, the Pilgrims, who landed at Plymouth Rock. By 1931 over 100,000 cars rolled off the assembly line which placed Plymouth firmly in third place behind Chevrolet and Ford.

1931 Plymouth Model 30U 2 Door Coupé, 32,155 miles from new, wire wheels, to original specification, very good overall condition.
£13,500-14,500 *S*

1948 Plymouth Convertible, excellent original condition.
£19,000-20,000 *FHF*

RAMBLER

1903 Rambler Roadster, fully restored condition.
£24,000-26,000 *FHF*

PREMIER

1910 Premier 40hp 4 Seater Tourer, good restored condition.
£32,000-38,000 *FHF*

1950 Plymouth Sedan, 6 cylinder in line engine, 217.8cu in, 97bhp at 3600rpm, 3 speed manual gearbox, 4 wheel drum brakes, coil spring front suspension, leaf spring rear, left hand drive, very good overall condition, excellent original interior, 19,000 recorded miles.
£3,500-5,000 *CNY*

RELIANT

1975 Reliant Scimitar SR5A, V6 engine, 3 litres, good condition. **£4,000-4,500** *GW*

1977 Reliant Scimitar SE6A, V6 engine, 3 litres, restored, good condition.
£7,250-7,750 *GW*

RELIANT Model	ENGINE cc/cyl	DATES	CONDITION		
			1	2	3
Sabre 4 Coupé & Drophead	1703/4	1961-63	£4,500	£2,750	£1,000
Sabre 6 " "	2553/6	1962-64	£5,000	£3,250	£1,000
Scimitar GT Coupé SE4	2553/6, 2994 V6	1964-70	£4,500	£2,500	£1,000
Scimitar GTE Sports Estate SE5/5A	2994/V6	1968-75	£4,500	£2,000	£750
Scimitar GTE Sports Estate SE6/6A	2994/V6	1976-80	£6,000	£3,500	£1,250
Scimitar GTE Sports Estate SE6B	2792/V6	1980-86	£8,000	£5,000	£2,000
Scimitar GTC Convertible SE8B	2792/V6	1980-86	£12,000	£8,000	£5,500

1987 Reliant Scimitar SS1,
1809cc, turbo-charged, optional
hard top.
£5,000-5,500 *GW*

1986 Reliant Scimitar GTC,
2.8 litres, optional hard top, excellent
condition.
£15,250-15,750 *GW*

**1990 Reliant Middlebridge
Scimitar GTE,** 2.9 injection,
leather interior.
£12,750-13,250 *GW*

RENAULT

The Renault brothers established their
factory at Billancourt, near Paris, in 1898
and by the early 1900s were already winning
international motor races. Their first Grand
Prix win was in 1906.

The company was nationalized soon after
Louis Renault died in 1944. At this time
Renault was producing over 25% of all French
motor vehicles, and by the late 1970s were
looking to expand into North America. There
are many collectable Renaults from all eras.

**1910 Renault Open 4 Seater
Tourer.**
£14,000-16,000 *DB*

RENAULT Model	ENGINE cc/cyl	DATES	CONDITION 1	2	3
40hp	7540/6	1919-21	£30,000	£20,000	£10,000
SR	4537/4	1919-22	£10,000	£7,000	£5,000
EU-15.8HP	2815/4	1919-23	£5,000	£3,000	£2,000
GS-IG	2121/4	1920-23	£5,000	£3,000	£2,000
JP	9123/6	1922-29	£25,000	£20,000	£15,000
KJ	951/4	1923-29	£6,000	£4,000	£2,000
Mona Six	1474/6	1928-31	£7,000	£5,000	£3,000
Reinastella	7128/8	1929-32	£25,000	£20,000	£15,000
Viva Six	3181/6	1929-34	£10,000	£7,000	£3,000
14/45	2120/4	1929-35	£7,000	£5,000	£2,000
Nervahuit	4240/8	1931	£12,000	£10,000	£7,000
UY	1300/4	1932-34	£7,000	£5,000	£2,000
ZC/ZD2	4825/8	1934-35	£12,000	£10,000	£7,000
YN2	1463/4	1934-39	£7,000	£5,000	£2,000
Airline Super and Big 6	3620/6	1935	£10,000	£8,000	£5,000
18	2383/4	1936-39	£9,000	£5,000	£3,000
26	4085/6	1936-39	£12,000	£8,000	£5,000

Veteran pre-war models like the 2 cylinder AX, AG and BB are very popular, with values ranging between £6,000 and £15,000. The larger 4 cylinder cars like the AM, AZ, XB and VB are very reliable and coachbuilt examples command £25,000+.

1911 Renault Type AG 11hp Taxi, right hand drive, generally original condition. **£10,000-11,000** *HOLL*

1923 Renault Type KJ 8.3hp Roscata Runabout, 2 door, 3 seater, left hand drive, boat-tail body, good engine, good sound overall condition. **£3,500-4,000** *HOLL*

1911 Renault Type CC Coupé Chauffeur Landaulette, coachwork by Rothschild, 3564cc, D-fronted glass division with drop down centre panel and railway carriage windows to rear, Bleriot acetylene headlamps, scuttle mounted acetylene oil lamps, double-twist bulb horn, detachable rim wheels, sympathetically restored, museum stored. **£25,000-30,000** *S*

1914 Renault EK 9hp 2 Seater, older restoration, suffering from lack of use and now requires sympathetic restoration, museum stored. **£6,000-8,000** *S*

RENAULT Model	ENGINE cc/cyl	DATES	CONDITION 1	2	3
4CV	747/ 760/4	1947-61	£3,500	£2,000	£850
Fregate	1997/4	1952-60	£3,000	£2,000	£1,000
Dauphine	845/4	1956-66	£1,500	£1,000	£350
Dauphine Gordini	845/4	1961-66	£2,000	£1,000	£450
Floride	845/4	1959-62	£3,000	£2,000	£600
Caravelle	956/ 1108/4	1962-68	£4,500	£2,800	£750
R4	747/ 845/4	1961-86	£2,000	£1,500	£350
R8/R10	1108/4	1962-71	£1,800	£750	£200
R8 Gordini	1108/4	1965-66	£8,000	£5,000	£2,000
R8 Gordini	1255/4	1966-70	£8,000	£5,500	£2,500
R8S	1108/4	1968-71	£2,000	£1,200	£400

REO

The Reo takes its name from the initials of Ransom E. Olds, the founder of Oldsmobile. When he left Oldsmobile in 1904 he set up the R. E. Olds Company in Lansing, Michigan.

1910 Reo Model R 30hp 5 Seater Touring Car, very good condition throughout.
£22,000-24,000 *S*

1925 Reo 6 Golfer's Coupé Open 2 Seater With Dickey, 6 cylinders, 3962cc, fully restored, in excellent condition throughout.
Est. £11,000-14,000 *COYS*

GEORGES RICHARD

Car production by the Paris based Georges Richard firm commenced in 1897. In 1901 production was moved to the Ivry-Port factory, with later cars bearing the name Richard-Brasier. The company collapsed in 1930.

1902 Georges Richard Twin Cylinder Rear Entrance Tonneau, equipped with period brass fittings, paintwork and upholstery in very good condition.
Est. £28,000-32,000 *S*

1905 Reo, single cylinder, with spares, in excellent condition.
£14,000-16,000 *FHF*

1911 Reo Single Cylinder Open Truck, equipped with oil lighting, generally good original condition.   **£4,500-5,000** *S*

RILEY

The first Riley was produced in 1898 but it was not until the Riley Nine appeared in 1926 that their first real success was achieved. Riley sports cars and saloons continued to sell well and Riley became part of the Nuffield empire in 1938. Several Badge Engineered Rileys were offered from the BMC range, but sadly the name disappeared in 1969.

1929 Riley 9hp Special, 2 overhead camshafts operated by pushrods, 4 speed gearbox, extensively restored, excellent condition.   **£7,500-8,500** *ADT*

1930 Riley Brooklands, 4 cylinders, 1087cc, engine and chassis fully overhauled, very original car.
Est. £35,000-45,000 *COYS*

1931 Riley Monaco, 4 cylinders, 1089cc, original
structure dismantled and completely rebuilt,
original leather interior. **Est. £7,000-9,000** *ADT*

1933 Riley Monaco, very
good overall condition.
£6,250-6,750 *CC*

1933 Riley 9hp Tourer, very
good overall condition.
£7,000-8,000 *CC*

1934 Riley 9hp Gamecock,
4 cylinders, 1089cc, rebuilt
engine, in good condition.
Est. £14,000-18,000 *ADT*

RILEY Model	ENGINE cc/cyl	DATES	CONDITION		
			1	2	3
9hp	1034/2	1906-07	£9,000	£6,000	£3,000
Speed 10	1390/2	1909-10	£10,000	£6,000	£3,000
11	1498/4	1922-27	£7,000	£4,000	£2,000
9	1075/4	1927-32	£10,000	£7,000	£4,000
9 Gamecock	1098/4	1932-33	£14,000	£10,000	£6,000
Lincock 12hp	1458/6	1933-36	£9,000	£7,000	£5,000
Imp 9hp	1089/4	1934-35	£35,000	£28,000	£20,000
Kestrel 12hp	1496/4	1936-38	£8,000	£5,000	£2,000
Sprite 12hp	1496/4	1936-38	£40,000	£35,000	£20,000

1934 Riley 9 Special Tourer, chassis-up rebuild,
re-bodied as a Special Tourer in the 1950s, good,
sound condition. **£6,000-7,000** *LF*

**1936 Riley Monaco 9hp Sports
Saloon,** special series engine
with high compression pistons,
stronger valve springs, twin
carburettors, Wilson pre-selector
gearbox, aluminium coachwork,
engine overhauled, original
specification, fair to good overall
condition. **£6,250-6,750** *S*

**1937 Riley 9 Special 4 Seater
Sports,** 4 cylinders, 1084cc,
new body in 1980s, in very
good condition.
£8,500-9,000 *Mot*

1949 Riley RMC 2½ Litre 2 Seater Roadster, completely rebuilt to a high standard, very good condition.
£17,500-18,500 *BKS*

Rarely seen in right hand drive form, the Riley RMC 2½ litre Roadster was principally intended for export markets.

1949 Riley 1½ Litre, 4 cylinders, 1496cc, rack-and-pinion steering, 4 speed gearbox and torque tube transmission, very good condition throughout.
£4,400-4,800 *ADT*

1964 Riley 4/72 4 Door Saloon, leather upholstery, polished wood fascia, bucket type front seats, generally sound overall condition.   **Est. £900-1,200** *S*

The Riley 4/72 was 'badge engineered' and produced alongside similar models from Morris (Oxford), MG (Magnette), Wolseley (16/60) and Austin (Cambridge), the Riley being distinguishable by its traditional radiator grille and blue diamond badge.

1951 Riley RME 1½ Litre Sports Saloon, to factory specification in all major respects, excellent condition.
£8,500-9,000 *S*

1966 Riley Kestrel 4 Door Saloon, mechanically sound, chassis and bodywork in good condition.
£1,300-1,500 *S*

1962 Riley Elf, 4 cylinders, 848cc, in good condition throughout.
Est. £1,200-2,000 *ADT*

RILEY Model	ENGINE cc/cyl	DATES	CONDITION 1	2	3
1½ litre RMA	1496/4	1945-52	£5,000	£3,500	£1,500
1½ litre RME	1496/4	1952-55	£5,000	£3,500	£1,500
2½ litre RMB/F	2443/4	1946-53	£9,000	£7,000	£3,000
2½ litre Roadster	2443/4	1948-50	£15,000	£12,000	£9,000
2½ litre Drophead	2443/4	1948-51	£20,000	£18,000	£10,000
Pathfinder	2443/4	1953-57	£3,500	£2,000	£750
2.6	2639/6	1957-59	£3,000	£1,800	£750
1.5	1489/4	1957-65	£4,000	£2,000	£850
4/68	1489/4	1959-61	£1,500	£700	£300
4/72	1622/4	1961-69	£1,600	£800	£300
Elf I/II/III	848/4	1961-66	£1,500	£850	£400
Kestrel I/II	1098/4	1965-67	£1,500	£850	£400

ROLLS-ROYCE

Harry Royce, an engineer, was so angry when his new car, a Decauville, refused to start that he took it apart and remade it adopting his perfectionist standards, or so the legend has it.

The Hon. Charles Rolls, a pioneer motorist, started business as a motor trader and was introduced to Royce by a mutual friend. Rolls agreed to sell Royce's cars and a formal agreement was set up. The first Rolls-Royce appeared by the end of 1904. Rolls-Royce sounded better than Royce-Rolls. The rest is history.

1920 Rolls-Royce 40/50 Silver Ghost Alpine Eagle Boat-Tail Roadster, 2 seater coachwork probably built in the 1960s, polished wood pointed tail, later 21in wheels, Marchal headlamps, windscreen mounted swivel searchlight and an electric klaxon, museum stored, needs mechanical attention.
£30,000-35,000 *S*

1914 Rolls-Royce Silver Ghost London-Edinburgh Style Open Tourer.
£120,000-130,000 *BLE*

1922 Rolls-Royce Silver Ghost Open Tourer, ex-works demonstrator, coachwork by Barker & Co. Ltd., 6 cylinders, 7428cc, open touring body, polished aluminium bonnet, full weather equipment, rear Auster screen, very good condition throughout.
£75,000-78,000 *COYS*

1923 Rolls-Royce 40/50 Silver Ghost, replica coachwork by Wilkinson & Son, Derby, 6 cylinder in line, side valve engine, 7428cc, 85bhp, 4 speed gearbox, cone clutch, rear drum brakes, semi-elliptical front spring suspension, rear cantilever springs, right hand drive, in excellent condition throughout.
Est. £57,000-65,000 *CNY*

1923 Rolls-Royce Silver Ghost Tourer, coachwork by Barker, in excellent overall condition.
£85,000-120,000 *FHF*

1924 Rolls-Royce 20 Tourer, 6 cylinders, 3127cc, 3 speed gearbox, no front wheel brakes, correct horizontal shuttered radiator surround, modern body described as a Sedancalette De Ville.
Est. £14,000-16,000 *ADT*

1926 Rolls-Royce Silver Ghost Limousine.
£37,000-39,000 *HWA*

1927 Rolls-Royce Phantom I Cabriolet, modified coachwork by Hibbard & Darrin, 6 cylinders, overhead valve, 7668cc, 95bhp, 2750rpm, 4 speed manual gearbox, all-round drum brakes, semi-elliptic leaf springs front suspension, rear cantilever leaf springs, right hand drive, original wind-up windows, handles, lamps, instruments and windscreen, new hood, bare metal respray, good overall condition. **Est. £25,000-30,000** *C*

1926 Rolls-Royce 20 Doctor's Coupé, excellent condition. **£38,000-40,000** *FHF*

1927 Rolls-Royce Phantom I 40/50 Fixed Head Doctor's Coupé, coachwork by Roger Cook of Swindon and Carmichael's of Bournemouth and completed by Mike Collis of Holcombe, carefully stored and regularly started-up and run. **£22,000-24,000** *S*

1927 Rolls-Royce Phantom I Open Tourer, 6 cylinders, 7668cc, Brewster style tourer body, regularly maintained, excellent condition throughout. **£42,000-45,000** *COYS*

1928 Rolls-Royce Phantom I Limousine, coachwork by Gurney Nutting. **£28,000-30,000** *BLE*

ROLLS-ROYCE Model	ENGINE cc/cyl	DATES	CONDITION 1	2	3
40/50	7035/6	pre-WWI	£350,000	-	£50,000
40/50	7428/6	post-WWI	£110,000	£70,000	£38,000
20hp (3 speed)	3127/6	1922-25	£29,000	£23,000	£18,000
20hp	3127/6	1925-29	£30,000	£24,000	£18,000
Phantom I	7668/6	1925-29	£36,000	£28,000	£22,000
20/25	3669/6	1925-26	£23,000	£18,000	£15,000
Phantom II	7668/6	1929-35	£36,000	£30,000	£20,000
Phantom II Continental	7668/6	1930-35	£50,000	£40,000	£28,000
25/30	4257/6	1936-38	£24,000	£18,000	£12,000
Phantom III	7340/12	1936-39	£38,000	£28,000	£16,000
Wraith	4257/6	1938-39	£38,000	£32,000	£25,000

Prices will vary considerably depending on heritage, originality, coachbuilder, completeness and body style. A poor reproduction body can often mean the value is dependent only upon a rolling chassis and engine.

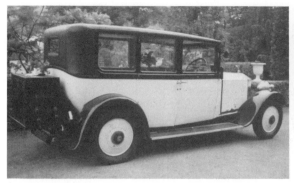

1929 Rolls-Royce 20/25 Limousine, coachwork by Barker.
£18,000-20,000 *Cum*

1928 Rolls-Royce Phantom I Open Tourer, coachwork by Wilkinson.
£44,000-46,000 *BLE*

1930 Rolls-Royce 20/25 Saloon, 4 light sports coachwork by William Arnold Ltd., 6 cylinders, 3128cc, good overall condition.
£18,500-20,000 *ADT*

1930 Rolls-Royce Phantom II 40/50 Tourer, original coachwork by Hooper, now modified, good overall condition.
£40,000-42,000 *S*

Formerly the property of H. H. Maharaja of Reiva.

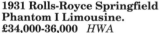

1931 Rolls-Royce Springfield Phantom I Limousine.
£34,000-36,000 *HWA*

1930 Rolls-Royce 20/25 4 Door Tourer, originally a limousine, now a 4 seater open tourer, in good, sound condition.
£16,500-17,000 *RCC*

1933 Rolls-Royce 20/25 Owner/Driver Sports Saloon, coachwork by Barker, engine completely rebuilt, repainted, original leather interior, in good condition throughout.
£26,000-28,000 *S*

1933 Rolls-Royce 3.7 Litre 20/25 6 Light Saloon, coachwork by H. J. Mulliner, Brooks trunk containing 2 of the 3 original fitted suitcases, good overall original condition.
£18,000-20,000 *BKS*

1935 Rolls-Royce 20/25 Coupé,
coachwork by H. J. Mulliner,
6 cylinders, 3699cc, very good
restored condition.
£24,000-25,000 *COYS*

CROSS REFERENCE
**Commercial
Vehicles ——————► p289**

**1934 Rolls-Royce 20/25 Pick-
Up Truck,** mechanically correct,
new exhaust system, good
condition.
£11,000-12,000 *RCC*

1934 Rolls-Royce 20/25, Owen
Sedanca Drophead Coupé
coachwork by Gurney Nutting,
6 cylinders, 3699cc, 4 speed
gearbox, thermostatically
controlled radiator grille shutters
replacing previous manual
operation, a one-shot centralised
lubrication system, fully
overhauled 2 years ago.
£55,000-58,000 *COYS*

**1937 Rolls-Royce 25/30 All-
Weather Tourer,** coachwork by
Joseph Cockshoot Ltd., of
Manchester, 4¼ litre engine,
excellent original condition
throughout.
Est. £45,000-55,000 *BKS*

1937 Rolls-Royce 25/30 Saloon,
coachwork by Barker, 4 light,
with division, new exhaust
sytem, requires some attention,
good overall condition.
£15,000-16,000 *RCC*

1939 Rolls-Royce Wraith,
coachwork by Hooper, excellent
condition throughout.
£15,000-16,000 *LF*

**1937 Rolls-Royce 25/30
Drophead Coupé,** coachwork by
H. J. Mulliner, originally fitted
with James Young saloon body,
later changed to a 3 position
drophead coupé, museum stored,
in very good condition.
£25,000-27,000 *COYS*

**1948 Rolls-Royce Silver
Wraith Series B Limousine,**
coachwork by Park Ward & Co.,
bodywork, chassis and
transmission in good condition,
interior needs some restoration.
£9,000-10,000 *S*

**1951 Rolls-Royce Silver Dawn
Convertible.**
£84,000-86,000 *HWA*

1952 Rolls Royce Silver Wraith,
coachwork by Freestone & Webb.
£14,000-16,000 *DB*

1952 Rolls-Royce Silver Dawn,
6 cylinders, 4500cc, rarely fitted
manual gearbox, in excellent
condition generally, including the
leather interior.
Est. £19,000-23,000 *ADT*

**1953 Rolls-Royce Silver
Wraith,** coachwork by Park
Ward, fair condition.
£4,000-7,500 *BA*

**1953 Rolls-Royce Silver
Wraith Touring Limousine,**
coachwork by H. J. Mulliner,
6 cylinders, 4566cc, coachwork
extensively restored, interior
re-upholstered, in good condition
throughout.
£19,000-20,000 *COYS*

**1954 Rolls-Royce Silver Dawn
Saloon,** very good condition.
£25,000-26,000 *S*

*In 1949 Rolls-Royce adopted the
policy of a standard steel factory
built body on their own chassis,
a policy already used successfully
by Bentley with their Mk VI
model in 1946. The Silver Dawn
was initially built for export and
785 examples were produced.*

**1954 Rolls-Royce Silver
Wraith,** coachwork by Park
Ward, excellent condition
throughout.
£14,000-15,000 *LF*

*The Silver Wraith was only
available in chassis form for
specialist coachmakers to body,
unlike the Bentley which was
available with a factory body.*

1956 Rolls-Royce Silver Cloud,
coachwork by James Young.
£7,500-8,500 *DB*

1960 Rolls-Royce Phantom V Touring Limousine, coachwork by James Young, single headlamps, full air conditioning, drinks cabinet with crystal decanters and glasses, one owner and 40,000 miles from new, excellent condition.
£42,000-45,000   *COYS*

1959 Rolls-Royce Silver Cloud I Drophead Coupé, coachwork by H. J. Mulliner, 6 cylinders, 4887cc, superb restoration to Concours winning standard.
Est. £75,000-90,000   *COYS*

1963 Rolls-Royce Series A Phantom V 6 Seater Limousine, showing signs of wear but good original condition.
£35,000-40,000 *S*

1964 Rolls-Royce Silver Cloud III 2 Door Drophead Coupé, coachwork by H. J. Mulliner/ Park Ward.
£55,000-65,000 *FHF*

1964 Rolls-Royce Silver Cloud III 6.2 Litre 2 Door Saloon, coachwork by H. J. Mulliner/Park Ward, good overall condition.
Est. £20,000-25,000 *BKS*

The quadruple headlamps were angled downwards, thus giving the design its 'Chinese Eye' nickname.

ROLLS-ROYCE Model	ENGINE cc/cyl	DATES	CONDITION 1	2	3
Silver Wraith LWB	4566/ 4887/6	1951-59	£22,000	£15,000	£9,000
Silver Wraith SWB	4257/ 4566/6	1947-59	£20,000	£12,000	£9,000
Mark VI	4257/6	1946-54	£20,000	£12,000	£7,000
Mark VI Coachbuilt	4257/6	1946-54	£22,000	£13,000	£6,000
Silver Wraith Drophead	4257/ 4566/6	1947-59	£50,000	£35,000	£25,000
Silver Dawn St'd Steel	4257/ 4566/6	1949-52	£30,000	£15,000	£10,000
Silver Dawn St'd Steel	4257/ 4566/6	1952-55	£30,000	£20,000	£15,000
Silver Dawn Coachbuilt	4257/ 4566/6	1949-55	£35,000	£25,000	£18,000
Silver Dawn Drophead	4257/ 4566/6	1949-55	£70,000	£50,000	£35,000
Silver Cloud I	4887/6	1955-59	£20,000	£10,000	£8,000
SCI Coupé Coachbuilt	4887/6	1955-59	£30,000	£20,000	£15,000
SCI Conv (HJM)	4887/6	1955-59	£80,000	£60,000	£40,000
Silver Cloud II	6230/8	1959-62	£19,000	£10,000	£8,000
SCII Conv (HJM)	6230/8	1959-62	£80,000	£75,000	£40,000
SCII Conv (MPW)	6230/8	1959-62	£60,000	£40,000	£32,000
Silver Cloud III	6230/8	1962-65	£25,000	£12,000	£10,000
SCIII Conv (MPW)	6230/8	1962-65	£75,000	£45,000	£35,000
Silver Shadow	6230/ 6750/8	1965-76	£11,000	£8,000	£6,000
S Shadow I Coupé (MPW)	6230/ 6750/8	1965-70	£15,000	£10,000	£8,000
SSI Drophead (MPW)	6230/ 6750/8	1965-70	£33,000	£25,000	£18,000

1966 Rolls Royce Phantom V Limousine, leather interior front compartment, cloth in rear with jump seats, 60,000 miles.
£37,000-40,000 *HWA*

1968 Rolls-Royce Silver Shadow 4 Door Saloon, low mileage, very good original condition.
£11,500-13,000 *S*

1970 Rolls-Royce Phantom VI Limousine, coachwork by H. J. Mulliner/Park Ward, fitted with occasional seats making an 8 seater, electric division, dual compartment, factory fitted air conditioning and electric windows, very good condition.
£36,000-38,000 *S*

1971 Rolls-Royce Silver Shadow Long Wheelbase Saloon, very good original condition.
Est. £11,000-13,000 *S*

1971 Rolls-Royce Silver Shadow, good overall condition.
£5,500-6,500 *DB*

1968 Rolls Royce Silver Shadow, leather interior, excellent original condition.
£8,750-9,250 *Bro*

1972 Rolls Royce Corniche Convertible.
£19,000-22,000 *BLE*

1972 Rolls-Royce Corniche, good overall condition.
£13,750-14,250 *Bro*

1972 Rolls-Royce Silver Shadow, good original condition.
£5,500-6,500 *DB*

1971 Rolls Royce Silver Shadow I, good condition.
£4,500-7,500 *BA*

1974 Rolls-Royce Silver Shadow Long Wheelbase Saloon, good overall condition.
£10,000-12,000 *S*

1975 Rolls-Royce Carmargue Fixed Head Coupé, 6750cc, excellent condition throughout.
Est. £27,000-30,000 *ALC*

In 10 years of production, only 136 Carmargue's were released to the U.K. market. The Carmargue was David Plaistow's attempt to make the most luxurious and expensive Rolls-Royce ever. He commissioned a totally new 2 door design from Pininfarina, to be coachbuilt by Mulliner/Park Ward. The new price in 1975 was £25,250, a world record and 50% more than the Corniche.

1976 Rolls Royce Silver Shadow I, full service history, excellent original condition.
£8,000-12,000 *VIC*

1976 Rolls-Royce Silver Shadow, 8 cylinders, 6725cc, used on Royal and official duties, excellent overall condition.
£13,000-14,000 *ADT*

1977 Rolls-Royce Corniche Convertible, coachwork by Mulliner/Park Ward.
£24,000-26,000 *Cum*

**1980 Rolls Royce Silver
Wraith II.**
£7,500-8,500 *DB*

**1978 Rolls-Royce Silver
Shadow II Saloon,** V8 engine,
6750cc, automatic gearbox,
excellent condition throughout.
Est. £12,000-14,000 *S*

1981 Rolls Royce Silver Spirit,
high mileage.
£14,500-15,500 *KSC*

1981 Rolls Royce Silver Spirit,
6750cc, slight damage to
paintwork.
£11,500-12,500 *Cum*

1982 Rolls Royce Silver Spirit,
6750cc, excellent original
condition. £14,000-14,500 *Cum*

1983 Rolls Royce Carmargue,
leather interior, Everflex top, low
mileage. £44,000-47,000 *HWA*

**1985 Rolls-Royce Silver Spur
Factory Limousine,** intercom
system, Panasonic colour TV and
VHS format VCR, crystal drinks
service, 11,418 miles, as new
condition. **£117,000-125,000** *HWA*

**1986 Rolls-Royce Corniche
Convertible,** low mileage.
£47,000-50,000 *HWA*

1987 Rolls Royce Silver Spur,
in excellent condition.
£30,000-32,000 *HWA*

1988 Rolls-Royce Silver Spur,
24,000 miles, excellent overall
condition.
£44,000-46,000 *HWA*

ROVER

John Starley used the Rover trade name for his range of safety bicycles as early as 1884. The Rover Cycle Co. Ltd., named in 1896, led the Coventry based cycle industry in producing machines with engines. The first Rover car appeared in 1904, although Rover motor cycles were still available in 1902.

Rover enjoyed a reputation for good vehicles aimed at the middle and professional classes. In 1966 they became part of the British Leyland Group. What was left of British Leyland became Austin Rover in 1982. In 1994 BMW purchased the controlling interest in the Rover Group.

1914 Rover 12hp 5 Seater Tourer, unrestored example, just 2 owners in its first 76 years, delivered new to Australia, requires restoring.
£15,500-18,500 *S*

1928 Rover 10/25 Saloon, 1124cc, Riviera fabric bodywork, artillery wheels, brass radiator, in need of some restoration after long storage.
£3,000-3,500 *ALC*

1935 Rover 12hp Saloon, 4 cylinders, 1425cc, original panelwork, full length sunroof, good overall condition.
Est. £4,500-5,500 *ADT*

1931 Rover 10/25 4 seater Coupé, coachwork by Weyman, rear trunk, twin bumpers, rear mounted spare wheel.
£6,000-6,500 *Bro*

1928 Rover 16hp Saloon, very good condition.
£10,000-11,000 *CC*

1931 Rover 10hp Sports Saloon, coachwork by Weyman.
£6,000-8,000 *FHF*

1935 10hp Rover, good overall condition.
£3,750-4,250 *CC*

1939 Rover 16hp Sportsman Saloon, good condition throughout.
£6,250-6,750 *CC*

ROVER Model	ENGINE cc/cyl	DATES	CONDITION 1	2	3
10hp	998/2	1920-25	£5,000	£3,000	£1,500
9/20	1074/4	1925-27	£6,000	£4,000	£2,000
10/25	1185/4	1928-33	£6,000	£4,000	£2,500
14hp	1577/6	1933-39	£6,000	£4,250	£2,000
12	1496/4	1934-37	£4,000	£3,000	£1,000
20 Sports	2512/6	1937-39	£5,000	£4,000	£2,500

1947 Rover Sportsman Saloon,
14hp, very good condition.
£6,750-7,250 *CC*

1947 Rover 12, 4 cylinders,
1595cc, excellent bodyshell, very
good original condition.
£3,000-3,300 *ADT*

1956 Rover 90 P4 Saloon,
6 cylinders, 2638cc, sound
condition. **£1,000-1,200** *ADT*

1949 Rover P3, 4 cylinders,
1389cc, 60hp, chassis-up rebuild,
dry stored for 10 years,
sympathetically restored.
£10,000-12,000 *ADT*

*The 1937 body style Rover P3
continued until 1948, with the
75hp model being made until 1950.*

1960 Rover 80 4 Door Saloon,
4 cylinders, 2286cc, overhead
inlet side exhaust engine, 4 speed
gearbox, manual overdrive,
leather upholstery, polished wood
interior, fair condition
throughout, requires restoration.
£900-1,100 *S*

1961 Rover 110, body renovated,
requires respraying, sound
condition. **£2,000-2,500** *Cum*

1961 Rover 80 Saloon, good
original condition.
£700-900 *ALC*

*One of the last coachbuilt Rovers,
this model was fitted with an
aluminium bonnet, doors and
boot lid.*

1966 Rover Mk III Coupé,
6 cylinders, 2995cc, needs slight
attention, otherwise good
condition. **Est. £4,500-5,500** *ADT*

1969 Rover P5 Coupé,
8 cylinders, 3531cc, reconditioned
automatic gearbox, very good
condition. **£3,500-3,800** *ADT*

1973 Rover 3 litre Saloon,
8 cylinders, 3528cc, good original
condition. **Est. £3,000-4,000** *ADT*

**1972 Rover 3500S 4 Door
Saloon**, 3.5 litres, good condition
throughout.
Est. £2,000-3,000 *BKS*

1973 Rover 3500 P6, automatic gearbox, full history, excellent condition. **£1,750-2,250** *Mot*

1974 Rover 2200 SC Sports Saloon, manual gearbox, good original condition. **£1,200-1,500** *S*

1974 Rover P6, 8 cylinders, 3528cc, automatic gearbox, bodywork in excellent condition. **Est. £2,300-2,800** *ADT*

1976 Rover 2200 SC Saloon, carefully maintained original car, very good condition. **£1,200-1,500** *S*

1975 Rover 2200 SC, automatic gearbox, good condition. **Est. £1,500-2,000** *ECC*

ROVER Model	ENGINE cc/cyl	DATES	CONDITION 1	2	3
P2 10	1389/4	1946-47	£2,900	£2,000	£500
P2 12	1496/4	1946-47	£3,200	£2,300	£600
P2 12 Tour	1496/4	1947	£6,500	£3,000	£1,000
P2 14/16	1901/6	1946-47	£4,000	£2,800	£700
P2 14/16 Sal	1901/6	1946-47	£3,700	£2,500	£700
P3 60	1595/4	1948-49	£2,900	£2,000	£500
P3 75	2103/6	1948-49	£3,800	£2,700	£600
P4 75	2103/6	1950-51	£2,800	£1,000	-
P4 75	2103/6	1952-64	£2,500	£900	-
P4 60	1997/4	1954-59	£2,300	£750	-
P4 90	2638/6	1954-59	£2,900	£1,100	-
P4 75	2230/6	1955-59	£2,500	£900	-
P4 105R	2638/6	1957-58	£3,000	£1,600	-
P4 105S	2638/6	1957-59	£3,000	£1,600	£250
P4 80	2286/4	1960-62	£2,500	£900	-
P4 95	2625/6	1963-64	£2,800	£1,600	-
P4 100	2625/6	1960-62	£3,200	£1,500	-
P4 110	2625/6	1963-64	£3,250	£1,600	-
P5 3 litre	2995/6	1959-67	£3,500	£2,000	£550
P5 3 litre Coupé	2995/6	1959-67	£5,000	£3,500	£750
P5B (V8)	3528/8	1967-74	£6,000	£4,000	£900
P5B (V8) Coupé	3528/8	1967-73	£6,000	£4,250	£1,250
P6 2000 SC Series 1	1980/4	1963-65	£2,200	£800	-
P6 2000 SC Series 1	1980/4	1966-70	£2,000	£800	-
2000 SC Auto Series 1	1980/4	1966-70	£1,500	£600	-
P6 2000 TC Series 1	1980/4	1966-70	£2,000	£900	-
P6 2000 SC Series 2	1980/4	1970-73	£2,000	£900	-
P6 2000 SC Auto Series 2	1980/4	1970-73	£1,500	£800	-
P6 2000 TC Series 2	1980/4	1970-73	£1,750	£900	-
P6 3500 Series 1	3500/8	1968-70	£2,500	£1,400	-
P6 2200 SC	2200/4	1974-77	£1,750	£850	-
P6 2200 SC Auto	2200/4	1974-77	£2,250	£900	-
P6 2200 TC	2200/4	1974-77	£2,000	£950	-
P6 3500 Series 2	3500/8	1971-77	£2,800	£1,700	-
P6 3500 S Series 2	3500/8	1971-77	£2,000	£1,500	-

SAAB

Saab stands for Svenska Aeroplan Aktiebolagel, the Swedish Aeroplane Company. They started to produce motor vehicles in 1947 and subsequently produced some of the worlds' foremost rally cars.

1978 Saab 96 V4 Souvenir Model, 4 cylinders, 1498cc, with certificate of registration and dashboard plaque, 376 recorded miles. **£7,800-8,200** *ADT*

SAAB Model	ENGINE cc/cyl	DATES	CONDITION 1	2	3
92	764/2	1950-53	£2,000	£1,000	£500
92B	764/2	1953-55	£2,000	£1,000	£500
93-93B	748/3	1956-60	£2,000	£1,000	£500
95	841/3	1960-68	£2,000	£1,000	£500
96	841/3	1960-68	£2,000	£500	-
96 Sport	841/3	1962-66	£2,000	£500	-
Sonnett II	1698/4	1967-74	£1,500	£500	-
95/96	1498/4	1966-80	£1,500	£500	-
99	1709/4	1968-71	£1,500	£1,000	-
99	1854/4	1970-74	£1,500	£1,000	-
99	1985/4	1972-83	£3,000	£1,000	£500
99 Turbo	1985/4	1978-83	£3,000	£1,000	£500

SIATA

1951 Siata 300BC Spyder, 4 cylinder in line engine, 1100cc, 4 speed manual gearbox, hydraulic drum brakes all-round, independent coil springs front and rear, left hand drive, aluminium bodywork, wire wheels, complete frame-up restoration.
Est. £27,000-30,000 *CNY*

The 300BC Spyder represents a model with the same basic attributes as the 208S, but with a 4 cylinder engine. There were only 21,300 BC Spyders exported to the US, most of which were very successful racers in the H-modified class.

SIDDELEY

1933 Siddeley Special Cabriolet, 5 litre straight 6 engine, 4 speed large Wilson pre-selector gearbox, restored over 5 years, excellent condition.
Est. £28,000-35,000 *S*

A total of 253 cars were built from 1933 to 1937, and 17 different coachbuilders produced a wide variety of body styles for these chassis.

SIMCA

1938 Simca Gordini Voiturette. **£30,000-45,000** *FHF*

1952 Siata 208S Spyder, V8 engine, 1100cc, 110bhp at 6000rpm, 4 speed manual gearbox, hydraulic drum brakes all-round, independent coil springs front and rear, left hand drive.
£29,500-32,500 *CNY*

The Siata company was founded in 1926 with the name Societa Italiana Auto Transformazione Accessori.

CROSS REFERENCE
Racing Cars ⟶ p301

SINGER

Singer made bicycles in Coventry, and like so many other motor manufacturers, progressed into motorcycles, and then automobiles in 1905. By the mid-1920s, Singer was the UKs third largest producer of automobiles after Morris and Austin.

Singer was acquired by the Rootes Group in 1956 and the name was used on top-of-the-range Hillman products. Chrysler acquired the Rootes Group in the mid-60s, and the Singer name passed into history.

1929 Singer 9 Junior, very good condition. **£5,250-5,750** *CC*

1934 Singer 9 4 Seater Saloon, 972cc, original leather seats, sunroof, picnic/luggage rack. **£3,500-4,000** *Bro*

1946 Singer 9 Tourer, 4 cylinders, 1074cc, dry stored, requires restoration. **£3,400-3,800** *ADT*

1951 Singer 9 Roadster, with Morris 1100cc engine, 48bhp, gearbox overhauled, repainted, good condition. **£4,800-5,200** *C*

1965 Singer Gazelle Mk V 4 Door Saloon, 1.6 litre engine, very good overall condition. **£2,400-2,800** *BKS*

The Gazelle was essentially a de luxe version of the Hillman Minx with a Singer grille. First launched in 1955 as a 1.5 litre overhead camshaft model, it utilised the 1.6 overhead valve engine in 1961 which it retained until 1965, when the Mk V was superceded.

1963 Singer Vogue Saloon, 1592cc, resprayed to a high standard, excellent condition. **£1,800-1,850** *ALC*

SINGER Model	ENGINE cc/cyl	DATES	CONDITION 1	2	3
10	1097/4	1918-24	£4,000	£2,000	£1,000
15	1991/6	1922-25	£6,000	£3,000	£1,500
14/34	1776/6	1926-27	£7,000	£4,000	£2,000
Junior	848/4	1927-32	£6,000	£3,000	£1,500
Senior	1571/4	1928-29	£7,000	£4,000	£2,000
Super 6	1776/6	1928-31	£7,000	£4,000	£2,000
9 Le Mans	972/4	1932-37	£12,000	£8,000	£5,000
Twelve	1476/6	1932-34	£10,000	£7,000	£6,000
1.5 litre	1493/6	1934-36	£3,000	£2,000	£1,000
2 litre	1991/6	1934-37	£4,000	£2,750	£1,000
11	1459/4	1935-36	£3,000	£2,000	£1,000
12	1525/4	1937-39	£3,000	£2,000	£1,000

SS

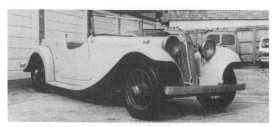

1932 SSI 4 Seater Tourer, 6 cylinder side valve engine, 2045cc, 53bhp at 4000rpm, 4 speed manual gearbox, 4 wheel drum brakes, leaf springs front and rear suspension, right hand drive, converted from an SSI coupé, chassis and engine are correct, new ash frame, bodywork in excellent condition, wire wheels, restoration incomplete. **£10,500-14,500** *C*

CROSS REFERENCE
Jaguar ──────→ p137

1934 SSI 2.1 litre Saloon, coachwork by Swallow Coachbuilding, 6 cylinders, 2154cc, 16hp, original leather trim. **£28,000-30,000** *BKS*

STANDARD

Founded by R. W. Maudsley in 1903, the Standard Motor Company was producing 6 cylinder motor cars as early as 1906. The Standard Nine was one of the best selling pre-war British cars. In 1945 Standard acquired Triumph and used the engine from the popular Standard Vanguard in the TR2 sports car. Standard Triumph was taken over by Leyland in 1961 and the Standard name soon disappeared.

1926 Standard Model V4 14hp 4 Door All Weather Tourer, original trim, steel artillery wheels, in the process of restoration, but no progress made for many years. **£5,000-5,500** *S*

CROSS REFERENCE
Restoration Projects ──────→ p305

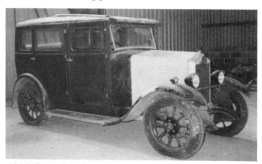

1929 Standard Teignmouth 9hp Fabric Saloon, original upholstery, instruments and all major engine ancillaries, mostly complete, found in a barn, suitable for restoration. **Est. £3,000-4,000** *S*

1931 Standard Big 9 4 Door Saloon, original slightly worn upholstery, good condition. **Est. £3,500-4,500** *S*

STANDARD Model	ENGINE cc/cyl	DATES	CONDITION 1	2	3
SLS	1328/4	1919-20	£5,000	£4,000	£1,000
VI	1307/4	1922	£5,000	£4,000	£1,000
SLO/V4	1944/4	1922-28	£5,000	£4,000	£1,000
6V	2230/6	1928	£10,000	£8,000	£5,000
V3	1307/4	1923-26	£4,000	£3,000	£1,000
Little 9	1006/4	1932-33	£4,000	£2,000	£1,000
9	1155/4	1928-29	£4,000	£3,000	£1,000
Big 9	1287/4	1932-33	£4,500	£3,250	£2,000
15	1930/6	1929-30	£6,000	£4,000	£2,000
12	1337/6	1933-34	£4,000	£3,000	£1,500
10hp	1343/4	1933-37	£4,000	£2,500	£1,000
9	1052/4	1934-36	£4,000	£2,500	£1,000
Flying 9	1131/4	1937-39	£3,000	£1,800	£750
Flying 10	1267/4	1937-39	£3,250	£2,000	£750
Flying 14	1176/4	1937-48	£4,000	£2,000	£1,000
Flying 8	1021/4	1939-48	£3,000	£1,800	£750

1936 Standard 10hp 4 Door Saloon, wooden door cappings, sunroof, very good condition.
£3,500-3,750 *S*

1947 Standard 8 Drophead Coupé, good overall condition.
£3,250-3,750 *CC*

STANDARD Model	ENGINE cc/cyl	DATES	CONDITION		
			1	2	3
12	1609/4	1945-48	£2,000	£950	£250
12 DHC	1509/4	1945-48	£3,200	£2,000	£500
14	1776/4	1945-48	£2,100	£950	£250
Vanguard I/II	2088/4	1948-55	£1,800	£750	£150
Vanguard III	2088/4	1955-61	£1,500	£750	£150
Vanguard III Est	2088/4	1955-61	£2,000	£800	£150
Vanguard III Sportsman	2088/4	1955-58	£2,000	£800	£200
Vanguard Six	1998/6	1961-63	£1,500	£700	-
Eight	803/4	1952-59	£1,250	£500	-
Ten	948/4	1955-59	£1,400	£800	-
Ensign I/II	1670/4	1957-63	£1,000	£800	-
Ensign I/II Est	1670/4	1962-63	£1,000	£850	-
Pennant Companion	948/4	1955-61	£1,800	£850	£300
Pennant	948/4	1955-59	£1,650	£825	£250

1948 Standard 12hp Drophead Coupé, 4 cylinders, 1609cc, original interior trim, good condition.
£6,250-6,500 *ADT*

STANLEY

1918 Stanley Steamer 7 Passenger Tourer.
£22,000-25,000 *FHF*

One of the most powerful steamers, first to have battery start-up.

STAR

The Star Motor Company was one of the longest-lived British car makers. Production commenced in 1898 and continued until 1932, during which time they produced several successful commercial vehicles, along with army lorries and private cars.

1931 Star Little Comet 14.9hp 4 Door Coupé, 4 speed manual gearbox, 110in wheelbase, paintwork needs attention, sound condition, dry stored for some years. **£4,200-4,600** *S*

STUTZ

1928 Stutz Straight 8 BB Sedan, wire wheels, ground-up restoration to an excellent standard.
Est. £20,000-25,000 *Cen*

SUNBEAM

Sunbeam cars were first made by John Marston Ltd., at Wolverhampton in 1899. Their series of competition cars included Great Britain's first ever Grand Prix victory.

Sunbeam merged with Talbot and Darracq to form STD Motors Ltd., but the association did not work well and broke up in 1935. Sunbeam later became part of the Rootes Group, which was acquired by Chrysler, and the name disappeared by 1974.

1910 Sunbeam 12/16hp 5 Seater Tourer, mechanical rebuild, restoration needed to paintwork and upholstery. **£14,500-16,500** *S*

1922 Sunbeam 24/60 5 Seater Sports Tourer, completely rebuilt to Concours standard, replica body to original specification, excellent condition throughout. **£26,500-28,000** *S*

This car, which spent 40 years in dry storage, is complete but unrestored.

1927 Sunbeam 16.9hp Tourer, fully restored, engine rebuilt, repainted, new livery. **£17,000-17,500** *HOLL*

1931 Sunbeam 16 2 Door Coupé, new gearbox bearings, original upholstery, older respray, engine in working order. **£7,000-7,500** *S*

The Series M 16 cars (Treasury rating 18.2hp) featured Lockheed hydraulic braking, central chassis lubrication and Rotax lighting. This 2 door coupé has an opening windscreen, exterior sun visor and a side mounted spare wheel.

1929 Sunbeam 16.9hp 2 Seater Drophead Coupé, probably cut down from a closed car, running condition. **£3,200-3,600** *S*

1953 Sunbeam Alpine Special, 4 cylinders, 2267cc, completely restored. **£11,000-12,000** *ADT*

SUNBEAM Model	ENGINE cc/cyl	DATES	CONDITION		
			1	2	3
12/16	2412/4	1909-11	£20,000	£14,000	£9,500
16/20	4070/4	1912-15	£32,000	£22,000	£15,000
24	4524/6	1919-22	£28,000	£18,000	£10,000
3 litre	2916/6	1925-30	£48,000	£30,000	£20,000
16	2040/6	1927-30	£16,000	£12,500	£10,000
20	2916/6	1927-30	£22,000	£15,000	£10,500
Speed 20	2916/6	1932-35	£15,000	£10,000	£8,000
Dawn	1627/4	1934-35	£8,000	£5,000	£3,500
25	3317/6	1934	£10,000	£8,000	£4,000

Prices can vary depending on replica bodies, provenance, coachbuilder, drophead, etc.

**1947 Sunbeam-Talbot 10
4 Seater 2 Door Open Tourer,**
original upholstery, paintwork
fair, generally good condition.
£6,000-6,500 *S*

**1953 Sunbeam Alpine 2.3 litre
2 Seater Roadster,** sound
chassis, fair condition.
Est. £6,500-8,000 *BKS*

**1954 Sunbeam Talbot 90
Saloon ,** 4 cylinders, 2267cc,
original sunroof, very good
overall condition.
£2,800-3,400 *ADT*

**1954 Sunbeam Talbot Mk III
Saloon.**
£1,800-2,200 *DB*

1956 Sunbeam-Talbot Mk III,
4 cylinders, 2267cc, refurbished
gearbox with overdrive, very good
showroom condition.
£2,200-2,600 *ADT*

**1954 Sunbeam Alpine 2 Seater
Roadster,** 4 cylinders, 2267cc,
full body-off rebuild, very good
condition. **Est. £6,500-7,500** *ADT*

**1963 Sunbeam Alpine Series
III,** 4 cylinders, 1725cc, chrome
wire wheels, very good condition.
Est. £3,000-4,000 *ADT*

**1966 Sunbeam Tiger Sports
2 Seater,** V8 engine, 5 litres,
chassis-up rebuild.
Est. £12,000-13,000 *S*

*The engine has been rebuilt to
5 litre specification with matching
induction and exhaust manifolds,
and an extractor system with 2in
stainless steel pipes.*

1966 Sunbeam Alpine 1725cc Convertible,
left hand drive, upholstery retrimmed, good
condition throughout. **Est. £5,000-5,500** *S*

1967 Sunbeam Alpine Series V,
left hand drive, rebuilt
mechanically, new interior trim,
totally rust-free, Californian
import. **£4,800-5,200** *CCTC*

1967 Sunbeam Alpine Roadster,
1725cc, new chrome bolt-on wire
wheels, otherwise original, very
good condition.
Est. £3,500-5,000 *ALC*

1975 Sunbeam Rapier,
4 cylinders, 1725cc, manual
gearbox with overdrive on 3rd
and 4th gears, resprayed, good
overall condition.
Est. £1,500-2,000 *ADT*

1967 Sunbeam Alpine GT Mk V, 1.8 litres, Laycock
overdrive option, low mileage, very well preserved.
£6,750-7,250 *BKS*

1967 Sunbeam Tiger Mk II,
right hand drive, good condition.
£9,000-11,000 *CGOC*

SUNBEAM-TALBOT/ SUNBEAM Model	ENGINE cc/cyl	DATES	CONDITION		
			1	2	3
Talbot 80	1185/4	1948-50	£4,000	£2,250	£750
Talbot 80 DHC	1185/4	1948-50	£6,000	£4,500	£2,000
Talbot 90 Mk I	1944/4	1949-50	£4,000	£2,100	£750
Talbot 90 Mk I DHC	1944/4	1949-50	£7,000	£4,750	£2,000
Talbot 90 II/IIa/III	2267/4	1950-56	£5,000	£3,000	£1,500
Talbot 90 II/IIa/III DHC	2267/4	1950-56	£6,000	£4,500	£2,250
Talbot Alpine I/III	2267/4	1953-55	£9,000	£7,500	£3,750
Talbot Ten	1197/4	1946-48	£3,500	£2,000	£750
Talbot Ten Tourer	1197/4	1946-48	£7,000	£4,000	£2,000
Talbot Ten DHC	1197/4	1946-48	£6,500	£4,000	£2,000
Talbot 2 litre	1997/4	1946-48	£4,000	£2,500	£1,000
Talbot 2 litre Tourer	1997/4	1946-48	£7,500	£4,000	£2,250
Rapier I	1392/4	1955-57	£1,200	£700	£300
Rapier II	1494/4	1957-59	£1,800	£900	£300
Rapier II Conv	1494/4	1957-59	£3,000	£1,500	£450
Rapier III	1494/4	1959-61	£2,000	£1,200	£400
Rapier III Conv	1494/4	1959-61	£3,500	£1,600	£600
Rapier IIIA	1592/4	1961-63	£2,000	£1,200	£400
Rapier IIIA Conv	1592/4	1961-63	£3,600	£1,700	£650
Rapier IV/V	1592/ 1725/4	1963-67	£2,000	£700	£250
Alpine I-II	1494/4	1959-62	£6,000	£3,500	£1,800
Alpine III	1592/4	1963	£6,500	£4,000	£1,250
Alpine IV	1592/4	1964	£6,500	£4,000	£1,250
Alpine V	1725/4	1965-68	£7,000	£4,000	£1,250
Harrington Alpine	1592/4	1961	£8,000	£4,750	-
Harrington Le Mans	1592/4	1962-63	£10,000	£6,500	-
Tiger Mk 1	4261/8	1964-67	£12,000	£9,000	£5,000
Tiger Mk 2	4700/8	1967	£9,000	£7,500	£5,000
Rapier Fastback	1725/4	1967-76	£1,100	£700	£250
Rapier H120	1725/4	1968-76	£1,500	£800	£300

TALBOT

1932 Talbot 75 Close-Coupled Sportsman's Saloon, excellent all-round condition.
£15,000-20,000 *BC*

1933 Talbot 65 4 Door Fixed Head Coupé, 6 cylinder overhead valve engine, 1700cc, pre-selector gearbox, good restored condition.
£11,500-12,000 *Mot*

1934 Talbot AV 105, with replica Brooklands Team Car coachwork, rebuilt engine, aero-screens, tonneau, headlamp stone guards, knock-off wire wheels. **Est. £30,000-35,000** *S*

This 1934 car was rebodied in the 1970s, modelled on the team cars owned and restored by the late Anthony Blight.

1936 Talbot Airline Coupé, 4 cylinder, 1185cc engine, restored 3 years ago, very good condition overall. **£4,400-4,800** *ADT*

CROSS REFERENCE
Sunbeam Talbot ⟶ p254

1935 Clement Talbot 65 Sports Saloon, sound bodywork and chassis, original upholstery, good condition.
£5,500-6,500 *C*

TALBOT Model	ENGINE cc/cyl	DATES	CONDITION 1	2	3
25hp and 25/50	4155/4	1907-16	£35,000	£25,000	£15,000
12hp	2409/4	1909-15	£25,000	£15,000	£9,000
8/18	960/4	1922-25	£8,000	£5,000	£2,000
14/45	1666/6	1926-35	£16,000	£10,000	£5,000
75	2276/6	1930-37	£22,000	£12,000	£7,000
105	2969/6	1935-37	£28,000	£20,000	£15,000

Higher value for tourers and coachbuilt cars.

TALBOT-LAGO

c1951 Talbot-Lago T26 Chassis, 4 wire wheels, drum brakes, fuel tank, Wilson pre-selector gearbox, rear axle, front suspension, steering arm and wheel.
£1,800-2,000 *C*

CROSS REFERENCE
Restoration Projects ⟶ p305

1948 Talbot-Lago Grand Sport Vanden Plas Body, originally fitted on a Lago Grand Sport Chassis, in need of restoration, retains a Liège-Rome-Liège sticker on the windscreen.
£3,200-3,500 *C*

TATRA

The Tatra company based in Koprivnice, Czechoslovakia, has been manufacturing automobiles since 1897. Not widely recognised in the West, they paved the way for rear mounted engines and V8 air-cooled systems.

A car with a body style that continued until 1975. The type T603, produced from 1964 until 1975, was the last passenger model to be produced and the later cars were fitted with V8, 2.5 litre, 98bhp engines, disc brakes all-round and 4 speed column gearchange.

1932 Tatra 57 Cabrio, opposed 4 cylinder engine, air-cooled engine, central tubular frame, swing axles, fully restored.
Est. £5,000-6,000 *ALC*

1972 Tatra T2-603 6 Seater Sports Saloon, 2.9 litre air-cooled overhead camshaft engine, good condition.
Est. £3,000-4,000 *S*

THORNEYCROFT

The Thorneycroft Steam Wagon Company of Chiswick and Basingstoke entered the world of motor car production in 1903. In 1948 they built some of the largest trucks including the Mighty Antar. AEC took control of the company in 1961 which was again taken over in 1969 by the American-owned Eaton Company.

Miller's is a price Guide not a price List
The price ranges given reflect the average price a purchaser should pay for a similar vehicle. Condition, rarity, provenance, racing history, originality and any restoration are factors that must be taken into account when assessing values. When buying or selling, it must always be remembered that prices can be greatly affected by the condition of any vehicle. Unless otherwise stated, all cars shown in Miller's are of good merchantable quality, and the valuations given reflect this fact. Vehicles offered for sale in exceptionally fine condition or in poor condition may reasonably be expected to be priced considerably higher or lower respectively than the estimates given herein.

1903 Thorneycroft 10hp 2 Seater, self contained acetylene brass lamps and oil sidelamps, dated by The Veteran Car Club.
Est. £30,000-35,000 *S*

The present 2 seater coachwork may not be original.

1967 Toyota S800 Targa Sports 2 Seater Coupé, probably the only example in the UK, in good condition throughout.
Est. £4,000-4,500 *S*

Japanese cars of the 1960s were not imported into the UK in very large numbers, and therefore few have survived.

TOYOTA

TRIUMPH

Triumph produced bicycles and more famously motorcycles. Surprisingly they did not make their first motor car until 1923.

Sir John Black's Standard Motors acquired Triumph at the end of WWII and set about producing a range of affordable saloons and competitive sports cars, the TR range being the most popular. Standard Triumph eventually became part of the BL Group and although the Triumph name was used for the Acclaim, made in assocation with Honda, the Triumph marque disappeared by 1984.

1929 Triumph Super 7, designed by Gordon England, 4 cylinders, 858cc, excellent order throughout. **£3,300-3,800** *ADT*

The vehicles were supplied in 3 formats, a basic saloon, tourer and the top of the range model, the Fabric Saloon.

1936 Triumph Vitesse 6 Light Saloon, factory body, external boot, good all-round condition. **Est. £4,000-5,000** *S*

1934 Triumph Gloria Southern Cross 4 Seater Tourer, needs restoring. **£13,500-14,500** *FHF*

TRIUMPH Model	ENGINE cc/cyl	DATES	CONDITION		
			1	2	3
TLC	1393/4	1923-25	£6,000	£4,000	£1,500
TPC	2169/4	1926-30	£6,000	£4,000	£2,000
K	832/4	1928-34	£4,000	£2,000	£1,000
S	1203/6	1931-33	£5,000	£3,000	£1,500
G12 Gloria	1232/4	1935-37	£6,000	£4,000	£2,000
G16 Gloria 6	1991/6	1935-39	£7,000	£4,500	£2,000
Vitesse/Dolomite	1767/4	1937-39	£14,000	£10,000	£6,000
Dolomite	1496/4	1938-39	£7,000	£4,000	£2,000

1951 Triumph Mayflower, sound chassis and underbody, original condition throughout. **£3,750-4,250** *Bro*

1949 Triumph 2000 Roadster, 4 cylinders, overhead valve, 68hp at 4200rpm, 3 speed manual fully synchronised gearbox, 4 wheel drum brakes, independent coil spring front suspension, rear semi-elliptic leaf springs, right hand drive, complete engine rebuild and chassis-off restoration, requires new hood, in excellent condition throughout. **Est. £10,000-15,000** *C*

1962 Triumph Courier Car-O-Van, 1.2 litre engine, optional rear folding seats, with photographic record of restoration of this rare car. **£2,200-2,600** *BKS*

1964 Triumph Vitesse Convertible, 6 cylinders, 1998cc, in good condition. **£1,000-1,200** *ADT*

1969 Triumph Vitesse 2 litre Mk II Saloon, engine stripped and rebuilt, gearbox, brakes and suspension overhauled, Webasto sunroof, 22,820 miles from new. **£3,400-3,800** *S*

1973 Triumph Toledo 1300, excellent condition. **£1,000-1,200** *Cen*

1980 Triumph Dolomite Sprint, manual gearbox with overdrive, mechanics and interior in good condition, bodywork needs restoration. **£400-600** *LF*

1955 Triumph TR2 Sports 2.1 litre 2 Seater, with replica TR3A fibreglass body. **£3,800-4,200** *BKS*

1955 Triumph TR2 Roadster, body-off restoration to Concours standard, original right hand drive. **£8,800-9,200** *ALC*

1960 Triumph TR3A, 4 cylinders, 1991cc, original engine and gearbox, full body-off rebuild using original outer panels, in very good condition. **£9,000-10,000** *ADT*

1962 Triumph TR3B, 4 cylinders, 2138cc, recently resprayed, very good original condition. **£9,000-10,000** *COYS*

1962 Triumph TR4, 4 cylinders, 2138cc, with overdrive, originally exported to the USA, left hand drive, recently resprayed, in very good condition. **£4,000-4,500** *COYS*

1965 Triumph TR4A Surrey,
engine, suspension, gearbox,
brakes and chassis restored,
good overall condition.
£9,750-10,250 *WES*

1966 Triumph TR4A,
4 cylinders, 2138cc, restored
to a high standard.
£9,000-10,000 *ADT*

1967 Triumph TR4A,
4 cylinders, 2138cc, in
good condition.
£3,900-4,400 *COYS*

1968 Triumph TR250, to USA specification without
fuel injection, left hand drive.
£4,500-5,000 *CCTC*

Wire wheels and overdrive options increase the value.

1971 Triumph TR6, 150bhp,
excellent restored condition.
£7,750-8,250 *Mot*

1972 Triumph TR6, good
overall condition.
£7,000-9,000 *FHF*

**1970 Triumph TR6 2 Seater
Sports Roadster,** with overdrive
on 3 gears, chassis-off restoration.
£8,250-8,750 *S*

1973 Triumph TR6, totally
rebuilt to a very high standard.
Est. £5,000-6,000 *ADT*

*Designed by Karmann of
Germany, the TR6 became the
most numerous of the TR range of
sports cars. Introduced in 1969,
the 2.5 litre petrol injected, 6
cylinder, engine developed
150bhp, coupled with a 4 speed
gearbox and electric overdrive.*

**1973 Triumph TR6 2 Seater
Sports Roadster,** good restored
condition.
£7,250-8,250 *S*

c1969 Triumph Spitfire Mk I,
2.5 litre Triumph straight 6
engine, extensive modification,
fibreglass bonnet, prepared for
club racing.
£500-600 *ADT*

**1973 Triumph GT6 Mk III
Sports Coupé,** requires restoring.
£3,800-4,200 *S*

TRIUMPH Model	ENGINE cc/cyl	DATES	CONDITION 1	2	3
1800/2000 Roadster	1776/ 2088/4	1946-49	£12,000	£7,500	£2,500
1800	1776/4	1946-49	£4,200	£2,000	£950
2000 Renown	2088/4	1949-54	£4,200	£2,000	£950
Mayflower	1247/4	1949-53	£1,700	£750	£350
TR2 long door	1247/4	1953	£10,000	£8,000	£5,000
TR2	1247/4	1953-55	£9,000	£6,000	£5,000
TR3	1991/4	1955-57	£9,000	£8,500	£3,500
TR3A	1991/4	1958-62	£9,500	£8,500	£3,500
TR4	2138/4	1961-65	£9,000	£6,000	£3,000
TR4A	2138/4	1965-67	£10,000	£6,500	£3,000
TR5	2498/6	1967-68	£11,500	£8,500	£4,000
TR6 (PI)	2498/6	1969-74	£10,500	£7,500	£3,500
Herald	948/4	1959-61	£800	£400	£150
Herald FHC	948/4	1959-61	£1,200	£550	£300
Herald DHC	948/4	1960-61	£2,000	£800	£350
Herald 'S'	948/4	1961-64	£800	£400	£150
Herald 1200	1147/4	1961-70	£1,100	£500	£200
Herald 1200 FHC	1147/4	1961-64	£1,400	£800	£300
Herald 1200 DHC	1147/4	1961-67	£2,000	£900	£350
Herald 1200 Est	1147/4	1961-67	£1,300	£700	£300
Herald 12/50	1147/4	1963-67	£1,250	£600	£250
Herald 13/60	1296/4	1967-71	£1,300	£600	£200
Herald 13/60 DHC	1296/4	1967-71	£2,000	£1,200	£400
Herald 13/60 Est	1296/4	1967-71	£1,500	£650	£300
Vitesse 1600	1596/6	1962-66	£2,000	£1,250	£550
Vitesse 1600 Conv	1596/6	1962-66	£2,800	£1,350	£600
Vitesse 2 litre Mk I	1998/6	1966-68	£1,800	£800	£300
Vitesse 2 litre Mk I Conv	1998/6	1966-68	£3,000	£1,500	£650
Vitesse 2 litre Mk II	1998/6	1968-71	£2,000	£1,500	£300
Vitesse 2 litre Mk II Conv	1998/6	1968-71	£4,000	£1,750	£650
Spitfire Mk I	1147/4	1962-64	£2,000	£1,750	£300
Spitfire Mk II	1147/4	1965-67	£2,500	£2,000	£350
Spitfire Mk III	1296/4	1967-70	£3,500	£2,500	£450
Spitfire Mk IV	1296/4	1970-74	£2,500	£2,000	£350
Spitfire 1500	1493/4	1975-78	£3,500	£2,500	£750
Spitfire 1500	1493/4	1979-81	£4,500	£3,000	£1,200
GT6 Mk I	1998/6	1966-68	£6,000	£4,000	£1,200
GT6 Mk II	1998/6	1968-70	£7,000	£4,500	£1,400
GT6 Mk III	1998/6	1970-73	£8,000	£5,000	£1,500
2000 Mk I	1998/6	1963-69	£2,000	£1,200	£400
2000 Mk III	1998/6	1969-77	£2,000	£1,200	£500
2.5 PI	2498/6	1968-75	£2,000	£1,500	£900
2500 TC/S	2498/6	1974-77	£1,750	£700	£150
2500S	2498/6	1975-77	£2,500	£1,000	£150
1300 (FWD)	1296/4	1965-70	£800	£400	£150
1300TC (FWD)	1296/4	1967-70	£900	£450	£150
1500 (FWD)	1493/4	1970-73	£700	£450	£125
1500TC (RWD)	1296/4	1973-76	£850	£500	£100
Toledo	1296/4	1970-76	£850	£450	£100
Dolomite 1500	1493/4	1976-80	£1,350	£750	£125
Dolomite 1850	1854/4	1972-80	£1,450	£850	£150
Dolomite Sprint	1998/4	1976-81	£8,000	£5,500	£1,000
Stag	2997/8	1970-77	£7,000	£4,250	£2,000
TR7	1998/4	1975-82	£3,000	£1,200	£500
TR7 DHC	1998/4	1980-82	£4,500	£3,500	£1,500

1967 Triumph GT6 Coupé,
original factory specification,
wire wheels, good condition.
£4,000-5,000 *S*

**1974 Triumph GT6 2 litre
Mk III Sports Coupé,** wire
wheels, stainless steel twin
sports exhaust, fully restored.
Est. £3,800-4,200 *BKS*

1972 Triumph Stag, 8 cylinders,
2997cc, manual gearbox,
mechanically sound, bare
metal respray.
£4,250-4,500 *ADT*

1974 Triumph Stag Mk II,
V8 engine, 2998cc, excellent
restored condition.
£6,750-7,250 *COYS*

*The Mk II version appeared in
February 1973, distinguished by
black painted sills and tail panel,
twin coachlines and the deletion
of the soft top's rear quarter
windows. Improvements included
a standard fitment hardtop, a
sealed cooling system, higher
compression ratio, and alloy
rather than wire wheels.
Production ended in June 1977.*

1977 Triumph Stag Convertible,
very good original condition.
£4,600-5,200 *ALC*

**1972 Triumph Stag 3 litre
2+2 GT,** manual gearbox, good
original condition.
£5,000-5,500 *S*

1974 Triumph Stag, rebuilt
engine, reconditioned gearbox,
excellent condition.
Est. £5,500-6,500 *ADT*

1975 Triumph Stag, original
engine, automatic gearbox, new
aluminium wheels, good
condition throughout.
£3,300-3,600 *ADT*

1978 Triumph TR7, 4 speed
gearbox, correct tartan trimmed
seating, in remarkably good
condition for an early model.
Est. £2,500-3,500 *ADT*

1980 Triumph TR7 2 Seater Sports Convertible, 2 litres, 5 speed gearbox, full body restoration.
Est. £2,500-3,500 *BKS*

1980 Triumph TR7 2 Seater Sports Convertible, excellent condition throughout.
Est. £3,500-4,500 *S*

1981 Triumph TR8, 8 cylinders, 2500cc, Holly carburettors, fuel injection system removed and retained in boxes, low mileage, very good original condition.
Est. £6,900-7,900 *ADT*

1980 Triumph TR7, very good overall condition.
£2,200-2,400 *CC*

TROJAN

1963 Trojan 200 Bubble Car, 1 cylinder, 200cc, totally stripped and repainted, excellent order throughout.
£2,400-2,600 *ADT*

1964 Trojan Cabin Cruiser, engine and gearbox in good order, good condition throughout.
£1,700-1,900 *ADT*

CROSS REFERENCE	
BMW ──────▶	p81
Heinkel ──────▶	p132
Messerschmitt ──▶	p188

TVR

1964 Trojan Cabin Cruiser, excellent restored condition.
£3,600-4,000 *ADT*

1975 TVR Taimar, stage 3 engine, 1700cc, GRP removable roof, one of only 3 hatchbacks built, total body-off rebuild.
£5,750-6,250 *TVR*

1963 TVR Grantura Mk II.
£14,500-15,500 *FHF*

1975 TVR 3000M, very good
restored condition.
Est. £3,000-3,500 *Cen*

**1980 TVR Taimar SE Wide
Body Hatchback**, 15in split rim
compomotive wheels, Concours
condition throughout.
£13,000-14,000 *TVR*

1980 TVR Taimar, Wolfrace
wheels, as new condition.
£10,250-10,750 *TVR*

TVR Model	ENGINE cc/cyl	DATES	CONDITION 1	2	3
Grantura I	1172/4	1957-62	£4,000	£3,000	£2,000
Grantura II	1558/4	1957-62	£4,300	£3,000	£2,000
Grantura III/1800S	1798/4	1963-67	£5,000	£3,000	£2,200
Vixen S2/3	1599/4	1968-72	£5,000	£3,000	£1,500

VAUXHALL

Vauxhall, under the influence of Laurence
Pomeroy, produced superb touring cars but
were in deep financial trouble by the 1920s.
General Motors took over the company and in
1964 Vauxhall reached its peak production
period producing 247,782 cars.

**1924 Vauxhall OE 30/98
4¼ litre 4 Seater Velox Tourer,**
frame reunited with original body
and both restored, good overall
condition. **£96,000-98,000** *BKS*

**1915 Vauxhall D-Type 25hp
Kingston Tourer,** 4 litre engine,
body recreated around the
original bonnet, scuttle and dash,
mechanical specification believed
original in all respects.
£35,000-37,000 *S*

*The touring version of the Prince
Henry was the D-Type 25hp car
with the same 4 litre engine, a
longer wheelbase and more space
for the family motorist. The
D-Type was well known for
military service in WWI.*

1924 Vauxhall 30/98 OE Type Fast Light Tourer,
4 cylinder, overhead valve engine, 4225cc, 112bhp at
3500rpm, 4 speed and reverse gearbox, 4 wheel
mechanical brakes, foot operated front and
transmission brake, hand operated on rear drums,
semi-elliptic leaf springs suspension and Hartford
dampers, right hand drive, new Velox body using
original blueprints with original bonnet, scuttle
vent and fittings attached. **Est. £60,000-80,000** *C*

1935 Vauxhall 25hp Newmarket,
very good condition throughout.
£7,750-8,250 *CC*

1936 Vauxhall DX Saloon.
£3,800-4,200 *DB*

1931 Vauxhall 80 Tourer,
very rare model.
£18,000-20,000 *FHF*

*Modelled directly on General
Motors' Chevrolet, but with
Vauxhall radiator.*

1947 Vauxhall J 14/4 Door Saloon,
straight 6 overhead valve engine, 1781cc,
synchromesh gearbox, mechanically good,
body and paintwork in need of restoration,
original interior.   **£1,800-1,900** *LF*

VAUXHALL Model	ENGINE cc/cyl	DATES	CONDITION		
			1	2	3
D/OD	3969/4	1914-26	£35,000	£30,000	£25,000
E/OE	4224/4	1919-28	£40,000	£33,000	£25,000
Eighty	3317/6	1931-33	£10,000	£8,000	£5,000
Cadet	2048/6	1931-33	£7,000	£5,000	£3,000
Lt Six	1531/6	1934-38	£5,000	£4,000	£1,500
14	1781/6	1934-39	£4,000	£3,000	£1,500
25	3215/6	1937-39	£5,000	£4,000	£1,500
10	1203/4	1938-39	£4,000	£3,000	£1,500
Wyvern LIX	1500/4	1948-51	£3,000	£1,000	£500
Velox LIP	2200/6	1948-51	£3,000	£1,000	£500
Wyvern EIX	1500/4	1951-57	£3,000	£1,320	£400
Velox EIPV	2200/6	1951-57	£3,000	£1,650	£400
Cresta EIPC	2200/6	1954-57	£3,000	£1,650	£400
Velox/Cresta PAS/PAD	2262/6	1957-59	£2,850	£1,300	£300
Velox/Cresta PASY/PADY	2262/6	1959-60	£2,700	£1,500	£300
Velox/Cresta PASX/PADX	2651/6	1960-62	£2,700	£1,300	£300
Velox/Cresta PASX/PADX Est	2651/6	1960-62	£2,700	£1,300	£300
Velox/Cresta PB	2651/6	1962-65	£1,600	£800	£100
Velox/Cresta PB Est	2651/6	1962-65	£1,600	£800	£100
Cresta/Deluxe PC	3294/6	1964-72	£1,500	£800	£100
Cresta PC Est	3294/6	1964-72	£1,500	£800	£100
Viscount	3294/6	1964-72	£1,700	£900	£100
Victor I/II	1507/4	1957-61	£2,000	£1,000	£250
Victor I/II Est	1507/4	1957-61	£2,100	£1,100	£300
Victor FB	1507/4	1961-64	£1,500	£900	£200
Victor FB Est	1507/4	1961-64	£1,600	£1,000	£300
VX4/90	1507/4	1961-64	£2,000	£900	£150
Victor FC101	1594/4	1964-67	£1,600	£900	£150
Victor FC101 Est	1594/4	1964-67	£1,800	£1,000	£200
101 VX4/90	1594/4	1964-67	£2,000	£1,500	£250
VX4/90	1975/4	1969-71	£700	£600	-
Ventora I/II	3294/6	1968-71	£500	£375	-
Viva HA	1057/4	1963-66	£500	£350	-
Viva SL90	1159/4	1966-70	£500	£350	-
Viva Brabham	1159/4	1967-70	£1,200	£500	-
Viva	1600/4	1968-70	£500	£350	-
Viva Est	1159/4	1967-70	£500	£400	-

1958 Vauxhall Victor F Series Estate, 1.5 litre engine, restored to high standard, winner of several car of show awards.
£6,000-6,500 *BKS*

Only 6 Series I Victor estates are known to exist worldwide out of a total production run of 10,000 cars.

1972 Vauxhall Victor SL Saloon, 4 cylinders, 2279cc, automatic gearbox, paintwork in excellent condition.
£1,900-2,100 *ADT*

VELIE

VOLKSWAGEN

1912 Velie 40hp Raceabout, very good condition.
£35,000-55,000 *FHF*

1967 Volkswagen Beetle, 4 cylinders, 1192cc, with painted bonnet, roof and rear stripe.
£2,750-3,000 *ADT*

1969 Volkswagen Beetle 1300, resprayed, very good condition.
Est. £1,000-1,200 *Cen*

1969 Volkswagen Karmann Ghia Coupé, right hand drive, lowered suspension, Porsche wheels, excellent condition throughout.
£5,000-5,500 *CCTC*

1971 Volkswagen Karmann Ghia Convertible, 1584cc, semi-automatic gearbox, original specification, very good condition throughout.
£14,000-16,000 *S*

1969 Volkswagen Karmann Ghia Sports Coupé, reasonable condition throughout.
Est. £5,500-6,000 *S*

VOLKSWAGEN Model	ENGINE cc/cyl	DATES	CONDITION 1	2	3
Beetle (split rear screen)	1131/4	1945-53	£5,500	£3,500	£2,000
Beetle (oval rear screen)	1192/4	1953-57	£4,000	£2,000	£1,000
Beetle (slope headlamps)	1192/4	1957-68	£2,500	£1,000	£600
Beetle DHC	1192/4	1954-60	£7,000	£4,500	£2,000
Beetle 1500	1493/4	1966-70	£3,000	£2,000	£1,000
Beetle 1302 LS	1600/4	1970-72	£2,500	£1,850	£850
Beetle 1303 S	1600/4	1972-79	£3,000	£2,000	£1,500
1500 Variant/1600	1493/ 1584/4	1961-73	£2,000	£1,500	£650
1500/1600	1493/ 1584/4	1961-73	£3,000	£2,000	£800
Karmann Ghia/I	1192/4	1955-59	£4,000	£3,000	£1,000
Karmann Ghia/I DHC	1192/4	1957-59	£8,000	£5,000	£2,500
Karmann Ghia/I	1192/4	1960-74	£4,000	£3,000	£1,800
Karmann Ghia/I DHC	1192/4	1960-74	£6,000	£4,500	£2,000
Karmann Ghia/3	1493/4	1962-69	£3,000	£2,500	£1,250

1975 Volkswagen 1303LS Karmann Convertible,
4 cylinders, 1584cc, left hand drive, good condition.
£5,000-5,500 *ADT*

1971 Volkswagen Karmann Ghia Sports Coupé, 1600cc, bare metal respray, very good restored condition.
£6,000-6,500 *S*

1973 Volkswagen SSP2 Sports Coupé, thorough restoration.
Est. £9,000-11,000 *S*

Designed and built in Brazil, this SP2 sports coupé utilises conventional running gear from Volkswagen, including a flat 4, 1678cc, rear mounted, air-cooled engine, pressed steel chassis, 4 speed gearbox, dual circuit braking and steel bodywork. Less than 100 models are thought to have been built.

Miller's is a price GUIDE not a price LIST.

1972 Volkswagen Variant 1600E, automatic gearbox, fuel injection, right hand drive, 17,000 miles, one owner from new, all original,
Est. £4,000-4,500 *PC*

VOLVO

1964 Volvo PV544, 4 cylinders, 1798cc, low mileage, excellent original condition.
£5,250-5,500 *ADT*

1961 Volvo P122S Saloon,
4 cylinders, low mileage, good original condition.
£3,200-3,500 *ADT*

The P120 series, introduced in 1956, was the forerunner of quality family motoring for the Volvo company.

VOLVO Model	ENGINE cc/cyl	DATES	CONDITION		
			1	2	3
PV444	1800/4	1958-67	£4,000	£1,750	£800
PV544	1800/4	1962-64	£4,000	£1,750	£800
120 (B16)	1583/4	1956-59	£3,000	£1,000	£300
121	1708/4	1960-67	£3,500	£1,500	£350
122S	1780/4	1960-67	£4,500	£1,500	£250
131	1780/4	1962-69	£4,000	£1,500	£350
221/222	1780/4	1962-69	£2,500	£1,500	£300
123Gt	1986/4	1967-69	£3,000	£2,500	£750
P1800	1986/4	1960-70	£3,500	£2,000	£1,000
P1800E	1986/4	1970-71	£4,000	£2,500	£1,000
P1800ES	1986/4	1971-73	£5,000	£3,000	£1,000

1968 Volvo 122S 2 Door Saloon, slight paintwork damage and rust.
Est. £1,500-2,000 *S*

1972 Volvo 1800ES, 4 cylinders, 1986cc, generally good condition.
£2,800-3,200 *ADT*

1970 Volvo 144 Saloon, 4 cylinders, 1986cc, glass sunroof, tow bar, 26,000 miles, very good original condition. **£2,800-3,200** *ADT*

1980 Volvo 240GL Saloon.
£3,000-3,300 *DaD*

1963 Volvo P1800, 4 cylinders, 1780cc, engine reconditioned and rebuilt, good condition.
Est. £4,500-5,500 *ADT*

This 1963 car was one of the Jensen bodied models, referred to as the P1800, after which production moved to Sweden, and became the 1800S.

WANDERER

Wanderer-Werke AG of Siegmar (originally Schonau), started as bicycle makers. They began building experimental cars in 1904, and launched into production in 1911. During the 1930s, in addition to 4 cylinder models, the company also built a range of Porsche-designed 6 cylinder models with pushrod operated overhead valve engines.

1937 Wanderer W25 Cabriolet, single Solex carburettor, Bosch coil ignition, wire spoked wheels, rear-mounted spare wheel, left hand drive, unused since restoration. **Est. £40,000-50,000** *S*

The cabriolet version of the W25 Wanderer carried coachwork by Glaser and an un-supercharged, 6 cylinder, 1950cc, Porsche designed, overhead valve pushrod engine.

1938 Wanderer W25K 2 Seater Supercharged Sports, excellent condition, with photographic record of restoration. **Est. £80,000-100,000** *S*

WHITE

The White Manufacturing Co., was set up in 1866 to produce sewing machines. Later a subsidiary company, The Cleveland Automatic Machine Co., was established to develop cars. Their first steam car, designed by Rollin H. White, went into production in 1900. By 1906 the motor business, which now included truck production, became a separate company, the White Co., located in Ohio.

1902 White Steamer 6hp Stanhope with postilion seat, engine rebuilt, new flash boiler fitted, wheels rebuilt, new tyres, only 2 owners from new.
£9,700-10,500 *S*

Believed to be the oldest White Steamer surviving in the UK, having a VCC dating certificate. It has been converted to run on propane gas, however, all the original fittings are available to convert back to petrol.

1911 White Model GA 30hp Torpedo Tourer, 4 cylinder side valve engine, 3685cc, 4 speed manual gearbox, rear wheel drum brakes, semi-elliptic leaf spring front suspension, three-quarter elliptic rear, full set of brass lamps, acetylene tank, Stepney spare wheel, wood spoked wheels, folding brass windscreen, right hand drive.
£18,000-19,000 *C*

Locate the source
The source of each illustration in Miller's can be found by checking the code letters below each caption with the list of contributors.

WILLYS

John North Willys was a successful motor dealer of which Overland was one of his agencies. When Overland ran into financial difficulties Willys stepped in to offer financial advice and found himself leading the company. In 1909 the company was moved to Toledo, Ohio and the name changed to Willys-Overland Co. Most of the cars produced then were the conventional 4 cylinder, 25-40hp models. By 1911 Willys was the third largest automobile manufacturer in the USA.

Willys continued expanding his empire by acquiring the majority of stocks in the Garford company in 1912 and purchasing the Gramm Motor Truck Co. of Lima, Ohio in 1913 and Edwards Motor Co. in 1914.

1927 Willys-Knight Model 70A Roadster, engine running well, fair condition, left hand drive.
£5,400-5,600 *C*

CROSS REFERENCE
Military Vehicles ➝ p292

1927 Willys-Overland Roadster, 4 cylinder sleeve valve engine.
£9,000-11,000 *FHF*

1929 Willys Whippet, 4 cylinders, 2387cc, right hand drive, good condition.
£8,400-8,800 *ADT*

WOLSELEY

Wolseley gained a reputation for producing good reliable vehicles between the first and second world wars. Herbert Austin, and later John Siddeley, were both influential in Wolseley's auto development prior to forming their own companies. Wolseley was declared bankrupt in 1927 at which time the company was bought by William Morris and renamed Wolseley Motors (1927) Ltd.

1910 Wolseley Roi de Belges Tourer, original coachwork, excellent condition.
£27,000-29,000 *FHF*

1913 Wolseley 16/20hp 5 Seater Tourer, engine partially dismantled for refurbishment, leather upholstery original, bodywork appears sound, but needs repainting.
£14,200-14,700 *S*

1913 Wolseley Type C6 16/20hp Limousine Landaulette, brass acetylene headlights, oil sidelamps and rear lamp, and matching brass driving mirrors, excellent restored condition.
£32,000-34,000 *S*

1931 Wolseley Hornet 4 Seater Sports, 6 cylinders, overhead camshaft, 1298cc, older restoration, good condition.
£8,500-9,000 *Mot*

1957 Wolseley 15/50 Saloon, original condition, paintwork needs restoration, right hand drive.
£1,300-1,500 *C*

WOLSELEY (Veteran & Vintage) Model	ENGINE cc/cyl	DATES	CONDITION		
			1	2	3
10	987/2	1909-16	£16,000	£12,500	£9,000
CZ (30hp)	2887/4	1909	£18,000	£13,000	£9,000
10 and E3	1320/4	1920-24	-	-	-
7 and H7	840/2	1922-24	-	-	-
15hp and A9	2614/4	1920-27	£12,000	£10,000	£8,000
20 and C8	3921/ 3862/6	1920-27	-	-	-
E4 (10.5hp)	1267/ 1542/4	1925-30	-	-	-
E6 and Viper and 16hp	2025/6	1927-34	£18,000	£15,000	£10,000
E8M	2700/8	1928-31	£22,00	£18,000	£14,000
Hornet	1271/4	1931-35	£10,000	£8,000	£4,500
Hornet Special	1271/ 1604/6	1933-36	£12,000	£8,000	£5,000
Wasp	1069/4	1936	£7,000	£5,000	£3,500
Hornet	1378/6	1936	£8,000	£6,000	£4,000
21/60 and 21hp	2677/ 2916/6	1932-39	£11,000	£6,000	£4,000
25	3485/6	1936-39	£11,000	£6,500	£4,000
12/48	1547/4	1937-39	£5,000	£3,000	£1,750
18/80	2322/6	1938-39	£11,000	£6,750	£4,000

Early Wolseley cars are well made and very British and when housing coachbuilt bodies command a premium of at least +25%.

1967 Wolseley 6/110 Mk II.
£1,800-2,200 *CVPG*

1970 Wolseley 18/85 Mk II,
4 cylinders, 1798cc, all original,
good condition.
£1,100-1,200 *ADT*

WOLSELEY Model	ENGINE cc/cyl	DATES	CONDITION 1	2	3
8	918/4	1939-48	£1,800	£1,000	£500
10	1140/4	1939-48	£2,500	£1,000	£500
12/48	1548/4	1939-48	£2,500	£1,000	£500
14/60	1818/6	1946-48	£2,500	£1,200	£500
18/85	2321/6	1946-48	£3,000	£1,200	£500
25	3485/6	1946-48	£2,500	£1,000	£500
4/50	1476/4	1948-53	£1,900	£600	£300
6/80	2215/6	1948-54	£2,000	£1,000	£400
4/44	1250/4	1952-56	£1,850	£850	£350
15/50	1489/4	1956-58	£1,850	£850	£350
1500	1489/4	1958-65	£2,000	£1,000	£500
15/60	1489/4	1958-61	£1,500	£700	£300
16/60	1622/4	1961-71	£1,600	£800	£300
6/90	2639/6	1954-57	£2,000	£1,000	£500
6/99	2912/6	1959-61	£2,000	£1,000	£500
6/110 MK I/II	2912/6	1961-68	£1,500	£800	£400
Hornet (Mini)	848/4	1961-70	£1,250	£450	£250
1300	1275/4	1967-74	£1,250	£750	£200
18/85	1798/4	1967-72	£950	£400	£150

1969 Wolseley Hornet,
4 cylinders, 998cc, reconditioned
automatic gearbox, engine
refurbished, repainted.
£2,600-2,800 *ADT*

1968 Wolseley Hornet,
4 cylinders, 998cc, automatic
gearbox, good condition.
£1,500-1,700 *ADT*

YALE

1971 Wolseley 16/60 Saloon,
good original condition.
£1,500-1,700 *S*

1903 Yale, 2 cylinders, underfloor flap, automotive inter-valve,
American.
£25,000-28,000 *FHF*

A bronze bust of a motorist at the wheel, by C. Loreniani, signed, c1908, 6in (15cm) high, with marble base, repaired, on original wooden base.
Est. £3,000-3,500 *S(Z)*

A Rolls-Royce silver plated ashtray, with 'Spirit of Ecstasy' figure, c1928, 4in (10cm) high.
£280-320 *S*

A pair of Luxor motoring goggles, with original case, 1930s.
£140-160 *BCA*

A bronze and ivory figure of Madame du Gast, after Théophile Françoise Somme, c1903, 7½in (19cm) long, on marble base.
Est. £2,800-3,200 *S(Z)*

An album of 1st Argentine Grand Prix 1953 photographs, signed by competing drivers, hard cover with enamel badge, and a menu card for the Competitors' Dinner.
£575-600 *BKS*

A French pocket knife, signed Courselle, c1910.
£110-130 *BCA*

The first production model 'Mini Chair', No. 001, with flashing headlamps and reading light, 55 by 50in (140 by 127cm). **£625-650** *S*

A 'Spirit of Ecstasy' bronze showroom display statue, signed Charles Sykes, No. 5, mounted on a green marble base, 19¾in (50cm) high overall.
£5,200-5,500 *S*

Believed to be one of 9 original castings given to Rolls-Royce dealers.

Three Edwardian glass and silver plated flower vases.
£80-150 each *BCA*

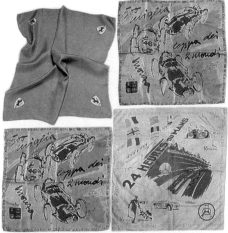

Four silk scarves, purchased at race events and autographed by the participating drivers during the actual events, and a Scuderia Ferrari scarf, given by Enzo Ferrari as a present to one of his mechanics in 1953.
£1,700-1,800 *COYS*

A Brooklands Aeroclub enamel badge, No. 379, c1930, 4in (10cm) high, on a wooden base.
£480-520 *S*

A Steering Wheel Club enamel badge, No. 44, 5in (12.5cm) high.
£300-325 *S*

A BRDC Silverstone Club Member's enamel badge, No. 54, 5½in (14cm) high.
£580-600 *S*

An RAC Life Member's polished brass badge, No. B1110, with enamel Union Jack centre, c1908, 6¼in (16cm) high, on a wooden display base.
£250-270 *S*

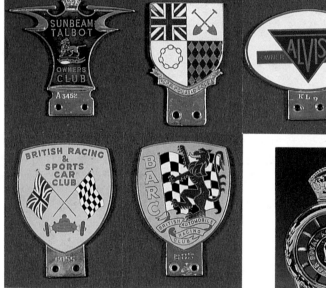

A collection of enamel car badges, comprising: Sunbeam Talbot Owners' Club, Monte Carlo Rally participants' badge, Alvis Owners' Club, BR&SCC and BARC.
£375-400 *S*

An RAC Full Member's badge, with enamel Union Jack centre, No. D3835, 5½in (14cm) high, on a wooden base.
£125-150 *S*

An RAC Full Member's badge, with enamel circular Union Jack centre, No. DJ658, c1912, 5in (12.5cm) on display base.
£180-220 *S*

A Nassau, Bahamas enamel badge, c1930, 5in (12.5cm) high, on a wooden base.
£600-625 *S*

An RAC Associate Member's polished brass badge, No. N42513, with enamel Union Jack centre, c1920, 5in (12.5cm) high.
£200-225 *S*

r. A French enamel and nickel plated dashboard plaque, by N. Perot, 'Les Vieux du Volant', No. 7650, signed, dated 1910, 4in (10cm) high.
£125-130 *S*

A German car badge, 1938.
£75-80 *BCA*

A bronze dealer's plaque, presented by Austin Motor Co.
£250-260 *HOLL*

A BARC Brooklands enamel badge, No. 374, in 7 colours, 3¾in (9.5cm) high, mounted on a display base.
£275-300 *S*

A 14ct gold and gilded Huguenin Frères Motor Club car badge, from the Balkan States, in original presentation case.
Est. £850-1,200 *BKS(M)*

An RAC Life Member's cast brass and enamel badge, No. B2276, c1910, 6¾in (17cm) high.
£620-640 *S*

A Shell double-sided illuminated sign, 1920s. **£390-410** *MSMP*

l. An RAC member's badge, by Elkington & Co., No. DB814, with enamel centre, 5¼in (13cm) high, on a wooden base.
£200-250 *S*

l. Eleven assorted German motor club badges and plaques, 8 enamelled, mounted on a display board.
£550-650 *S(Z)*

A Moskvich pedal car, pressed steel body, electric lights and horn, no E.C. type approval, c1992.
£75-100 *CARS*

Based on the famous Russian car.

A Bentley Continental Convertible pedal car, produced by Tri-ang Sharna Ltd., for H.R.H. Prince William, with electric motor, lights, horn and indicators.
£3,000-5,000 *CARS*

Donated to 'Children in Need' Appeal.

A Ford Mustang Convertible pedal car, by Tri-ang Toys Ltd., pressed steel, working lights and horn, Lines Bros. Ltd., 1960s.
£200-250 *CARS*

A Ferrari 500 F.2 Grand Prix one-third scale model car, with rear mounted Minarelli engine, fibreglass body, and tubular aluminium frame, unused.
£10,000-11,000 *COYS*

A Mercedes-Benz 540K, with a Fichtel & Sachs 50/AD LX petrol engine, No. 11100320, fibreglass body, Bosch headlamps, Momo steering wheel, walnut dashboard, 108in (274cm) long. **£6,000-6,250** *S*

A Swiss rear compartment car clock, 1930s.
£80-100 *BCA*

A 1926 Bugatti Type 52 Short Nose electric powered toy car, 4 wheel drum brakes, semi-elliptic front springs and enclosed rear axle.
£20,000-22,000 *CNY*

A silver plated St. Christopher dashboard plaque, German, 1930s.
£95-100 *BCA*

A Rolls-Royce presentation clock, by Saunders and Shepard, c1927.
£1,600-1,700 *S*

A silver Automobile Club de Cannes, dashboard rally plaque, post-war.
£230-240 *BCA*

A silver and enamel St. Christopher dashboard plaque, French, 1930s.
£120-130 *BCA*

A Cartier silver gilt St. Christopher dashboard plaque, with garnet mounted screws, Baccarat glass central motif, hallmarked, 1938, 3in (8cm).
£3,250-3,500 *BKS(M)*

An MG flag, by Piggott Brothers & Co. Ltd., from the MG Factory in Abingdon, 72in (182.5cm) wide.
£575-600 *S(Z)*

l. A bezel-wind dashboard clock, by Boselli, Italy, c1938.
£150-200 *BCA*

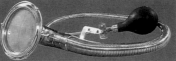

A pair of Lucas R100 Bentley electric headlamps, marked, late 1930s, 10½in (26.5cm) diam.
£500-550 S

A pair of Lucas RB 67S Bi-Flex long range headlamps, restored, lens 8in (20cm) diam.
£250-275 S

A Zeiss handlamp, with fork mounting bracket, suitable for a Speed Six or 8 litre Bentley, lens 7in (18cm) diam.
£840-880 S

A Boa Constrictor horn, with mesh, brass bodied with rubber bulb and mounting brackets, c1910, 72in (183cm) long.
£525-550 S

A Lucas PLG-40 centre spotlamp, with enamel top hinge badge and tri-bar bulb holder, restored.
£575-625 S

A Stephan Grebel hand spotlamp, with pillar mounted articulated bracket, handle to rear of case, original etched glass lens, c1930, 4¼in (11cm) diam.
£840-880 S

l. A pair of Swiss Scintilla SPN rear lights, with mounting brackets, restored, 4¼in (11cm) wide. **Est. £800-1,000**
l.c. A pair of Ace sidelights, by Cornercroft Ltd., each with frosted bull's-eye lens, 6¼in (16cm) long. **£525-575**
r.c. A pair of Marchal streamlined sidelights, each with original rubber base, 6in (15cm) long. **£275-300**
r. A Stephan Grebel electric pillar-mounted tail light, 1930s, lens 3in (7.5cm) diam. **£800-875** S

A pair of Lucas R100L Rolls-Royce electric headlamps, unused, in original box, polished cases, ribbed reflectors, vertical bulb shade bars marked RR Lucas, lens 10½in (26.5cm) diam.
Est. £1,300-1,500 S

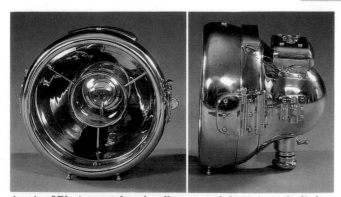

A pair of Bleriot acetylene headlamps, each lamp brass bodied, fork mounted, simple flat chimney with maker's plate, mirrored and polished reflectors, signed Bleriot, marked Patent 26889-1904, 4in (10cm) diam, bull's-eye lens behind 10in (25cm) diam bevelled glass lens. **Est. £3,000-4,000** S

A pair of Bosch electric headlamps, each pillar mounted with ribbed reflectors and ribbed glass diffuser, restored, 1929-36, 10in (25cm) diam.
£980-1,050 S

A radiator mascot, 'Nude on Broomstick', by Louis Lejeune, Paris, late 1920s.
£440-460 *BCA*

A Guy Motors Ltd., lorry or bus mascot, 'Feathers In Our Cap', on original cap, 1930-50.
£90-110 *MSMP*

A bronze radiator mascot, signed L. Maurel, French, c1920.
£630-660 *BCA*

A nickel plated mascot, depicting a mythical figure of a woman with a griffin body, c1920, 6½in (16.5cm) high.
£1,400-1,500 *S(Z)*

A Vauxhall griffin radiator mascot, c1920.
£330-360 *BCA*

A Tête d'Aigle clear glass mascot, embossed R. Lalique, France, 1928-39, 4¼in (11cm) high, on a radiator cap.
Est. £1,500-1,800 *S*

A 'Chrysis' glass mascot, etched R. Lalique.
Est. £1,400-1,500 *S(Z)*

A radiator mascot in the form of a butterfly, made from nickel, crystal and a butterfly wing, French, c1920.
£780-820 *BCA*

A 'Victoire' clear satin finished glass mascot, indistinctly marked R. Lalique, France, 1928-39, 10in (25.5cm) long, mounted in a metal ring, on a wooden display base. **Est. £6,200-7,000** *S*

A Rolls-Royce Phantom 'Spirit of Ecstasy' mascot, signed by Charles Sykes, 1929, 5in (13cm) high, on wooden base.
£260-280 *S(Z)*

A stylised Pegasus nickel plated brass mascot, by Alexandre, signed and inscribed, c1920, 5¾in (14.5cm) high, mounted on a radiator cap.
£2,650-2,750 *S*

A tortoise and hare mascot, by H. Petrilly, signed, c1910, 6½in (16.5cm) high, on a radiator cap, now used as a paperweight.
£1,400-1,500 *S(Z)*

A 'Bright Young Things' mascot, number 19, signed Ruffony, marked AN Paris, 5in (13cm) high, on a wooden base.
£480-520 *S(Z)*

A stylised swift mascot, by F. Bazin, signed, 5½in (14cm) wingspan, mounted on a radiator cap.
£210-230 *S(Z)*

A solid nickel 'Crystal Gazer' mascot, by M. Guiraud Rivière, signed, c1930, 4¾in (12cm) high, on a radiator cap.
£1,300-1,500 *S(Z)*

A 'Scotch Egg' mascot, by A. Dugès, signed, marked bronze, the bird with sprung nodding head, c1920, 3½in (9cm) high, on a radiator cap.
£900-950 *S(Z)*

A Rolls-Royce kneeling 'Spirit of Ecstasy' mascot, signed C. Sykes, 1934-39, 3½in (9cm) high. **£500-550** *S*

A hollow cast mascot of a circus elephant, holding a whip in its trunk, signed M. Frecourt, 1920s, 6½in (16.5cm) high, mounted on a radiator cap.
£2,100-2,200 *S*

A Rolls-Royce Phantom II 'Spirit of Ecstasy' mascot, signed Charles Sykes, 1929, 5in (12.5cm) high, on a radiator cap.
£400-440 *S*

A cat's head mascot, with green glass eyes, marked MAR/LD/DEP, c1910, 3½in (9cm) high, on a marble base.
£650-700 *S(Z)*

A Rolls-Royce Phantom II 'Spirit of Ecstasy' mascot, signed Charles Sykes, 1929, 5in (12.5cm) high.
£380-420 *S*

A model of the 1936/37 Auto-Union C Type V16 pre-war Grand Prix racing car, with moving components, Continental rubber tyres on detachable wheels, excellent condition, 24in (60cm) long.
Est. £23,500-35,250 *BKS(M)*

A tinplate model of an Alfa Romeo P2, by CIJ, German, late 1920s.
£1,580-1,620 *BCA*

A stylised model of a Type 35 Grand Prix Bugatti, by Richard Cardew, wooden body, cast alloy spoked wheels, rubber tyres, brass axles, starting handle, and steering wheels, 21½in (55cm) long. **£350-400** *S(Z)*

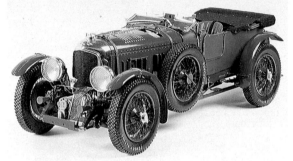

A model of the Supercharged Le Mans Bentley 4½ litre Blower, nickel plated brightwork, fold-flat screen, opening racing style filler caps, full instruments, set of miniature tools, and a miniature BRDC badge.
£12,500-13,500 *BKS*

Detail of the Hispano-Suiza, showing nickel plated radiator, lamps and brightwork.

A model of the Hispano-Suiza, by Rex Hays, raced by André Dubonnet in the 1924 Targa Florio, 20in (51cm) long.
Est. £8,000-12,000 *BKS(M)*

Gamy, La Voiture Th. Schneider 1912 gagne à Dieppe Dinant et à la Sarthe vitesse et régularité Magneto Bosch Carburateur Claudel Roues Riley, lithograph in colours, 15¼ by 33¼in (39 by 84cm).
£750-800 *CNY*

Gamy, Tour de France 1914, lithograph in colours, 11¼ by 29in (28.5 by 74cm).
£750-800 *CNY*

A colour lithograph poster depicting a Jaguar C-Type and Aston Martin passing the pits by night, original design by Roy Nockolds, c1953, 20 by 30in (76 by 50cm).
£500-550 *BKS*

Gamy, Grand Prix d'Amérique, Goux le gagnant sur Peugeot à Indianapolis, lithograph in colours, 16 by 34in (41 by 13.5cm).
£700-800 *CNY*

A Gilbarco Salesmaker pump, 1950s. **£800-850 excluding globe** *PPP*

An Avery Hardoll pump, restored, late 1950s. **£660-680 excluding globe** *PPP*

A Gilbarco Salesmaker pump, 1950s. **£800-850 Globe: £125-150** *PPP*

l. An Avery Hardoll pump, restored, 1930s. **£1,500-1,600 excluding globe** *PPP*

A Gilbarco Salesmaker pump, restored, 1950s. **£800-850 excluding globe** *PPP*

A Gilbarco Salesmaker pump, 1950s. **£800-850 Globe: £250-300** *PPP*

A Bowser hand pump, restored, 1920s. **£1,050-1,100 excluding globe**

l. A Gilbarco Calcometer pump, restored, 1930s. **£1,600-1,700 excluding globe** *PPP*

An Avery Hardoll pump, early 1960s. **£780-820 excluding globe** *PPP*

l. A Gilbarco Salesmaker pump, restored, c1950. **£800-850 excluding globe** *PPP*

A Bulldog plastic globe, 1970s.
£30-40 *PPP*

An Esso Extra globe,
1950s.
£140-160 *PPP*

A reproduction Buffalo
Gasoline globe.
£80-90 *PPP*

A Fina globe, 1950s.
£290-310 *PPP*

A BP Regular globe,
1960s.
£140-160 *PPP*

A Russian Oil Products
globe, 1930s.
£190-210 *PPP*

A Jet plastic globe,
1960s.
£40-50 *PPP*

A Shell Mex globe.
£240-260 *MSMP*

A Regent globe, 1960s.
£140-160 *PPP*

A Power globe, 1950s.
£140-160 *PPP*

A Super Shell globe, 1950s.
£220-230 *PPP*

A Cleveland Premium globe,
1950s.
£240-260 *PPP*

A Mobil globe, 1950s.
£140-160 *PPP*

A National Benzole globe,
slight damage.
£90-100 *PPP*

A Regent TT globe, slight
damage, 1940s.
£85-95 *PPP*

A 'Not For Resale' globe.
£60-70 *PPP*

A Pink Paraffin globe, 1960s.
£70-80 *PPP*

A BP Super globe,
late 1950s.
£140-160 *PPP*

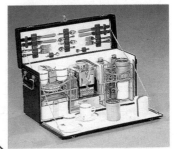

An Esso Mixture globe,
1950s.
£140-160 *PPP*

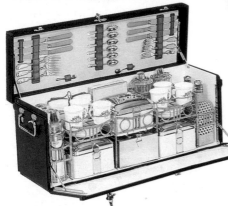

A Coracle 6 person picnic
case, with black Rexine
covered case, c1920, 30in
(76cm) wide.
£3,000-3,500 *S(Z)*

A Coracle 4 person picnic
set, with Rexine covered
case, c1920, 24in (61cm)
wide.
Est. £4,000-5,000 *S*

A Drew & Sons 'En Route'
2 person picnic set, the oak
case with leather edging,
c1910, 13in (33cm) wide, with
key. **£1,300-1,400** *S(Z)*

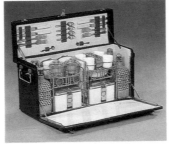

A Coracle 4 person running board picnic
case, the leather case with brass edged lid
with foot rest, c1910, 29in (73.5cm) wide.
£1,400-1,500 *S*

A Coracle 4 person picnic set,
with leather covered case,
c1910, 22in (56.5cm) wide.
£900-950 *S*

A Coracle 4 person picnic set,
with leatherette case, c1925,
24½in (62cm) wide.
Est. £2,500-3,000 *S*

An Asprey 4 person picnic case,
the leather case with wooden
lining, c1910, 22½in (57cm) wide.
£1,800-1,900 *S*

r. A Drew & Sons 6 person
picnic case, with black Rexine
covered case, c1920, 21in
(54cm). **£2,200-2,600** *S(Z)*

A Mercedes-Benz enamel sign, c1950. **£170-180** *MSMP*

A BP enamel sign, showing a Sunbeam racing car, c1920. **£1,900-2,000** *BCA*

An AA enamel sign for the village of Kingston in Dorset, 1919-30. **£140-160** *MSMP*

An enamel sign, R. Maddox & Co. Ltd., 1920s, 39 by 60in (99 by 152cm). **£580-620** *MSMP*

A Road Junction sign, restored, 1950s. **£140-160** *PPP*

An AA nearside road marker, 1920s, 8in (20cm). **£90-110** *MSMP*

l. A Shell double-sided enamel sign, 1920s, and *r.* A Shell single-sided printed tin sign. **£280-320 each** *MSMP*

A Mobiloil tin sign, c1920. **£75-85** *MSMP*

l. A Blackstone Oil Engines enamel sign, pre-WWI. **£290-310** *MSMP*

r. A Level Crossing road sign, restored. **£140-160** *PPP*

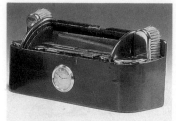

A vanity set and smoker's companion, the wooden case inset with an 8-day clock, with silver gilt accessories hallmarked London 1920, 11in (28cm) wide.
£580-620 *S*

A Continental vesta case in the shape of a Panhard-Levassor radiator, hallmarked, c1910.
£240-260 *BCA*

A French silver vesta case in the shape of a Chenard-Walcker radiator, 1921.
£210-230 *BCA*

A vanity set, with tortoiseshell and silver case, red enamel French silver and silver gilt pieces, and a matching 8-day clock by De Francia, Paris, c1920, 12in (30.5cm) wide.
£1,300-1,400 *S*

A vanity set, the bowfronted wooden case inset with a white faced clock, the silver backed brushes hallmarked Birmingham 1913, 11¾in (30cm) wide.
Est. £1,500-1,700 *S*

A gold and Continental silver vesta case, 1910.
£90-100 *BCA*

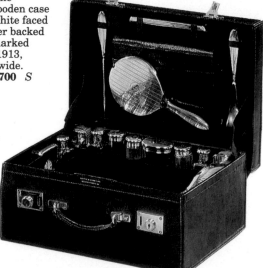

A Mappin & Webb Ltd., gentleman's overnight vanity case, with a dark green leather case, silver topped bottles, silver backed brushes, manicure set, leather writing case and jewellery box, hallmarks from 1913-19, 18in (45.5cm) wide.
£750-850 *S*

A pair of vanity sets, with matching inlaid wooden cases, silver gilt accessories, including notebook, card case, ashtray and vesta cases, c1909, each case 8in (20cm) wide.
£480-540 *S*

Frederick Gordon Crosby, the Maserati 4CL dicing with the B-Type ERA, charcoal heightened with white, signed and inscribed Donington, dated 1939, 17 by 25in (44 by 64cm). **£3,000-3,200** *BKS*

Frederick Gordon Crosby, Brooklands Double Twelve 1931, charcoal heightened with white, signed, 15 by 29in (38 by 74cm). **£1,100-1,200** *BKS*

l. Frederick Gordon Crosby, George Eyston at Pendine Sands, 1932, charcoal, signed, 14 by 29in (36 by 74cm). **£2,200-2,400** *BKS*

A. de la Maria, watercolour depicting a V12 rear engine Auto Union racing past a crowd in the rain, 16 by 20in (40.5 by 50.5cm), mounted. **£1,800-2,200** *S(NY)*

Frederick Gordon Crosby, J. C. C. Brooklands, 1928, Campbell racing Balls, charcoal, signed, 14 by 28in (36 by 70cm). **£1,500-1,600** *BKS*

Frederick Gordon Crosby, Tourist Trophy Race, Donington 1938, a Delage D6 leading a Darracq, charcoal, signed, inscribed and dated, 14 by 27in (36 by 70cm). **£2,100-2,300** *BKS*

Frederick Gordon Crosby, British Empire Trophy Race, Donington 1937, Raymond Mays in the winning ERA R4D, charcoal, signed, inscribed and dated, 17 by 22in (44 by 56cm). **Est. £2,000-3,000** *BKS*

A. de la Maria, Carlo Pintacuda in an Alfa 2.9, oil on canvas, signed, 39 by 32in (99 by 81cm). **£2,500-3,000** *S(NY)*

Peter Helck, Targa Florio: Divo Wins His Second Targa, Divo driving the Bugatti Type 35B in 1929, gouache, signed and dated '67, 18½ by 35in (47 by 89cm).
£10,000-10,500 *CNY*

Peter Helck, Giant's Despair: Haupt's Winning Chadwick, gouache, signed, 16 by 19½in (40.5 by 49cm).
£9,000-9,500 *CNY*

Peter Helck, 1955 Mille Miglia: Moss's Record Run, Stirling Moss and Denis Jenkinson in the Mercedes-Benz 300SLR, gouache, signed and dated '69, 20½ by 34in (52 by 86cm).
£15,500-16,000 *CNY*

Francesco Scianna, Studio, depicting the Mille Miglia Storica, 1987, the Coppa d'Italia, 1985, the Donington 100 Mile Race, 1988, and the Silverstone 100 Mile Race, 1990.
£3,600-4,000 *COYS*

Peter Helck, Mount Washington: Climb To The Clouds, Bill Hilliard reaching Mount Washington's peak in his Napier in 1905, gouache, signed, 20¼ by 29⅜in (51 by 75cm).
£40,000-42,000 *CNY*

Peter Helck, Robinson Comes Through, George Robinson in his Locomobile 'Old No.16' racing to the first American victory in the Vanderbilt Cup Race of 1908, gouache, signed, 26 by 37½in (66 by 95cm).
£60,500-61,500 *CNY*

l. Peter Helck, 1914 Grand Prix de l'A.C.F: Pilette at Speed, gouache, signed and dated '68, 20½ by 34¾in (52 by 88cm).
£15,500-16,000 *CNY*

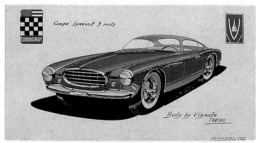

Michelotti, two coloured designs for two different Cunningham Coupés, gouache, signed, 9 by 15in (22.5 by 38cm).
£1,000-1,500 *CNY*

Michael Wright, Mille Miglia 1931, depicting Caracciola's Mercedes SSKL with Nuvolari's Alfa Romeo 8C 2300, watercolour and gouache, signed, mounted, framed and glazed, 34 by 41in (86 by 104cm). **£875-925** *BKS(M)*

Michael Wright, Stirling Moss leading Luigi Musso through Spoltore, in the Grand Prix, Pescara 1957, watercolour and gouache, signed, 16 by 24in (40.5 by 61cm). **£1,100-1,300** *BKS*

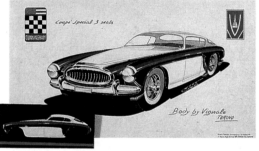

Michelotti, Coupé and Convertible, two coloured designs for the same Cunningham motor car, gouache, signed, 9 by 15in (22.5 by 38cm).
£1,000-1,500 *CNY*

Michelotti, Coupé and Convertible, two coloured designs for Cunningham motor cars, signed, gouache, one dated 4-10-52, 9 by 15in (22.5 by 38cm). **£2,500-3,000** *CNY*

r. Tony Smith, BRM V16, Froilan Gonzalez leading Rosier's Ferrari at Silverstone, oil on canvas, signed, dated 1981, 21 by 25in (54 by 64cm). **£300-330** *BKS*

l. Michael Wright, Le Mans 1930, Bentley-v-Mercedes, watercolour and gouache, signed, 16 by 24in (40 by 60cm). **£2,200-2,400** *BKS*

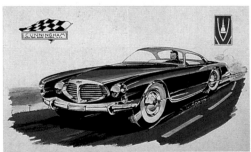

Michelotti, a coloured design of a green and black coupé for Cunningham Motor Cars, gouache, signed, 9 by 14¾in (22.5 by 37cm), and 2 black and white photographs for the Cunningham C3 road car.
£300-350 *CNY*

Nicholas Watts, Targa Florio 1932, Tazio Nuvolari leading in an Alfa Romeo 8C 2300 Monza, signed, acrylic on canvas, mounted and framed, 40 by 51in (100 by 130cm).
£1,800-2,400 *BKS(M)*

BICYCLES

c1885 Ordinary 50in Bicycle, sprung leather saddle, mounting step, turned wooden handles.
£1,600-1,700 *S*

A 'Platform' Tricycle, the 2 wheeled platform pivoted from frame to allow steering.
£275-300 *S*

A Phillips Heavy Duty Military Pedal Cycle, rod brakes, helmet mudguards, restored, tyres 26 x 2in (66 x 5cm). **£220-240** *S*

A BSA Paratrooper's WWII Folding Bicycle, restored, tyres 26 x 1⅜in (66 x 3cm).
£380-420 *S*

COMMERCIAL VEHICLES

1932 Albion LK51 6 Ton Flat Bed Lorry with Canvas Tilt, older restoration.
£7,750-8,250 *Bro*

Only 2 of these lorries are known to exist.

c1950 Sunbeam Winkie Child's Tricycle, 16in (40.5cm) spoked wheels.
£50-60 *ALC*

1927 Austin Heavy 12/4 Pick-Up, good war-time conversion.
£5,750-6,250 *Mot*

1923 Austin 20 Pick-Up, excellent condition.
£19,000-20,000 *FHF*

1933 Austin 7 Pick-Up,
good overall condition.
£1,400-1,600 *CC*

**1970 Austin/Morris Minor
6cwt Pick-Up,** 1098cc, 28,400
miles, original canvas tilt, good
original condition.
£2,400-2,600 *S*

**1937 Commer Type N1 25cwt
Delivery Van,** 13.95hp engine,
steel artillery wheels, restored.
£5,750-6,250 *Bro*

*This is the original Lyons Tea
van from the Cadby Hall factory.*

*The first Bedford commercial
vehicles appeared in 1931 under
the auspices of Vauxhall Motors
Ltd., with production based at the
Luton factory.*

**1934 Bedford WL 2 Ton
Dropside Truck,** good
mechanical condition.
£6,000-6,500 *S*

**1948 Commer 60cwt
Superpoise Recovery Truck,**
restored, very good useable
condition.
Est. £5,000-6,000 *S*

**1921 Ford Model T Depot
Hack,** imported from Florida,
good condition throughout.
Est. £5,000-7,000 *LF*

1922 Ford Model T Panel Van,
completely restored, very good
condition.
Est. £8,000-9,000 *S*

**1929 Morris Cowley Light
Van,** bodied as a van by the
Cooke Company, very good
restored condition.
Est. £6,000-8,000 *ALC*

1929 Ford Model A Flat Bed Truck, 4 cylinder in line engine, 200.5cu in, 40bhp at 2200rpm, 3 speed manual gearbox, 4 wheel mechanical drum brakes, front solid axle, transverse leaf spring suspension, rear solid axle, completely restored, excellent condition, left hand drive. **£9,000-9,500** *CNY*

1927 Morris One Ton Light Van, 4 cylinders, 1500cc, restored 4 years ago, excellent condition. **Est. £8,500-9,500** *ADT*

1946 Morris 8 Post Office Telephone Van, excellent museum condition. **£4,500-5,000** *Bro*

1946 Post Office Delivery Van, by Morris Commercial LES, chassis-off restoration, winner of many trophies. **£7,500-8,000** *Bro*

FIRE APPLIANCES

1934 Morris Minor 8hp 5cwt Van, totally rebuilt, restored to a very high standard. **£5,000-5,500** *S*

Morris Light Vans produced 2 models for 1934, the 8/10cwt, 14/32hp and the smaller 5cwt, 8hp model.

1960 Austin Gypsy Short Wheelbase Fire Tender, with 1939 Portable Coventry Climax Model FF3 Trailer Pump, complete with bell, ladder and hoses, good general condition. **£2,500-2,750** *S*

1959 Morris Commercial Van. **£2,400-2,600** *CVPG*

1936 Dennis Ace Fire Engine, fully equipped, restored. **£9,750-10,250** *Bro*

1955 Bedford Miles A-Type.
£1,400-1,600 *CVPG*

c1939 Dennis Merryweather
Fire Engine.
£5,500-6,000 *TSh*

1957 Commer Auxiliary Fire
Service 3 Ton Lorry, by Rootes,
2,900 miles, 2 new 15ft 6in
rubber Bikini rafts, 9 new Godiva
lightweight fire pumps with
Coventry Climax engines, fire
hoses, nozzles, wellies and all
original fittings.
£3,750-4,250 *Bro*

1928 Sanford Empire 600 Fire
Truck, complete and original
condition, straightforward
restoration project.
Est. £5,000-6,000 *S*

The Sanford Motor Truck Co. of
Syracuse, New York, commenced
truck production in 1912 and
continued for 23 years. They were
to achieve major recognition as
suppliers of fire appliances and
operated a special Motor Fire
Apparatus Division.

1955 Dennis F8
Fire Engine,
Rolls-Royce engine,
8,000 miles, fully
restored throughout.
£4,750-5,250 *Bro*

MILITARY VEHICLES

1839 Shand Mason
Horsedrawn Manual Fire
Engine.
£7,500-7,750 *TSh*

Austin 8hp Series AP Military Tourer,
finished in military livery, engine in running
order, seats from a later car, hood frame present
but cover missing, careful restoration required.
£2,000-2,400 *S*

The Military Tourer version of the 8hp was
produced from 1939 to 1941, with only 35 8hp
cars leaving the factory after August 1942.

**Austin 10hp 'Tilly' Model
G/YG,** folding seats recessed in
rear floor, spare wheel and shovel
mounted on cab roof.
£2,400-2,800 *S*

**c1940 Austin Series K2/Y
2 Ton 4 x 2 Ambulance,**
extended vertical exhaust for
river crossings, good condition.
£3,500-3,800 *S*

*Fitted with a 6 cylinder, 63bhp
petrol engine and 4 speed
gearbox, the K2/Y was the most
common chassis for British heavy
ambulances used by all services.
This ambulance was featured in
the film* A Bridge Too Far.

**1952 Austin WN1 Champ
4 x 4¼ Ton Truck,** engine and
gearbox restored, newly painted,
original in all major respects.
Est. £3,000-4,000 *S*

*The Rolls-Royce engined Austin
Champ was introduced in 1952
adopting the 4 cylinder, B40,
2838cc engine. It had a 5 speed
gearbox driving either to the rear
wheels only or to all 4 wheels.*

**c1957 Clark Model FCT 30RS
Airfield Tractor,** 6 cylinder
Dodge engine.
£740-780 *S*

Used for filming in A Bridge Too Far.

**c1941 Bedford QLD(C) 3 Ton
4 x 4 Truck,** engine in working
order, paintwork in good condition.
£2,300-2,600 *S*

**1964 Auto-Union Munga
Utility,** 3 cylinders, permanent
4 wheel drive, left hand drive.
Est. £800-1,400 *ALC*

*The Munga was introduced in
1955 as a cross country car for the
German Army, and went into
production in 1956.*

1942 Chevrolet G4100 1½ Ton 4 x 4 Cargo Truck, good overall condition.
Est. £4,000-4,500 *S*

This truck has been used in the TV series, The Darling Buds of May.

1943 Daimler Dingo Mk II Armoured Scout Car, 6 cylinder, rear mounted 2520cc petrol engine, 5 speed pre-selector gearbox with fluid flywheel, independent suspension and drive to all 4 wheels, good all-round condition.
£5,600-6,000 *S*

Daimler Ferret Mk 5 Light Scout Car/Reconnaissance Vehicle, reconditioned Rolls-Royce engine, good condition throughout.
Est. £4,500-5,000 *S*

c1944 Dodge T222/D15 4 x 2 15cwt Water Tanker, replacement engine valves, requires starter ring, fair condition, right hand drive.
£2,300-2,600 *S*

Hillman 10hp Light Utility, folding rear seats and canvas tilt, straightforward restoration project. £1,700-2,000 *S*

c1942 Diamond T 980 12 Ton 6 x 4 Prime Mover, now fitted with Leyland 6 cylinder diesel engine, gauges/dials missing or broken, fair to good condition.
£1,200-1,400 *S*

Ford GPW ¼ Ton 4 x 4 Jeep, 4 cylinder side valve engine, 3 speed variable ratio gearbox with 2 or 4 wheel drive option, short wheelbase, finished in US Army colours, with shovel and axe, jerry cans, spare wheel, totally restored.
£7,200-7,700 *S*

c1942 GMC 353 2½ Ton 6 x 6 Model ST5 Radio/Workshop, coachwork by The Superior Coach Corporation, Lima, Ohio, unused for some time, brakes require attention.
£1,400-1,600 *S*

**c1941 International M5A1
Half Track Armoured Car,**
repainted, dummy machine gun
over cab, Tulsa winch, pick,
shovel and jerry cans.

Used in the film A Bridge Too Far.

**1961 Leyland Hippo Model
19H/1E Aircraft Refueller,**
original specification, correct
RAF livery, good general
condition.
Est. £2,000-3,000 *S*

Scammell Pioneer SV/2S Recovery Vehicle,
with Herbert Morris crane, original specification,
good condition. **£2,400-2,800** *S*

*The 6LW engine had a capacity of 8367cc developing
102bhp and driving through a 6 speed gearbox
to the rear wheels.*

**1950 Mercedes-Benz 170S
4 Door Saloon,** desert sand
livery, museum housed, engine
in working order.
£3,800-4,200 *S*

Used in the making of many films.

**1977 Thornycroft Nubian
Model TFB 881 Trencher,** good
original condition throughout.
Est. £4,000-5,000 *S*

**c1945 Universal T16 Bren Gun
Carrier,** steering by levers with
one side braking for sharper
turns, Horstmann type
suspension.
£5,000-5,500 *S*

This is an ideal museum exhibit.

**c1955 Volvo Military
Command Car,** bodywork in
generally good condition.
Est. £3,000-4,000 *S*

MOTORCYCLES

1956 AJS 16H 350cc Jampot Motorcycle, unrestored.
£650-680 *MR*

1955 Ariel Square Four 1000cc Motorcycle, with Watsonian Albion single seat sidecar, fully restored and running.
£3,000-3,500 *MR*

1960 AJS 31 DL 350cc Motorcycle, excellent condition.
Est. £2,400-2,800 *ECC*

1925 BSA Roundtank 2.49hp Solo Motorcycle, an early original model, excellent condition.
Est. £2,500-3,000 *ALC*

1951 BSA B31 Single Cylinder 349cc Trials Model Replica Motorcycle, overhead valve, 21in diam. front wheel, reasonable paintwork, in good working order.
£700-800 *PS*

Basically this motorcycle is a standard B31 road-going model, converted for on/off road use.

1934 BSA Sloper 600cc Motorcycle, extensively refurbished, engine and wheels rebuilt, all metalwork repainted.
£2,250-2,500 *DDM*

1955 BSA Gold Star 350cc Motorcycle, in original touring trim, good condition throughout.
£5,000-5,500 *S*

1952 BSA C11 250cc Motorcycle, side valve engine, original condition.
£450-550 *MR*

1960 BSA A7 Shooting Star 500cc Motorcycle, excellent condition.
£2,500-2,800 *MR*

1968 BSA Lightning Unit-Construction Twin 654cc Motorcycle, originally exported to Canada, modified chromium plated petrol tank and side panels, very good condition.
£1,300-1,400 *PS*

1989 Ducati 851 Superbike, V2, 851cc engine, in excellent condition. **£7,500-8,000** *COYS*

This machine was bought in 1989, complete in race trim with slick tyres, at a cost of around £20,000. It has never been road registered or used on the track.

1987 Harley-Davidson FXLR Custom Motorcycle, 1591cc rebuilt engine.
£4,800-5,200 *DDM*

1957 Francis Barnett Plover, 125cc, in good original condition and running order.
Est. £400-500 *HOLL*

1970 Honda CB 750K1 4 Cylinder 736cc Motorcycle, single overhead camshaft.
£1,800-2,000 *PS*

c1952 Maserati SS50 Racing Motorcycle, mostly original, lacks chains and minor mechanical items.
£2,400-2,800 *BKS(M)*

c1919 Kenilworth Scooter, 142cc, overhead valve engine, made by the Norman Engineering Co., Leamington Spa, thought to have been a prototype model, unrestored, in sound condition.
£800-850 *C*

1990 Norton F1 Motorcycle, UK delivery example, never registered, in excellent condition.
£7,500-8,000 *COYS*

1959 Raleigh Automatic 49cc Moped, restored, very good condition.
£85-95 *PS*

1966 Royal Enfield Turbo Twin Sports 2 Stroke 249cc Motorcycle, Villiers 4T engine unit, complete and original, requires restoration.
£270-290 *PS*

1930 Scott Flyer Squirrel Solo 498cc Motorcycle, 1932 short stroke Flyer engine, gearbox and clutch are period, replica frame with girder forks, requires some restoration.
£1,900-2,100 *ALC*

c1985 Sinclair C5 Electric Tricycle, with wing mirrors, horn, indicators, side screens, signed by the inventor.
£400-420 *S*

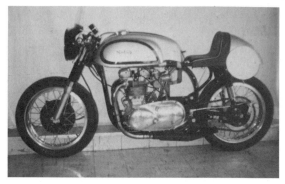

1991 Triton 750cc Motorcycle, alloy barrelled Morgo engine, Triumph T120R bottom end, Manx pattern tank, Norton featherbed frame and Roadholder forks.
£2,200-2,500 *MR*

1961 Triton Vertical Twin 744cc Motorcycle, Triumph T140 tuned engine, Norton featherbed wideline frame, excellent condition.
Est. £2,200-2,500 *PS*

1966 Triumph 5TA 500cc Motorcycle Combination, Swallow Jet 80 sidecar, excellent restored condition.
£3,000-3,500 *Mot*

1970 Triumph Bonneville 650cc Solo Motorcycle, restored to original specification.
£2,800-2,900 *ALC*

1966 Triumph Tiger 90 350cc Motorcycle, in running order.
£800-850 *MR*

PASSENGER VEHICLES

1950 Bristol Model KS5G Low Bridge 55 Seater Double Decker Bus, coachwork by Eastern Coachworks, Lowestoft, overhauled Gardner 5LW diesel engine, very good condition throughout.
£5,750-6,000 *S*

1925 Ford Model TT Jitney 10 Passenger Bus, carefully rebuilt.
£6,400-6,800 *S*

1929 Dennis 16 Seater Bus, mechanically in good order, to original specification.
Est. £9,000-11,000 *S*

1914 Daimler Type DG3C 21 Seater Charabanc, 4 cylinder engine with pair-cast cylinders, 2 plugs per cylinder, 4 speed gearbox, modern indicators, 5 rows of seats behind the driver, solid rubber tyres, fully restored. **£55,000-60,000** *S*

1936 Lanchester 10hp Special Coach, coachwork by Mervyn Gibson, 1442cc, 4 cylinder overhead valve engine, Mulliner saloon body, aluminium coachwork with sliding nearside door, Widney type windows including an Ace half-drop, mechanically in good order.
Est. £2,750-3,750 *S*

PEDAL CARS

An Edwardian Pedal Car, with maroon coachwork.
£110-120 *ALC*

A Tri-ang 'Veteran' Pedal Car, with solid tyres, Boa Constrictor type horn, 36in (91.5cm) long.
£250-275 *S*

c1930 Rolls-Royce Style Child's Pedal Car, crank driven, original trim, with rear view mirror, hand klaxon, wood rimmed steering wheel, single opening door and boot, dummy headlamps, sidelamps, restored.
Est. £1,600-1,800 *S*

1930s Eureka Pedal Car, French, spring suspension, handbrake, horn, removable bonnet, radiator with badge, spare wheel on side, 54in (137cm) long.
Est. £900-1,200 *S*

c1932 Vauxhall Type Pedal Car, by Lines Brothers, with mascot, lights, dashboard, opening boot, pneumatic tyres, 57in (145cm) long.
£830-850 *S*

c1925 Lines Brothers Pedal Car, with luggage rack, trunk, headlamps, windscreen, running board mounted petrol can, crank driven, 45in (114cm) long.
Est. £800-1,000 *S*

c1960 MG TD Child's Pedal Car, by Leeway & Co., moulded fibreglass, with electric lights, rubber tyres, comprehensive dashboard detail, 48in (122cm) long.
£670-700 *BKS*

c1935 Pedal Monoplane, possibly by Lines Brothers,, wheels with solid rubber tyres, 45in (114cm) wingspan.
Est. £700-900 *S*

c1935 Pedal Car, by Lines Brothers, with solid rubber tyres.
£185-200 *ALC*

c1948 Austin Pathfinder Racing Pedal Car, pressed steel body, finished in red, original seat, lacking windscreen, some dents to front, 61in (155cm) long.
£600-640 *S*

c1955 Tri-ang Ford Zephyr Pedal Car, pressed heavy gauge steel body with chrome fittings, working headlamps, fully restored.
£250-350 *CARS*

c1960 Child's Police State Patrol Car, by Leeway & Co., with heavy gauge pressed steel body, original steering wheel, wheels with chrome hub caps, windscreen missing, repainted.
£150-200 *CARS*

> **Miller's is a price GUIDE not a price LIST.**

RACING CARS

1969 Alexis Mk 15 Formula Ford, restored in 1993 by Jester Racing. **£9,500-10,500** *Car*

1954 Cooper-Norton Mk VIII, now fitted with short stroke Manx Norton engine, extremely good condition.
£11,000-12,000 *COYS*

1972 GRD 272 Formula 2 Racing Car, 2 litre, BDA 295bhp engine, restored.
£16,500-17,500 *Car*

1963 Ford Cortina GT 4 Door Saloon, 1650cc, original Lawrence tune engine, original interior.
£4,750-5,000 *Car*

1964 Alfa Romeo Giulia Sprint GT Coupé, 4 cylinders, 1570cc, coupé coachwork by Bertone, excellent condition.
£9,500-9,750 *COYS*

1971 Ensign LNF 371 Formula 3 Racing Car.
£11,500-12,500 *Car*

1959 Elva BMC Formula Junior.
£12,750-13,500 *Car*

1951 HAR Jaguar Formula 2 Monoposto Racing Car, Jaguar 3.8 litre engine, completely restored in South Australia, excellent condition. **Est. £55,000-60,000** *S*

The HAR was designed and built by Horace A. Richards of Smethwick in 1951, primarily for participation in Formula 2 racing. This Car is one of only 3 cars believed to have been built.

1976 Formula Ford Hawke DL 19. £3,250-3,750 *Car*

1954-56 Jaguar D-Type 3.4 Litre Shortnose 2 Seater Sports Racer, an extremely important historic racing car. **Est. £500,000-600,000** *BKS*

1957 Jaguar XK150 Race Modified Fixed Head Coupé, 6 cylinder, 3781cc, double overhead camshaft engine, 265bhp at 5500rpm, triple SU carburettors, 4 speed manual gearbox with overdrive, all-round disc brakes, independent torsion bar front suspension, semi-elliptic leaf springs rear, right hand drive, modified for racing with much of the original trim removed, Sparco racing seats, 5-part harness, will no longer comply with any current racing series. **Est. £10,000-15,000** *C*

1967 Lola-Aston Martin Sports Racing Coupé, V8 engine, 5340cc, excellent condition, fully race ready. **£160,000-170,000** *COYS*

This car is one of only 2 Lola-Aston Martins ever built.

1961 Lotus 18 Racing Car, original old race car. **£28,000-35,000** *FHF*

1979 Lola T492 Sports 2000 2 Seater Racing Car, 4 cylinder, Ford Pinto 2 litre overhead camshaft engine, Hewland Mk IX 4 speed gearbox mounted on the transaxle, restored to full race specification, excellent condition throughout. **Est. £10,000-12,000** *S*

1980 March 803 Single Seater Racing Car, 4 cylinder, 2000cc engine, an F3 car with advanced aerodynamic package and inboard rocker-arm suspension, up-rated to 1982 specification, good condition throughout. **£7,500-8,000** *COYS*

1972 Formula Ford Rostron CT4 Racing Car. *A typical pre-1974 club racer.* £5,000-6,000 *Car*

1989 MG Metro 8R4 Coupé, V8 engine, 3500cc dry sump engine, big valve head, 4 twin choke Dellorto carburettors, breakerless ignition, twin works fuel tanks with solenoid changeover, power steering, adjustable Recaro seats, 6-point harnesses, central locking, electric windows, excellent condition. £11,000-11,500 *COYS*

1986 Tyrrell-Renault 015 Racing Car, 6 cylinder, 1494cc turbo engine, injectors and electronic boxes missing. £14,500-16,000 *COYS*

REPLICA VEHICLES

1980 Auburn Speedster, power steering, fold away hood, fly screens but no sidescreens. Est. £17,000-19,000 *ADT*

1988 Autocraft Python Roadster, a fibreglass copy of the AC Cobra, Chevrolet V8 engine, revised Jaguar front and rear suspension, Jaguar brakes, leather seating, very good condition. £7,000-7,500 *ADT*

1959 Ferrari California Spyder. £25,000-35,000 *HWA*

1991 Teal Replica Bugatti Type 35, 4 cylinder, 1788cc engine, Teal design chassis, aluminium bodywork, good all-round condition. £7,500-7,900 *ADT*

c1980 King Replica Bugatti Type 35, mainly Triumph Vitesse running gear, 6 cylinder, 1596cc engine, 4 speed manual gearbox, aluminium bodywork. Est. £7,000-8,000 *ADT*

1963 Ferrari 330 Testarossa,
V12, 4 litre engine from a 330GT,
chassis shortened to give the
correct wheelbase, new
aluminium body.
£55,000-57,000 *COYS*

1951 Jaguar C-Type Roadster,
3.4 litre engine, 4 speed gearbox,
3,613 miles recorded, excellent
condition throughout.
£20,000-25,000 *HWA*

1990 Stardust D-Type,
aluminium prototype model,
Ford Pinto 4 cylinder, 2 litre
engine, gas flowed head and twin
40 DCOE carburettors, 5 speed
Ford gearbox, hand built
aluminium panelwork over a
square sectioned mild steel
space frame.
Est. £9,000-10,000 *ADT*

**c1990 Jaguar D-Type
Shortnose,** 3.4 litre Jaguar
engine, overdrive gearbox,
triple twin choke Weber
carburettors, leather trimmed,
1,000 recorded miles.
£15,000-16,000 *Bro*

1990 Ferrari Nobel P4,
professionally built, fitted with
3 litre Renault V6 engine.
£13,000-15,000 *Car*

1990 GTD 40 2 Seater Sports Coupé, 302cu in
Ford Motorsport 5 litre V8 engine, Renault Alpine
5 speed transaxle, twin fan cooling with manual
override, 1,250 miles recorded, excellent condition
throughout. **Est. £22,000-28,000** *BKS*

**c1985 Westfield Lotus 11 Le Mans Replica
Sports,** 948cc Austin-Healey Sprite engine,
4 speed gearbox, axles and running gear,
mechanically good, bodywork excellent.
Est. £7,000-8,000 *S*

**Mercedes-Benz LG63 6 x 4
Cargo Truck,** built specifically
for film work by Lamanva,
6 cylinder petrol engine.
£1,300-1,400 *S*

*Painted in desert camouflage for
the film* Raiders of the Lost Ark.

1986 Naylor 1700TF, excellent condition.
£11,000-11,500 *Cen*

RESTORATION PROJECTS

1933 Austin 10/4.
£900-1,000 *CC*

1949 Bentley Mk VI, saloon
coachwork by Freestone & Webb.
£6,250-6,750 *DB*

1934 Delage D8-15 Chapron Pillarless Saloon,
4700cc engine, partially restored original car.
£2,200-2,400 *HOLL*

1938 Delage D6-70, coachwork by University
Coachwork, 3000cc engine, manual gearbox, totally
original. **£11,000-11,500** *HOLL*

1939 Humber Convertible.
£3,000-3,250 *DB*

1935 BMW 319 Cabriolet, work
completed includes removal of
body and checking of chassis for
straightness and sound condition,
rebuilding of axles and
differential, overhauling hubs,
brakes, bearings, springs and
shock absorbers, engine re-bored
and refurbished, gearbox stripped
and rebuilt, new body floor
inserted, complete in all major
respects. **Est. £5,000-7,000** *S*

1935 Bentley 3½ litre Convertible, coachwork
by James Young.
£17,000-18,000 *DB*

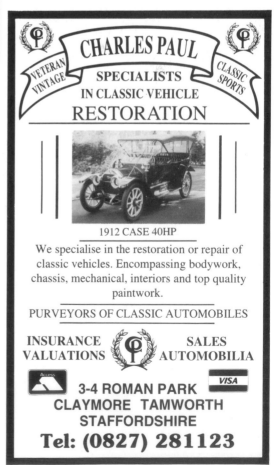

c1959 Facel Vega HK500, right
hand drive, a restoration project
or for use as spares, no engine,
bootlid, sunroof, interior trim,
door furniture, windscreen
wipers, headlamps, bumper
or front grille.
£150-200 *ADT*

1952 Jaguar XK120 Roadster,
an original unrestored car, worn
interior, running.
£16,000-17,000 *CCTC*

**1934 Lagonda M45 2 Door
Drophead Coupé,**
4½litre engine, stored in poor
conditions for about 30 years,
some rot in wood framing of the
Vanden Plas bodywork.
£32,000-34,000 *S*

**1951 Lea-Francis 14hp 4 Door
Saloon,** coachwork by A.P.
Coachwork of Coventry, fairly
sound and complete.
£850-900 *S*

1973 Mercedes 280CE,
non- running car.
£280-320 *CCTC*

1968 MGB Roadster, left hand
drive, imported from USA, rust
free, wire wheels, overdrive,
complete car.
£2,200-2,600 *CCTC*

1923 Minerva 20hp Model UU, engine requires
attention, remaining mechanical components good,
interior and bodywork need restoration, right
hand drive. **£24,000-26,000** *WES*

**1934 Morris Minor 2 Seater
Tourer,** in need of complete
restoration.
£1,800-2,200 *CC*

1963 Porsche 356B Coupé,
partially dismantled but complete
in all major respects.
Est. £3,000-4,000 *S*

**1929 Rolls-Royce Phantom I
Saloon. £14,000-16,000** *DB*

**1935 Rolls-Royce Sedanca.
£5,000-7,000** *DB*

1967 Sunbeam Alpine Series V,
left hand drive, imported from
USA, rustfree, much mechanical
work undertaken.
£1,800-2,200 *CCTC*

1961 Triumph TR3A, left hand
drive, imported from California,
complete. **£2,600-3,000** *CCTC*

**c1918 Republic Truck Rolling
Chassis,** Continental 4 cylinder
side valve engine, to original
mechanical specification.
Est. £2,000-2,500 *S*

*This vehicle is believed to have
originally been a fire truck.*

**c1948 Riley RM Rolling
Chassis and Spares,** restoration
to bodywork commenced.
£440-480 *C*

STATIONARY ENGINES

Bosch Benzin Portable Generator, No. 5781, retrieved from a crashed zeppelin, comprising approx. 400cc horizontally opposed 2 cylinder 4 stroke engine, producing 9hp at 3000rpm, generator producing D.C. 65v x 15amps or 80v x 12amps. **£1,100-1,200** *TSh*

Associated Manufacturers Co., Hired Man, 2¼hp, open crank, low tension, American. **£400-500** *AD*

The Carbrooke Engine (Stover) by Hunton & Son (T.H. Page), K-Type 4hp Petrol/Paraffin Engine, No. 12 25, on an excellent quality trolley, with L.T. tri-polar ignition. **£850-900** *TSh*

This engine is one of the earliest of its type, produced from 1923-25.

c1912 Crossley HHE Horizontal Engine, No. 07825, open crank, approx. 2hp, a small oil engine which has been crudely converted to petrol, Bosch magneto, but could be restored by re-introducing tube ignition. **£2,400-2,600** *TSh*

A Small Horizontal Gas Engine by Dudbridge Ironworks, open crank, on trolley, very rare, eccentric operation of the inlet and exhaust, inertia governor on the gas valve and early style tube ignition. **£8,400-8,800** *TSh*

1915-19 Fairbanks Morse Type Z 6hp Engine, low tension throttle governed open crank, produced in Beliot, Wisconsin, USA. **£640-660** *TSh*

Lister Junior 3½hp Petrol Engine, on good quality trolley probably by Lister.
£320-340 *TSh*

1936 J. Fowler & Co. (Leeds) Ltd.,1½hp 1PA, believed to be the only one surviving from 23 originally produced.
£140-160 *AD*

c1914 Melco 1¼hp Single Cylinder Horizontal Petrol Engine, now fitted with a BTH magneto, imported by Melotte Separator Sales Co. Ltd., Bristol for use with their cream separators and milking equipment.   **£740-780** *TSh*

1931 Lister J-Type, on original Lister trolley.
£220-240 *AD*

Make the most of Miller's

Condition is absolutely vital when assessing the value of a vehicle. Top class vehicles on the whole appreciate much more than less perfect examples. However a rare, desirable car may command a high price even when in need of restoration.

1922 PetterAcorn Top.
£300-400 *AD*

1929 Petter 5hp Apple Top.
£400-500 *AD*

1916 Petter 5hp Junior,
2 stroke, on original type trolley.
£540-560 *AD*

1935 3hp Apple Top Petter.
£540-560 *AD*

1924 Lister A-Type,
single fly wheel.
£130-150 *AD*

1924 Little Pet 1⅓hp,
exhibited in Paris.
£640-680 *AD*

FURTHER READING
Stationary Engine Magazine,
Kelsey Publishing, Kelsey
House, 77 High Street,
Beckenham, Kent BR3 1AN.
Tel: 081 658 3531

**1923 Ruston &
Hornsby 10hp
Industrial
Paraffin
Engine,**
low tension.
£1,800-2,400 *AD*

**Ruston & Hornsby Horizontal
Steam Engine,** period heavy
duty trolley with solid rubber
tyres. **£1,200-1,300** *TSh*

1912 Victoria 3hp.
£840-880 *AD*

TAXIS

1937 Austin Taxi, Landaulette body by Jones, interior good, body fair condition.
£13,000-14,000 *Mot*

1934 Lanz Bulldog Model N Type D.8500 Tractor, single cylinder diesel, started with a blow lamp, partly dismantled. **£5,000-5,400** *TSh*

1947 Fordson Major E27N Petrol/TVO Tractor, belt pulley, low speed top gear, running order.
£1,200-1,300 *TSh*

c1947 Field Marshall Series 2 Tractor, excellent condition. **£4,200-4,500** *TSh*

TRACTORS

1937 Cletrac HG Rowcrop Model E Track Laying Tractor, 4 cylinder side valve TVO engine, apparently complete, American. **£800-850** *TSh*

FURTHER READING
Farm & Horticultural Equipment Collector, Kelsey Publishing, Kelsey House, 77 High Street, Beckenham, Kent BR3 1AN.
Tel: 081 658 3531

c1939 Fordson Standard Tractor.
£640-660 *AD*

AUTOMOBILIA

A wooden cigarette box, in the form of a car, with glazed windows and rubber tyred wheels, 11in (28cm) long.
Est. £200-300 *S*

A pair of German nickel silver driving mirrors, 4⅓in (11cm) diam.
£1,500-1,600 *S*

A Chad Valley wooden interlocking jigsaw puzzle, depicting bluebird, with original box, 10 by 11¼in (25 by 29cm).
Est. £300-350 *S*

The chassis plate from Sir Henry Royce's prototype Phantom II Continental, plate No. EX69GX, together with a picture of Sir Henry Royce.
£160-180 *S*

An electroplated veteran car condiment set, 1920s, 6½in (16cm) high.
Est. £600-700 *S*

A French motorists' penknife, embossed 'Coursolle', c1920s, 3½in (9cm) long. **£130-150** *BKS*

A Doxa Automobile dashboard clock, c1910, 2⅓in (6cm) diam.
£550-575 *S*

A Rolls-Royce calorimeter, 3⅓in (9cm) high, on display base.
£175-195 *S*

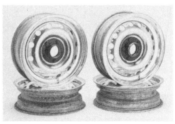

A set of 4 original cast aluminium peg-drive knock-off wheels for a D-Type Jaguar.
£3,000-3,250 *BKS*

A nickel plated motor racing helmet, goggles and gloves trophy, mounted on wooden base, 7in (18cm) wide. **Est. £300-500** *C*

A flat 16, 1495cc, FWMW Coventry-Climax H16 display engine.
£8,600-9,000 *C*

Every sports racing car from the Lotus Mark 9 to 19 was designed to use a Climax engine and these were also used in every Lotus Formula One car from the first Lotus 12s to the end of 1965.

A hub spinner from the Ecurie Ecosse Jaguar D-Type, the 1956 Le Mans winning car, mounted on an ebony plinth, with plaque inscribed 'To Sir William Lyons, Le Mans 1956'.
£1,800-2,000 *BKS*

A walnut veneered occasional cocktail cabinet, with ashtray and radio speaker, 24in (61cm) high.
Est. £800-1,000 *S*

This cabinet was designed to be fitted into the space left when an occasional seat was removed.

A silver plated sweetmeat dish table decoration, c1930, 8in (20cm) long.
£320-340 *S*

Advertising Displays

An MG neon illuminated sign, by Brillite Signs Ltd., in working order, with transformer, 20in (51cm) wide. **£400-425** *S*

A Rolls-Royce cast aluminium retailer's sign, with polished raised lettering and black painted background, 26in (66cm) wide. **£500-525** *S*

A Meccano shop display model of Sir Malcolm Campbell's Bluebird 1935 record car, manufactured by the factory from contemporary constructor set components, blue and gold, pre-WWII, 24in (61cm) long. **£300-320** *BKS*

A Desmo shop counter display stand, 20in (51cm) high. **£250-275** *S*

A collection of 21 painted advertising signs, including Krypton Test-Tune, post-WWII. **£270-290** *S*

An SS Cars dealer's showroom illuminated advertising sign. **£1,500-1,600** *BKS*

A Jaguar chromium plated 'Leaping Cat' totem, for dealer's external display purposes, 1960s, 66in (167.5cm) long. **£500-525** *BKS*

A Pratt's Perfection Spirit illuminated sign, 11¼in (28.5cm) high. **£125-145** *S*

A Rolls-Royce showroom display tower, with 6 fold-out shelves for sales literature. **£500-525** *S*

A Pyrene advertising display board, fitted with 2 fire extinguishers, dated 1928, the board 17½in (44.5cm) wide. **£300-325** *S*

A Price's Oils advertising lubrication board, with twin oil dispenser and a grease gun, the board 30½in (77cm) high. **£225-250** *S*

Badges

A Brooklands Aero-Club enamel badge, 1930s, 4in (10cm) high. **£480-520** *S*

A British Salmson enamel badge, c1936. **£45-55** *MSMP*

A BARC Brooklands enamel
badge, 1930s.
£480-520 *MSMP*

A Junior Car Club
member's enamelled
hadge, 3½in (9cm)
high, on display base.
£190-210 *S*

A nickel plated brass
swastika mascot and
a DDAC chromed
brass car badge, with
decorative enamelling,
German, c1936.
£820-850 *BKS(M)*

A Pioneer Automobile Touring
club USA badge, 1960s.
£140-160 *MSMP*

A chromed brass pre-WWII
Prince Birabongse ERA
Club member's badge,
inscribed 'B. Bira' to base,
mounted on a wooden
plinth, 5in (12cm) high.
£560-580 *BKS(M)*

Three RAC Associate members' badges, each
with different centres, enamel Union Jack
with 1924 disc, Hampshire Automobile
Club and Naval Motor Club with 1930 disc.
£480-520 *S*

A brass with enamelled centre
Lancashire Automobile Club RAC
Associate member's badge, 4½in
(11cm) high, on display base.
Est. £280-350 *S*

An AA 'red backed'
commercial badge,
5½in (14cm) high.
£190-210 *S*

A British Motor Racing
Marshals' Club enamel
badge, 5in (12cm) high.
£130-150 *S*

An SS Jaguar enamelled
silver badge, 2in (5cm)
high.
£400-420 *ONS*

A Winter Olympics 1936
enamel badge, 3½in (9cm)
diam. **£170-190** *S*

Four Continental car club
badges, pre-WWII.
£300-330 *BKS*

An AA member's badge, with
1916 red enamel heart, 4½in
(11cm) high.
£260-280 *S*

An RAC of Jordan enamel badge,
and an RAC of Jordan
competitions badge, with a
photograph of King Hussein's
Mercedes 300S, signed by King
Hussein.
£250-280 *S*

*The badges were removed from
King Hussein's Mercedes 300S.*

Books

l. A Bentley 4¼ Litre Instruction Book, 1930s.
£225-250
c. A Bentley 4¼ Litre Mk VI Handbook, with a Bentley 'R' Type Handbook.
£165-185
r. A Bentley Continental S2 Handbook, second edition.
£80-100 *S*

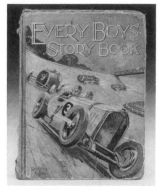

Five childrens' annuals, including *Every Boys' Story Book*.
Est. £150-220 *S*

Dashboard Plaques

A Car Mart Ltd., dashboard plaque, 1930s.
£30-50 *MSMP*

A French enamelled silver dashboard plaque depicting St. Christopher, c1930.
£340-360 *BKS*

Clothing

An Everoak crash helmet, Model TT MkI ACU, with stadium goggles, little used, in original box. **£110-130** *ONS*

A helmet worn by Nigel Mansell, by Arai, with part of intercom, with an Arai helmet bag and a certificate of provenance from Harrods, 1992.
£7,250-7,500 *S*

This helmet was worn by Nigel Mansell during his record breaking 1992 Formula 1 World Championship and was sold for charity.

A pair of Edwardian motorists' goggles, with tortoiseshell frames, tinted lenses and in original leatherette carrying case, French, c1910.
£100-120 *BKS*

Desk Ornaments

A white metal desk piece, engraved ADAC Wagenfahrt, 1913, 14½in (37cm) long.
Est. £5,000-7,000 *C*

This desk piece was presented as a trophy at an event organised in the summer of 1913 to celebrate the 25th anniversary of the Kaiser's reign.

A Bugatti silver plated desk calendar and clock, by Glyn, London, with inset 8-day car clock, 8½in (21cm) high.
£480-500 *S*

A Lorraine-Dietrich silver plated pewter motoring desk piece, stamped 'Kayser', 14in (36cm) long.
Est. £1,800-2,500 *BKS(M)*

An SS Jaguar chromium plated brass desk top ashtray, pre-WWII, 7in (17.5cm) diam.
£185-200 *BKS*

A German motoring desk piece, with bronze patination, c1910, 9in (23cm) wide.
£385-400 *S*

Enamel Signs

A Bugatti original advertising
sign, enamelled in 4 colours,
Emaillerie, Alsacienne,
Strasbourg, 19in (48cm) wide.
£675-800 *S(Z)*

A cut-out printed paper car park
attendant sign, laid on wooden
frame, together with an
advertising sign.
£180-190 *S*

An AJS Motor Cycles double-
sided enamel sign, together
with 4 other signs.
£425-450 *S*

A Fiat advertising sign,
enamelled in red, white and blue,
1920s, 30in (76cm) wide.
£200-240 *S*

A Prowodnik 'Columb' Tyres
enamel sign, 39in (99cm) wide.
£275-300 *S*

An Austin Sales and Service
enamel sign, in 3 colours,
pre-1940, 30in (76cm) high.
£625-650 *S*

Garage Equipment

Two W.B. Dick & Co. Ltd., 'Ilo'
oil pourers, 1936.
£45-55 each *MSMP*

A Shell hand-
cranked
petrol pump.
£1,200-1,500 *S*

A Reelair combined water and air
tower, restored, 39in (99cm) high.
£180-190 *S*

A Michelin 'Bibendum' portable
compressor, complete with
pressure charts and instructions,
c1930.
£240-260 *S*

A Bowes Seal Fast tyre and tube
repair bench, painted red,
restored, 61in (155cm) high.
£140-150 *S*

Horns

A pair of Lucas Windtone long trumpet horns, restored, 12in (30.5cm) long.
£450-475 *S*

A pair of Lucas short trumpet horns, 8in (20cm) long.
£160-180 *S*

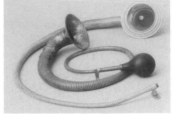

Two bulb flexible hose tapered horns, one marked CICCA, Paris, the other MTC, c1905.
£775-875 *S(NY)*

Lighting

A pair of Lucas Windtone long trumpet horns, 1930s, 13in (33cm) long.
£330-360 *S*

A Lucas Lorilite self-generating acetylene polished brass headlamp, early 1920s, 7in (17.5cm) diam. convex lens.
£260-280 *S*

A pair of Lucas King's Own oil illuminated brass sidelights, c1914, 3in (7.5cm) diam.
Est. £300-380 *S*

A pair of Stephen Grebel brass electric headlights, French, 1920s, 8½in (21cm) convex lenses.
£1,000-1,500 *S(NY)*

A pair of brass self-generating acetylene lamps, Italian, c1903, by Faysto & Pietro Carello Fratelli, Torino, lenses missing, 8in (20cm) lenses.
£1,600-2,000 *S(NY)*

A pair of Lucas King of the Road projector acetylene headlamps, c1908, 7¼in (18cm) diam lenses.
£420-450 *S*

A pair of Lucas short trumpet horns, restored, 8in (20cm) long.
£230-260 *S*

A pair of Lucas oil illuminated sidelights, restored, c1910.
Est. £500-600 *S*

A Lucas oil illuminated backlight numberplate lamp, restored, c1910. **£225-250** *S*

Two brass Autolyte fork mounted self-generating acetylene lamps, American, c1902, 6½in (16cm) lenses.
£3,200-3,700 *S(NY)*

A pair of Willocq Bottin acetylene headlamps, c1914, 8½in (19cm) diam. lens.
£410-450 *S*

Two Lucas oil illuminated sidelights, nearly identical, 1920s.
£225-250 *S*

A pair of Lucas oil illuminated rearlights, restored, c1910.
£460-480 *S*

Mascots

A carved ivory lion, 6in (15.5cm) long, mounted on a radiator cap.
Est. £1,500-2,000 *S*

Glass

A French fish, by Gueron, embossed, engraved Cazau, c1920, 4⅓in (11cm) high.
Est. £500-600 *S*

Metal

A Schneider nickel plated brass trophy, c1930, wingspan 6in (15cm), on a Phantom II radiator cap.
£480-500 *S*

A French plated brass athlete, 1930s, 7in (18cm) high, mounted on a radiator cap.
Est. £700-800 *S*

Bentley

A chromium plated backward sloping winged 'B' mascot, c1939, 2⅓in (6.5cm) high.
Est. £600-700 *S*

A forward sloping winged 'B' mascot, c1935, 2⅓in (6.5cm) high, mounted on original cap.
£220-240 *S*

A French green moulded glass bear, 1930s, 4¼in (11cm) long, mounted on a metal radiator cap, base stamped Le Ours Verte, Deposé.
£1,400-1,500 *S*

l. A Coq Nain glass mascot, beak chipped, marked R. Lalique France, 1930s, 8in (20.5cm) high.
£560-570
r. A Red Ashay Butterfly Girl, English, 1930s, 7¾in (19.5cm) high, mounted in an original Red Ashay illuminated base with 4 colour filters.
£1,900-2,000 *S*

A Chenard et Walcker pewter eagle car mascot, by T. Hingre, 1907, signed, wingspan 6½in (16.5cm).
Est. £150-200 *S*

A plated brass mascot, depicting Mickey Mouse, mid-1930s, 3¾in (9.5cm) high, mounted on a radiator cap.
£1,700-1,800 *S*

A Desmo chromium plated rugby player, 1930s, 4½in (11.5cm) high.
£250-270 *S*

A brass mascot of The Bomber, c1918, 5in (12.5cm) high, on a turned wooden base.
£340-380 *S*

A Morgan chromium plated brass winged 'M', 1939, 3¼in (8cm) long, mounted on a radiator cap.
£270-290 *S*

A Vauxhall Wyvern with pennant solid nickel mascot, marked Joseph Fray Ltd., Birmingham, 1929-30, mounted on an ashtray, 4¼in (11cm) high.
£220-240 *S*

A Humber Snipe mascot, late 1930s.
£75-85 *MSMP*

A nickel stylised cockerel, probably French, 1920s, 5in (12.5cm) long, mounted on a radiator cap.
Est. £200-300 *S*

A Renault racing car mascot, cast spelter with original lacquered finish, embossed Edite par Ponthieu Automobile, c1920, 6in (15cm) long.
£1,300-1,400 *BKS(M)*

A Schneider chromium plated brass trophy, worn and discoloured, 1920-30, wingspan 7in (18cm), mounted above a stepped wooden base.
£560-580 *S*

An English 'baby bobby', marked E & Co. Vernon, March 1908, on base, 4¼in (11cm) high.
£600-625 *S*

A French bronze Speed Head mascot, after an original design by Auscher, 1930s, 6in (15cm) long.
£225-250 *S*

A French Farman Icarus, by Colin George, signed with foundry marks, stamped Finnigans London, 1920s, 6in (15cm) high, mounted on a radiator cap.
£420-440 *S*

A French nickel plated brass cat in the moon, by Et Mercier, signed, 4in (10cm) high, mounted on a radiator cap.
£1,000-1,100 *S*

A Vauxhall nickel plated mascot, c1920.
£140-160 *MSMP*

A French nickel plated brass chicken, marked Floret FF, 1920s, 2¾in (7cm) high. **£55-65** *S*

A nickel plated metal golfer, 6in (15cm) high, mounted on a radiator cap. **£300-330** *S*

An English aluminium 'cock-a-snook', 1930s, 6in (15cm) high, mounted on a radiator cap. **£160-170** *S*

A British 'bobby', by J. Hassall, the brass body with ceramic head and brass helmet, 4¾in (12cm) high. **£240-260** *S*

A Radial Aero nickel plated engine, the rotating propeller stamped Robt. Beney & Co., 5in (13cm) high. **£420-440** *C*

A French Rolland-Pilain chromium plated brass winged sphinx, c1930, 8in (20cm). **Est. £800-1,200** *BKS(M)*

A French brass hare, by A. Becquerel, with brown patina, 1920s, 7in (18cm) high, mounted on a radiator cap. **£220-240** *S*

A nickel plated seated figure of Bibendum, with Michelin sash, 4¾in (12cm) high. **£520-540** *C*

Rolls-Royce

A Spirit of Ecstasy mascot, made with a flagstaff complete with flag, mounted on an original steam valve cap, pre-1939. **Est. £550-650** *S*

A 20/25hp Spirit of Ecstasy mascot, 1929, 4½in (12cm) high, mounted on a wooden display base. **£250-275** *S*

A Phantom II Spirit of Ecstasy mascot, signed Charles Sykes on base, marked R-R Ltd., 6-2-11, 1929, 5¾in (14.5cm) high. **£245-285** *S*

Models

An Alfa Romeo model of the Mille Miglia Spider 2 seater sports, by Pocher, 16in (41cm) long.
£440-460 *BKS*

A working model of the 1926 Delage 1½ litre Grand Prix car, fitted with 5cc 'glow plug' motor, English, c1930s, 20in (50cm) long.
£1,600-1,700 *BKS(M)*

A scratch built scale model of the Morgan Supersports 'beetle back' Matchless V-twin engined tricycle, complete with construction notes, in its original wooden carrying case, 19in (50cm) long.
£920-950 *BKS*

A wooden styling model of the Ford Anglia de luxe saloon, with full interior detail, chrome trim, fitted carrying case and mahogany base display mount, 18in (46in) long.
£350-375 *BKS*

This model, one of a pair commissioned by Ford Great Britain Ltd., was made by Mr. Joseph Cutt. The other model, retained by Ford, is now on display in the Science Museum.

A model of the Alfa Romeo 8C 2300 Monza, by Pocher, 18in (46cm) long.
£3,300-3,600 *BKS(M)*

A wooden styling model of the Bentley Mk VI, coachwork by James Young of Bromley, c1950, 23in (60cm) long
Est. £1,500-1,800 *BKS*

This model is nearly complete, but slightly damaged.

A scale model of the AC Cobra 289, 14in (36cm) long.
Est. £700-900 *BKS*

This model is made from laminated beech, covered with flexible plastic coating, and sprayed British Racing Green using 12 coats of cellulose and a further 6 of lacquer. The wheels are chrome plated brass with stainless steel spokes, the interior upholstered in leather and features dashboard details.

A scratch built model of a Rolls-Royce, with working features, 24½in (62cm) long.
Est. 400-500 *S*

A silver model of the 1907 Rolls-Royce 40/50 hp 6 cylinder car, The Silver Ghost, mounted on a base, hallmarked London 1990, 14½in (37in) long.
Est. £9,000-11,000 *S*

A Bugatti Type 57S Atlantic, No. 13 of a limited edition of 35, with carrying case and letter of authenticity, 22in (57cm) long.
Est. £3,500-5,000 *C*

Motoring Bronzes

A bronze model of the Blitzen Benz, numbered 2/10, originally sculpted by Vittorio Guttner, 23in (59cm) long.
£1,700-1,800 *ONS*

Petrol Pumps

A bronze model depicting Gabriel on the Mors, driving to win the Paris-Madrid road race of 1903, No. 3 of a limited edition of 21, by Laurence Braun, mounted on a carved hardwood plinth, 28in (70cm) long. **£1,850-2,000** *BKS*

A bronze bust of Sir Malcolm Campbell, signed and dated 'Myrander 1933', 25in (63cm) high.
Est. £1,500-2,000 *C*

Two Regent globes, c1940:
Miniature. **£480-500**
Large. **£265-285** *MSMP*

Petrol Pump Globes

A Bristol Pneumatic Tools Ltd., air tower, restored, 67in (170cm) high, fitted with a glass globe, 19in (48cm) high.
£950-1,000 *S*

l. A National Economy diamond pattern glass petrol pump globe, good condition, c1950s.
Est. 160-180
r. A Regent glass petrol pump globe, in good condition, possibly pre-war or late 1940s.
Est. 180-220 *BKS*

An American Gilbarco skeleton type hand operated petrol pump, refinished in red, with BP grade and price labels, in excellent restored condition, c1920s.
£600-650 *BKS*

An early Hammond visible sight hand operated petrol pump, painted red, with double glass reservoir, complete with hose, nozzle and Shell grade and price labels, in excellent restored condition, c1930.
£1,450-1,650 *BKS*

A Redline Super petrol pump globe, 1930s.
£290-320 *MSMP*

Photographs

A collection of 7 black and white photographs taken at Le Mans, including drivers sprinting to their cars, each approx. 11 by 15in (28 by 38cm).
£480-500 *CNY*

An Alan R. Smith monochrome photographic print of Juan Manuel Fangio, in the Alfa Romeo during the 1951 Swiss Grand Prix, signed by Fangio, 6 by 8in (15 by 20cm).
£300-320 *S(Z)*

A Louis Klemantaski action study photograph of Tazio Nuvolari, in the Auto-Union during the Swiss Grand Prix, Berne 1938, signed by the photographer, mounted, framed and glazed, 15 by 11in (38 by 28cm).
£220-240 *BKS(M)*

A photograph of the Earl of Derby's 1927 Rolls-Royce Phantom I Tourer, with coachwork by Hooper, mounted, 12 by 24in (30.5 by 61cm).
Est. £80-110 *S*

A photograph showing the cockpit of the Bentley 4½ litre No. 2, driven by Bertie Kensington-Moir, surrounded by the Bentley team members, at the Tourist Trophy Race Ards Circuit Belfast, 23rd August 1930, signed, 7½ by 9½in (19 by 24cm).
£150-200 *ONS*

No. 2 was the first finishing Bentley, placed eleventh, Birkin having had his first and only racing crash.

A Louis Klemantaski study of Stirling Moss in the Maserati 250F at the Monaco Grand Prix, 1956, signed by the driver and photographer, mounted, framed and glazed, 15 by 11in (38 by 28cm).
£480-500 *BKS(M)*

A Tom March study of BRM driver Ken Wharton, at the wheel of the V16 Mk I at Goodwood, signed by the photographer, mounted, framed and glazed, c1950, 15 by 18in (38 by 46cm).
£95-100 *BKS*

A Flewitt Coachwork photograph album, containing 43 photographs of body styles, including Rolls- Royce Phantom and 20hp cars. **£300-340** *S*

Picnic Cases
& Luggage

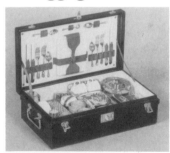

A Coracle 4 person picnic set, with fitted interior, including copper kettle and burner, in black Rexine covered suitcase, 23in (58.5cm) wide.
£1,000-1,200 *S*

A Coracle 4 person picnic set, including kettle, burner, food boxes, ceramic cups and saucers, enamel plates, glasses, bottles, Coracle butter and preserves jars and cutlery, in black Rexine covered case, 1920s, 25in (63.5cm) wide.
Est. £650-750 *S*

A Sirram 4 person picnic case, the blue case with leather edging, including Adams 'The Cube' teapot and other accessories, with original labels and keys in unopened envelope, unused, 21in (53cm) wide. **£275-295** *S*

Posters

Le Pneu Michelin Défie Toute Attaque, an original advertising poster by H. Detaspre, dry mounted, framed and glazed, 18½ by 13in (47 by 33cm).
Est. £750-850 *S*

Nunc est Bibendum, a first edition 1898 poster by O'Galop (Maurice Roussillon), dry mounted, framed and glazed, 18½ by 14in (47 by 35.5cm).
Est. 750-850 *S*

This design proved so successful with the Michelin Company that it was kept in use until 1920.

Gerber, 1959 Grosser Preis von Deutschland, a chromolithographic poster of a Dino Ferrari driven by Peter Collins on the Avus banking.
£480-500 *S*

The Green Helmet, an original chromolithographic poster for the MGM film, mounted, framed and glazed, c1961, 42 by 28in (107 by 72cm).
£450-475 *BKS(M)*

Grand Prix, an original chromolithographic poster, by John Frankenheimer for the MGM film, mounted, framed and glazed, c1967, 42 by 28in (107 by 72cm). **£280-300** *BKS(M)*

A Monaco Championship of the World drivers' poster, dated 19th May 1957.
£110-130 *P*

The Devil's Hairpin, an original chromolithographic poster for the Paramount film, mounted, framed and glazed, c1957, 26 by 32in (66 by 82cm).
£280-300 *BKS(M)*

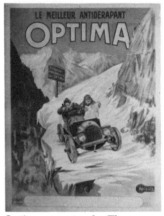

Optima, a poster, by Thor, mounted on linen, 1908, 63 by 47½in (160 to 120cm).
£430-460 *ONS*

J. Ramel, XVI Grand Prix, Monaco, 18th May 1958, a poster mounted on linen, 61 by 46in (155 by 117cm).
£540-580 *ONS*

Grand Prix de l'A.C.F., an advertising poster by Geo Bric, 1908, 48 by 63in (121 by 160cm).
£2,300-2,500 *ONS*

Steering Wheels

The original steering wheel taken from Innes Ireland's Lotus Type 21, Monaco 1961, after the tunnel accident during practice for the 1961 race.
Est. £550-850 *BKS(M)*

The original steering wheel from the Mercedes-Benz crashed by Richard Seaman during a test session at the Monza track in early 1937, and presented to him as a memento whilst convalescing by Alfred Neubauer.
Est. £5,800-8,200 *BKS(M)*

An Osram Car Bulb Kit tin, complete with contents, 1920-30, 4in (10cm) wide.
£4-10 *PC*

A 7lb tin of Carbide of Calcium, 1920-30, 7in (18cm) high.
£8-15 *PC*

Tins

Two one gallon petrol cans, originally 3 shillings each, 1920-30, 13in (33cm) high.
£5-10 each *PC*

Three Carbide Calcium cans, for cycle and motor lamps, 1920-30, 8in (20cm) high.
£3-10 each *PC*

Three cycle repair kits, 1920-30.
£1.50-4 each *PC*

A Dunlop cycle repair outfit hanging tin, 1920-30, 9in (23cm) high.
£20-25 *PC*

A Harris's Motorists Soap tin, 1920-30, 3½in (9cm) diam.
£10-15 *PC*

A one gallon can of Price's Motor Oil, 1920-30, 12½in (32cm) high.
£9-18 *PC*

Four Lodge Sparking Plug tins, 1920-30, 3 to 3½in (8 to 9cm) wide.
£1.50-5 each *PC*

Two Castrol Motor Oil cans, in excellent condition, 1920-30, 12 and 9in (31 and 23cm) high.
£15-25 *PC*

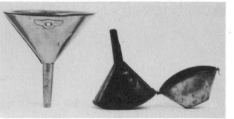

l. A nickel plated funnel mounted with Bentley winged 'B' badge, 7½in (19cm) long.
£140-150
r. A Joseph Lucas copper double funnel, marked 'water' and 'petrol', 6in (15cm) high.
£90-100 *ONS*

l. A Shell Lubricating Oil dummy conical-shaped tin, 8¼in (21cm) high.
£70-80
c. A collection tin in the form of a Pratts Spirit petrol pump, 10in (25cm) high.
£275-300
r. A Shell-a-Cyl printed tin can, 6½in (16cm) high.
£65-85 *ONS*

Two Shell Motor Oil cans, 1920-30, 11in (28cm) high.
l. **£25-50**
r. **£5-15** *PC*

A Brougham Brand Varnish tin, specially manufactured for the Indian climate, 1920-30, 7½in (19cm) high. **£18-20** *PC*

A Zero Radiator Glycerine printed tin can, 10⅜in (26cm) high.
£100-120 *ONS*

A Camberine Anti-Freeze tin, 1920-30, 9in (23cm) high.
£3-8 *PC*

Trophies

The Mobiloil Trophy for the British Empire Trophy Race, Donington Park, 1937, in the form of a bronze figure of Britannia mounted above a globe, on a wooden plinth, 19in (38cm) high overall.
Est. £2,000-3,000 *S*

The JCC International Trophy Brooklands 1934, replica of The MG Team Challenge Trophy, the applied silver plaque inscribed 'Presented by the MG Car Co. Ltd. Won by the Bugatti Team Drivers: Earl Howe, T. E. Rose-Richards and A. Esson-Scott', by F. Gordon Crosby, 8 by 4in (20 by 10cm). **£1,800-2,400** *BKS(M)*

A BARC silver tankard, presented to A. W. Fox, the owner of the Talbot driven by Brian Lewis, for 3rd Prize in The Founders Gold Cup Race, April 1931, hallmarked London 1930.
Est. £1,000-1,200 *S*

The Autocar Trophy, 1st Prize Class 2, RAC Rally, Bournemouth 1934, 13½in (34.5cm), on a marble base.
Est. £800-1,200 *P*

A silver salver, presented to Captain G. E. T. Eyston by the RAC for his successful attempt on World's Records, Salt Beds, Utah, September 1935, hallmarked London 1931, 12½in (32cm) wide.
£380-400 *S*

A BARC Brooklands silver Trophy, by William Comyns, hallmarked London 1910, Ford Car Race 1st Prize, 1st August 1910, 8in (20.5cm) high.
£900-950 *S*

The Ford Car Race was held over two miles. With a restricted list of entrants, only 12 Model T Fords competed for the cup.

AUTOMOBILE ART

Russell Brockbank, cartoon, original pen and ink monochrome drawing, signed, mounted, framed and glazed, 12 by 10in (30.5 by 25cm).
£240-280 *BKS*

Bryan De Grineau, Le Mans 1921, original colour painting, Duesenberg driven to victory by Jimmy Murphy, charcoal and watercolour highlighted with white, signed, captioned and dated 1921, 20 by 27in (51 by 69cm).
£1,700-1,800 *BKS*

F. Gordon Crosby, an original artwork cartoon of 1935 Le Mans winners Fontes & Hindmarsh in the 4½ litre Team Lagonda, charcoal and watercolour highlighted with white, signed and dated 1935, mounted, framed and glazed, 23 by 17in (58.5 by 43cm).
£2,400-2,600 *BKS*

Walter Gotschke, 1955 Monaco Grand Prix, watercolour and gouache, signed, 10 by 23in (25 by 58.5cm).
£6,000-6,500 *CNY*

Michael Watson, 1914 French Grand Prix, Mercedes, watercolour, signed, 20 by 14in (51 by 35.5cm).
£440-460 *C*

Peter Helck, 1908 Grand Prix de l'A.C.F., gouache, signed and dated '65, 13½ by 28¼in (34 by 72cm). **£18,000-19,000** *CNY*

Walter Gotschke, Stirling Moss in the Mercedes-Benz W196, monochrome, watercolour and gouache, signed, 21 by 31½in (53 by 80cm).
£5,500-6,000 *CNY*

A. De La Maria, untitled, watercolour and gouache, mounted, framed and glazed, 17 by 13½in (43 by 34cm).
£700-800 *S(NY)*

Frederic Nevin, Le Mans 1930, supercharged Bentley driven by Birkin, leading Caracciola's Mercedes-Benz, coloured pastel, from contemporary monochrome sketches, signed, mounted, framed and glazed, 22 by 25in (56 by 64cm).
£540-560 *BKS*

Bob Murray, Mansell at Surfer's Paradise 1993, watercolour, signed, mounted, framed and glazed, 12½ by 16½in (32 by 42cm).
£380-420 *S*

Peter Helck, 1952 Le Mans
Twenty-Four Hours: The
Cunningham Challenge, gouache,
signed and dated '73, 15½ by
21¾in (39 by 55cm).
£6,500-7,500 *CNY*

*Briggs Cunningham driving the
C4R to fourth place.*

Michael Turner, Jaguar XKSS,
Brands Hatch 1970, original
painting, oil on canvas, mounted
in gilded frame, signed by the
artist and dated, 28 by 43in
(71 by 109cm).
£700-740 *BKS*

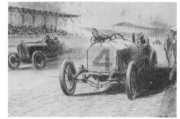

Peter Helck, 1912 Gallant Defeat,
alternative composition, pencil,
signed, 7¼ by 9½in (18 by 24cm).
£500-600 *CNY*

*DePalma and mechanic Jeffkins
are pushing their stricken
Mercedes in a last desperate effort
to win the $20,000 prize, after
having led the race for 6 hours.*

Ernest Montaut, Szisz sur voituré Renault Fres, Grand Prix de
l'A.C.F., 1907, lithograph in colours, 13½ by 30¾in (34 by 78cm).
£550-650 *CNY*

Michel Raimon, Clay Reggazzoni
in Ferrari 312B, original
painting, oil on canvas, signed by
the artist, mounted and framed,
30 by 22in (76 by 55.5cm).
£440-460 *BKS(M)*

Keith Woodcock, Rheims 12-
Hours 1965, Ferrari P2, original
painting, watercolour and
gouache, signed by the artist,
mounted, framed and glazed,
11½ by 28½in (29 by 72cm).
£440-460 *BKS(M)*

Frederic Nevin, Monaco - Grand
Prix 1933, original painting, oil
on board, based on original
contemporary sketches for *The
Motor* magazine, mounted and
framed, 15 by 20in (38 by 51cm).
£640-680 *BKS(M)*

Roy Nockolds, Targa Florio 1931,
Archille Varzi in the Bugatti, oil
on board, signed and framed, 17½
by 23½in (44 by 60cm).
£650-675 *S*

Roy Nockolds, 1952 Alpine Trials,
Ian Appleyard in his Jaguar
XK120 winning the first gold cup
ever to be presented for the
driver winning the premier
award 3 times, oil on canvas,
signed, 8½ by 14⅛in
(21 by 37cm).
£700-800 *CNY*

Michael Wright, 1950 Belgian
Grand Prix, watercolour and
gouache, signed, 21 by 23¾in
(53 by 60cm).
£740-780 *C*

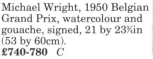

Michael Wright, Circuit de Biella
1935, original watercolour
painting, signed by the artist,
30 by 39in (76 by 99cm).
£1,900-2,000 *BKS*

GLOSSARY

We have attempted to define some of the terms that you will come across in this book. If there are any terms or technicalities you would like explained or you feel should be included in future please let us know.

All-weather - A term used to describe a vehicle with a more sophisticated folding hood than the normal Cape hood fitted to a touring vehicle. The sides were fitted with metal frames and transparent material, in some cases glass.

Berline - See Sedanca de Ville.

Boost - The amount of pressure applied by a supercharger or turbocharger.

Brake Horsepower - Bhp - This is the horse power of the combustion engine measured at the engine flywheel (See Horsepower).

Brake - A term dating from the days of horse drawn vehicles. Originally the seating was fore and aft, with the passengers facing inwards.

Cabriolet - The term Cabriolet applies to a vehicle with a hood which can be closed, folded half way, or folded right back. The Cabriolet can be distinguished from the Landaulette as the front of the hood reaches the top of the windscreen whereas the Landaulette only covers the rear quarter of the car.

Chain drive - A transmission system in which the wheels are attached to a sprocket, driven by a chain from an engine powered sprocket usually on the output side of a gearbox.

Chassis - A framework to which the car body, engine, gearbox, and axles are attached.

Chummy - An open top 2 door body style usually with a single door, 2 seats in the front and one at the rear.

Cloverleaf - A 3 seater open body style usually with a single door, 2 seats in the front and one at the rear.

Cone Clutch - One in which both driving and driven faces form a cone.

Convertible - A general term (post-war) for any car with a soft top.

Continental - This is a car specifically designed for high speed touring, usually on the Continent. Rolls-Royce and Bentley almost exclusively used this term during the 1930s and post-WWII.

Coupé - In the early Vintage and Edwardian period, it was only applied to what is now termed a Half Limousine or Doctor's Coupé which was a 2 door, 2-seater. The term is now usually prefixed by Drophead or Fixed Head.

Cubic Capacity - The volume of an engine obtained by multiplying the bore and the stroke.

De Ville - Almost all early coachwork had an exposed area for the driver to be in direct control of his horses, and so the motor car chauffeur was believed to be able to control the vehicle more easily if he was open to the elements. As the term only refers to part of the style of the car, i.e. the front, it is invariably used in connection with the words Coupé and Sedanca.

Dickey Seat - A passenger seat, usually for 2 people contained in the boot of the car without a folding hood (the boot lid forms the backrest). Known in America as a rumble seat.

Doctor's Coupé - A fixed or folding head coupé without a dickey seat and the passenger seat slightly staggered back from the driver's to accommodate the famous black bag.

Dog Cart - A horse drawn dog cart was originally used to transport beaters and their dogs to a shoot (the dogs were contained in louvred boxes under the seats, the louvres were kept for decoration long after the dogs had gone).

Dos-à-dos - Literally back-to-back, i.e. the passenger seating arrangement.

Drophead Coupé - Originally a 2 door 2 seater with a folding roof, see Roadster.

Dry Sump - A method of lubricating engines, usually with 2 oil pumps, one of which removes oil from the sump to a reservoir away from the engine block.

Engine - Engine sizes are given in cubic centimetres (cc) in Europe and cubic inches (cu in) in the USA. 1 cubic inch equals 16.38cc (1 litre = 61.02cu in).

Estate Car - See Brake.

Fixed Head Coupé - FHC, a coupé with a solid fixed roof.

Golfer's Coupé - Usually an open 2 seater with a square-doored locker behind the driver's seat to accommodate golf clubs.

Hansom - As with the famous horse drawn cab, an enclosed 2 seater with the driver out in the elements either behind or in front.

Horsepower - The unit of measurement of engine power. One horsepower represents the energy expended in raising 33,000lb by one foot in 60 seconds.

Landau - An open carriage with a folding hood at each end which would meet in the middle when erected.

Laudaulette - Also Landaulet, a horse drawn Landaulette carried 2 people and was built much like a coupé. A Landau was a town carriage for 4 people. The full Landau was rarely built on a motor car chassis because the front folding hood took up so much room between the driver's seat and the rear compartment. The roof line of a Landaulette has always been angular, in contrast to the Cabriolet and the folding hood, and very often made of patent leather. A true Landaulette only opens over the rear compartment and not over the front seat at all.

Limousine - French in origin, always used to describe a closed car equipped with occasional seats and always having a division between the rear and driver's compartments. Suffixes and prefixes are often inappropriately used with the term Limousine and should be avoided.

Monobloc engine - An engine with all cylinders cast in a single block.

Monocoque - A type of construction of car bodies without a chassis as such, the strength being in the stressed panels. Most modern mass produced cars are built this way.

OHC - Overhead camshaft, either single (SOHC) or double (DOHC).

OHV - Overhead valve engine.

Phæton - A term dating back to the the days of horse drawn vehicles for an open body, sometimes with a Dickey or Rumble Seat for the groom at the rear. It was an owner/driver carriage and designed to be pulled by 4 horses. A term often misused during the Veteran period but remains in common use, particularly in the United States.

Post Vintage Thoroughbred (PVT) - A British term drawn up by the Vintage Sports Car Club (VSCC) for selected models made in the vintage tradition between 1931 and 1942.

Roadster - An American term for a 2 seater sports car. The hood should be able to be removed totally rather than folded down as a drophead coupé.

Roi des Belges - A luxurious open touring car with elaborately contoured seat backs, named after King Leopold II of Belgium. The term is sometimes wrongly used for general touring cars.

Rotary engine - An engine in which the cylinder banks revolve around the crank, for example the Wankel engine with its rotating piston.

Rpm - Engine revolutions per minute.

Rumble Seat - A folding seat for 2 passengers, used to increase the carrying capacity of a standard 2 passenger car.

Runabout - A low powered light open 2 seater from the 1900s.

Saloon - A 2 or 4 door car with 4 or more seats and a fixed roof.

Sedan - See Saloon.

Sedanca de Ville - A limousine body with the driving compartment covered with a folding or sliding roof section, known in America as a Town Car.

Sociable - A cycle car term meaning that the passenger and driver sat side-by-side.

Spider/Spyder - An open 2-seater sports car, sometimes a 2+2 (2 small seats behind the 2 front seats).

Station Wagon - See Brake.

Supercharger - A device for forcing fuel/air into the cylinder for extra power.

Surrey - An early 20thC open 4 seater with a fringed canopy. A term from the days of horse drawn vehicles.

Stanhope - A term from the days of horse drawn vehicles for a single seat 2 wheel carriage with a hood. Later, a 4 wheeled 2 seater, sometimes with an underfloor engine.

Stroke - The distance a piston moves up-and-down within the cylinder. This distance is always measured in millimetres.

Tandem - A cycle car term, the passengers sat in tandem, with the driver at the front or at the rear.

Targa - A coupé with a removable centre roof section.

Tonneau - A rear entrance tonneau is a 4 seater with access through a centrally placed door at the rear. A detachable tonneau meant that the rear seats could be removed to make a 2 seater. Tonneau nowadays usually means a waterproof cover over an open car used when the roof is detached.

Torpedo - An open tourer with an unbroken line from the bonnet to the rear of the body.

Tourer - An open 4 or 5 seater with 3 or 4 doors, folding hood, with or without sidescreens, generally replaced the term torpedo, with seats flush with the body sides. This body design began in about 1910, but by 1920 the word tourer was used instead - except in France, where 'torpédo' continued until the 1930s.

Veteran - All vehicles manufactured before 31st December 1918, only cars built before 31st March 1904 are eligible for the London to Brighton Commemorative Run.

Victoria - Generally an American term for a 2 or 4 seater with a very large folding hood. If a 4 seater, the hood would only cover the rear seats.

Vintage - Any vehicles manufactured between the end of the veteran period and 31st December 1930. See Post Vintage Thoroughbred.

Vis-à-Vis - Face-to-face, an open car where one or 2 passengers sit opposite each other.

Voiturette - A French term meaning a very light car, originally used by Léon Bollée.

Waggonette - A large car for 6 or more passengers, in which the rear seats faced each other. Entrance was at the rear, and the vehicles were usually open.

Weyman - A system of construction employing Rexine fabric panels over a Kapok filling to prevent noise and provide insulation.

Wheelbase - The distance between the centres of the front and rear wheels.

MOTOR BOOKS

Leading specialists in automotive books for enthusiasts throughout the world.
All these books and thousands more in our book list for £1.00.

MOTOR BOOKS, 33 St Martin's Court, St Martin's Lane, London WC2N4AL   Tel: 071-8365376/6728/3800   Fax: 071-497 2539

MOTOR BOOKS, 8 The Roundway, Headington, Oxford OX3 8DH   Tel: (0865) 66215   Fax: (0865) 63555

MOTOR BOOKS, 241 Holdenhurst Road, Bournemouth BH8 8DA   Tel: (0202) 396469   Fax: (0202) 391572

MOTOR BOOKS, 10 Theatre Square, Swindon SN1 1QN   Tel: (0793) 523170   Fax: (0793) 432070

MAIL ORDER: *Inland:* add 10% of order value, minimum £1.50, maximum £3.00. Orders over £50.00 post free.

                Overseas: add 15% of order value on orders up to £150.00, minimum £5.00. Add 10% of order value

                on orders over £150.00. For large orders we prefer insured parcel post (usually by air) which we will quote for.

CREDIT CARDS: Visa, Access, Mastercard, Eurocard, Diners Club, TSB, AMEX Please quote full card number and expiry date.

TVRs VOL 1: GRANTURA TO TAIMAR.........0 947981 80 2
TVRs VOL 2: TASMIN TO CHIMERA. 0 947981 81 0
Graham Robson. A new edition now expanded into 2 volumes. The cars from one of Britain's small manufacturers. Each volume 128pp, 180 x 235mm, approx 120 ills, 8 colour, casebound. **£13.99**

BRM: THE SAGA OF BRITISH RACING MOTORS VOL 1: THE FRONT-ENGINED CARS 1945-60. ....0 947981 37 3
Doug Nye with Tony Rudd. This 'blockbuster' digs deep to tell the truth behind the drama. 400pp, 273 x 215mm, approx 300 ills, casebound. **£59.95**

FIAT X1/9. ....0 947981 83 7
Phil Ward. An important gap filler in the Collector's Guide series. Includes valuable practical information on restoration and maintenance. 128pp, 180 x 235mm, approx 130 ills, 8 colour, casebound.................**£13.99**

LOTUS SEVEN. 0 947981 71 3
Jeremy Coulter. One of two volumes replacing 'The Lotus and Caterham Sevens', this volume concentrates on the Seven from 1957 to 1973. Full supporting specifications, production and performance data. 128pp, 180 x 235mm, approx 130 ills, 8 colour, casebound. **£13.99**

CATERHAM SEVEN. 0 947981 72 1
Jeremy Coulter. This second volume covers all the Caterham Sevens from 1973 to date. Similar specifications etc. as previous book. 128pp, 180 x 125mm, approx 130 ills, 8 colour, casebound.................**£13.99**

ALFA ROMEO GIULIETTA GOLD PORTFOLIO 1954-1965.
Road Test book. ....1 85520 066 X
Large collection of road tests, long term and owner reports, restoration and tuning. 172pp, over 300 ills, 205 x 275mm, softbound. **£11.95**

ALFA ROMEO GIULIA-SPIDER OWNER'S WORKSHOP MANUAL 1962-1978. ....0 85416 128 X
Autobooks. Re-issue of Autobooks manual from 1300cc to 2000cc. Fully illustrated with photos and drawings. 176pp, 205 x 275mm, softbound. **£11.95**

AUSTIN-HEALEY 100/6 & 3000 WORKSHOP MANUAL.
BMC/BL. 0 948207 47 7
Official workshop manual. Covers 100/6, 3000 Mk I and Mk II. Plus Mk II and Mk III Sports convertibles (series BJ7 and BJ8). 400 pages, fully illustrated, softbound. **£19.95**

THE DE LOREAN 1977-1993. ....1 85520 230 1
Road Test book. Road Tests ∗ Launch ∗ Specifications ∗ Driving Impressions ∗ Technical Data ∗ DMC in Perspective ∗ Factory Report ∗ Comparisons ∗ Development ∗ History. 100pp, 205 x 275mm, fully illustrated. **£8.95**

PORSCHE 356 GOLD PORTFOLIO 1953-1965.
Road Test book. 1 85520 234 4
Road Tests ∗ Performance Data ∗ Touring Specifications ∗ History ∗ Comparisons ∗ Buying Used ∗ 1500 ∗ Super 75 and 90 ∗ 1600 ∗ Carrera ∗ SS ∗ SC ∗ GS ∗ 2 Litre. 200pp, 205 x 275mm, fully illustrated, softbound. **£11.95**

ISETTA: BMW ∗ Iso ∗ Velam. 1 85220 221 2
Road Test book. Road Tests ∗ New Model Introductions ∗ Comparisons ∗ Technical Data ∗ History ∗ Specifications ∗ Touring ∗ Isocarro 500 250 ∗ Monocoupé 300 ∗ 300 Plus ∗ 600. 100pp, 205 x 275mm, over 200 ills, softbound. **£8.95**

ROLLS-ROYCE SILVER SHADOW GOLD PORTFOLIO 1965-1980. ....1 85520 229 8
Road Test book. Road Tests ∗ Specifications ∗ Technical Data ∗ Model Introductions ∗ Comparisons ∗ Touring ∗ Factory Visit ∗ Buying Secondhand ∗ History ∗ Shadow ∗ II ∗ LWB ∗ Bentley T2 ∗ Corniche. 172pp, 205 x 275mm, approx 300 ills, softbound.................**£11.95**

LOTUS SPORTS RACERS GOLD PORTFOLIO 1953-1965.
Road Test book. 1 85520 223 9
The development of Chapman's early sports-racing cars - the 6 ,7, 8, 9, 10, 11, 14 (Elite), 15, 17, 19, 23, 23B, 26R (Elan), 30 and 40. Road and track tests, technical data. 172pp, 205 x 275mm, 200 ills, softbound. **£11.95**

A-Z OF WORKS RALLY CARS FROM THE 1950s TO THE 1990s. 1 870979 42 7
Graham Robson. From AC to Wartburg, via BMC, Ford and Lancia, here is an exhaustive guide to works rally cars built for International rallying. 176pp, 260 x 190mm, 250 b/w pics. casebound. **£19.95**

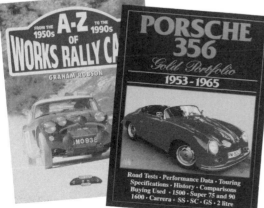

JAGUAR MARK VII TO 420G - THE COMPLETE COMPANION. 1 870979 41 9
Nigel Thorley. Here Nigel Thorley considers all the models in this long-lived line of large Jaguar saloons covering development, prototypes, design, history and production changes. 176pp, 260 x 190mm, 120 b/w ills, 50 colour, casebound. **£19.95**

ORIGINAL SPRITE 7 MIDGET - The Restorers Guide 1958-1979. ....1 870979 45 1
Terry Horley. The essential guide to evolution and 100% originality. Over 225 specially commissioned colour photographs of bodywork, interior and mechanical details. Original specs and equipment. 144pp, 295 x 225mm, 265 colour pics, casebound. **£19.95**

ORIGINAL VW BEETLE - Complete guide to European Models 1945-78. ....1 870979 46 X
Laurence Meredith. Guide to Beetle evolution and 100% originality with over 250 specially commissioned colour photos - includes Karmann. Bodywork, interior and mechanical details, illustrated. 128pp, 295 x 225mm, 225 colour pics, casebound. **£19.95**

TRIUMPH BY NAME - TRIUMPH BY NATURE.
Bill Piggott. 1 85443 107 2
The registrar of the Triumph Register gives the most complete account of the Triumph TR2/3/3A/3B ever and includes much previously unpublished data. 288pp, 233 x 208mm, over 350 b/w and colour ills, casebound.
Autumn 1994.. **£29.95**
Deluxe collector's edition **£49.95**
Limited leatherbound edition.................................. **£250.00**

RILEY - BEYOND THE BLUE DIAMOND. 1 85443 109 9
David G Styles. David Styles traces the success of the Riley family from their roots in Ireland during the 18th century, through their prosperity as leading weavers in Coventry, to William Riley Junior's new interest in bicycles and a whole panoply of creations from the world of cycles and motorcycles with an entry in the first ever international motorcycle Tourist Trophy on the Isle of Man in 1907. Finally he examines the roles of Victor Riley's Autovia Company and of Percy Riley's venture into PR Motors Ltd. 288pp, 350 x 210mm, over 300 b/w ills, casebound.
Autumn 1994.. **£24.95**
De Luxe collector's edition **£39.95**
Limited leatherbound edition.................................. **£225.00**

BROOKLANDS - A PICTORIAL HISTORY.....0 901564 15 X
G. N. Georgano. This updated edition of the original 1970's Dalton Watson Beaulieu Book recreates the unique atmosphere that was Brooklands - the place, the people and the machines. 112pp, 233 x 170mm, 227 colour and b/w ills, casebound.
Autumn 1994... **£12.95**

ASTON MARTIN LAGONDA: THE BEST OF BRITISH.
David G Styles. 1 85443 10 3
Presented in one volume from Wilbur Gunn's early exploits with Lagonda and the early successes in Russia through the many pre-war successes and the post-war re-emergence to winning the 1959 World Sports Car Championship and Aston Martin's Le Mans Victory. Since David Brown's departure the Company has remained the makers of cars which are undoubtedly 'The Best of British'. Hitherto unpublished data and all chassis/engine numbers since 1948, casebound.
Early 1995... **£39.95**
De Luxe collector's edition **£54.95**
Limited leatherbound edition..................................**£245.00**

CLASSIC CAR RESTORATION - The complete step-by-step guide. 1 85010 890 0
Lindsy Porter. This fully illustrated guide to the restoration of classic cars shows what to look for when buying a car - including the 'tricks of the trade' - and reveals the 'inside knowledge', usually known only by experts and vital for carrying out extensive restoration work covering bodywork, electrical and interior trim with advice on tools and equipment. 224pp, 270 x 210mm, 400 ills, casebound. **£14.99**

THE FRENCH SPORTS CAR REVOLUTION.
Anthony Blight...0 85429 944 0
Bugatti, Delage, Delahaye and Talbot-Darracq in competition 1934-39. Much previously unpublished information about the manufacturers, politics and personalities involved together with detailed technical analysis of the leading French sports car marques. 496pp, 270 x 210mm, 200 ills, casebound.
July 1994... **£75.00**

THE ENTHUSIAST'S GUIDE TO VINTAGE SPECIALS.
John Bateman. 0 85429 794 4
The great British special-building era began in the years
after the First World War and Vintage Specials presents a
representative selection of these and other types of sporting
car, to illustrate the evolution of this fascinating and
continually evolving branch of motor sporting activity.
192pp, 270 x 210mm, 90 ills, casebound. **£24.99**

AUSTIN SEVEN SPECIALS 2ND EDITION - Building, Maintenance & Tuning. 0 85429 955 6
L. M. (Bill) Williams. First published in 1958 and
subsequently reprinted several times and now re-issued to
meet the demand from the many present day devotees
this book covers overhauling, chassis design and
modification, gearboxes, suspension, brakes, steering,
electrical systems, making a sports car body, engine speed
and road speed charts etc. Caters for both standard and
special car owners. 176pp, 216 x 133mm, 82 photos and
diagrams, casebound....................................**£12.99**

BMW CLASSIC SERIES. ....1 85532 329 X
Jeremy Walton. Jeremy Walton's personal selection of
classic BMW's begins with the sporting six cylinder '300'
series of 1934-37. The rare 328 was outstanding and
delightful to look at and following the chaos of World War II
BMW restarted production with the portly 501 in 1952 and
Walton goes on to include the 3-series coupé and other
notable models. 228 x 210mm, 120 full colour ills,
paperback. **£10.99**

TRI-CHEVY LEGENDS: THREE GOLDEN YEARS.
Mike Key. 1 85532 422 9
A photographic tribute to the classic Chevrolets built in
1955, 1956 and 1957 *Tri Chevy II* includes excellent close
up photos and detailed descriptions of the various styling
changes, dashboard designs and V8 engine features across
the range of coupés, sedans and station wagons. 128pp,
227 x 210mm, 120 full colour ills, paperback..............**£10.99**

THE LAGONDA HERITAGE. ....1 85532 363 X
Richard Bird. A photographic tour de horizon of the various
Lagonda cars from Gunn's first 'Light Car' of 1913 to the
1938-39 LG6 (S-4). The only book of its kind * superb,
specially taken photographs * carefully researched, highly
detailed text. 127pp, 227 x 210mm, 120 full colour ills,
paperback. **£10.99**

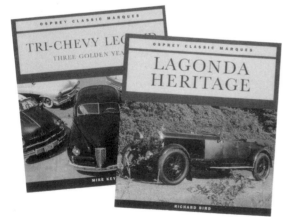

JAGUAR MKII - PORTRAIT OF A CLASSIC.
Martin Buckley. 1 872004 39 4
Jaguar MKII will give the complete history of the car from
introduction to end of production, will compare it with its
contemporary rivals and will depict its use in programmes
such as *'Inspector Morse'* and films such as *'Robbery'* and
'Villain'. It will provide full technical details and statistics, will
be illustrated with a mixture of contemporary pictures, factory
literature and previously unpublished colour photographs.
192pp, 297 x 210mm, 200 ills, 32 pages colour.
November 1994 ....**£35.00**
Limited edition of 200 signed and numbered..............**£60.00**

MG V8 TWENTY-ONE YEARS ON - From introduction to RV8. ....1 872004 89 X
David Knowles. David Knowles, Secretary of the MG
Car Club V8 Register has compiled a wealth of interesting
information on both the original cars and the new
version. Production history, road tests, technical data,
reminiscences, company literature, V8s overseas and
V8 conversions. 128pp, 297 x 210mm, 130 ills incl colour,
casebound. **£14.95**

CHOOSING AND BUYING YOUR VW BEETLE.
Peter Noad. 1 85915 020 9
Peter Noad explains exactly what to look for when buying
one and provides full information on specifications, chassis
numbers and engine type codes; lists major design and
production milestones from early prototypes to Mexican-built
cars and lots more including servicing requirements and
driving techniques. 112pp, 297 x 210mm, 130 ills,
paperback. **£12.95**

CHOOSING AND BUYING YOUR JAGUAR XJ6/XJ12.
Chris Horton. ....1 89515 025 X
A comprehensive buyer's guide to these popular Jaguar
models. Facts and figures, chassis numbers, guide to
establishing originality, advice on preparation for concours,
details of clubs and books and much more. 112pp,
297 x 210mm, 130 ills, paperback. **£12.95**

MINI-COOPER & S Classics in Colour 8. ....1 872004 08 3
Nigel Edwards. Portrays all versions of the Mini's famous
much loved high performance variant including the 'new'
Mini-Cooper introduced in 1989. 96pp, 260 x 190mm,
100-160 colour ills, paperback....................................**£11.95**

TRIUMPH SALOONS OF THE 1960s AND 1970s.
James Taylor. 1 872004 94 6
A complete history of the well-remembered Triumph saloons,
covering their introduction and development, production
changes, sales performance and where applicable,
competition history. Specifications, performance figures and
production tables included. 144 pp, 257 x 190mm, 140 ills,
hardback.
Autumn 1994...**£17.95**

MINI COOPER * THE REAL THING. 1 874105 22 7
John Tipler. Tipler tells the story from the beginning,
production history, the Cooper story, building the Cooper,
the Paddy Hopkirk file, rallying, racing, super Coopers,
clubbing, the Cooper comeback and modern Mini motoring.
160pp, 250 x 207mm, around 200 colour & b/w ills with line
ills, hardback. **£25.00**

CAR BODYWORK & INTERIOR - Care & Repair.
David Pollard. 1 874105 37 5
Pollard reveals professional 'secrets' and shows you how to
make your car showroom-fresh inside and out, increasing its
value and your pleasure in ownership. 80pp, 148 x 210mm,
around 100 colour & b/w ills, paperback.......................**£4.99**

CITROËN DS THE FAMILY ALBUM. 1 874105 30 8
Andrea & David Sparrow. David Sparrow has taken original
colour photographs capturing the essence of the DS's
extraordinary character and lifestyle in a remarkable
and thought-provoking way. Complementing David's
images are the words of his wife Andrea who introduces
the reader to the generations of the DS family and their
close relatives. 96pp, 250 x 207mm, 96 full-colour photos,
hardback. **£12.99**

COMPLETELY MORGAN - Four-wheelers 1936 to 1968.
Ken Hill. 1 874105 33 2
The first of what will be three volumes, covering all 4 cylinder
4-4 & 4/4 models series I-V and Plus 4 to 1968 covering
evolution, production and competition history, changes,
maintenance and repair, restoration and practical tips,
Morgan clubs and extensive appendices. 224pp,
250 x 207mm, around 200 colour and b/w ills, hardbound. ....
May 1994 ....**£35.00**

COMPLETELY MORGAN - Four-wheelers from 1968.
Ken Hill. 1 874105 34 0
Similar to the 1936 to 1968 volume this covers the story to
the present time. 192pp, 250 x 207mm, around 180 colour
and b/w ills, hardbound.
August 1994.. **£30.00**

ILLUSTRATED DUESENBERG BUYER'S GUIDE.
Josh Malks. 0 87938 741 6
High powered luxury cars of the '20s and '30s Duesenberg
was the epitome of superb craftsmanship, meticulous
engineering and grand styling. 128pp, 190 x 235mm,
200 b/w ills, softbound. **£12.95**

DAIMLER V8 SP250/'DART'. 1 874105 24 3
Brian Long. Daimler expert Brian Long tells the inside story
of 'Dart' (officially SP250) sportscar with an introduction to
the Daimler heritage with the usual details of prototypes,
production, the take over by Jaguar, competition history, the
SP252 story, the V8 saloons, SP specials, buying and
restoration and appendices. 160pp, 250 x 207mm, 200
colour and b/w ills and line drawings, hardback.
July 1994.. **£26.00**

MERCEDES-BENZ 300SL. ....0 97938 882 X
Dennis Adler. This book traces the phenomenal Mercedes-
Benz 300SL sports cars from development to production and
on to racing. Includes all the 300SL series cars: the
Roadsters, Gullwing coupés, prototypes, 300SLR and the
racers from 1952 through 1961. 160pp, 254 x 254mm,
150 colour & 50 b/w ills, hardbound.
July 1994.. **£38.95**

CORVETTE STING RAY 1963-1967 - Muscle Car Color
History. 0 87938 788 2
Mike Mueller. First-class colour and black & white
photography highlight the rare, limited production cars,
including the incredible rear-engined XP819 prototype.
Provides history and engineering commentary. 128pp,
228 x 266mm, 80 colour 40 b/w ills, softbound.
June 1994 .... **£15.95**

STUDEBAKER CARS. 0 87938 884 6
James H. Moloney. Your best source for the complete and
definitive history of the famous Studebaker car company.
1500 black & white photographs from the now destroyed
Studebaker factory archives cover each and every model
built by Studebaker through its long lifespan beginning with
horse drawn buggies in the mid-1800s through its demise in
1966. 392pp, 216 x 279mm, 1500 b/w ills, hardbound.
July 1994.. **£29.95**

ILLUSTRATED THUNDERBIRD BUYER'S GUIDE.
Paul McLaughlin. 0 87938 870 6
Each vehicle is reviewed by manufacturing year with
photographs and descriptions. Full descriptions of basic
model options, components and design changes.
Highlights common repair and restoration needs. Includes a
price guide for each model and information on what to look
for and what to avoid! 160pp, 190 x 235mm, 200 b/w ills,
softbound. **£12.95**

COBRA - THE REAL THING! 1 874105 05 7
Trevor Legate. Out of print for 10 years here is the original
and best Cobra history in fully updated and beautifully
produced form. Evolution, the Shelby connection, the first
cars, the MKII 289, the racing Cobras, the 427, the 1965
season, individual histories, after the Cobra, the replicas,
AC/Shelby/Cobra from 1983, facts and figures. 272pp, 250 x
207mm, around 300 colour & b/w ills, hardbound.
June 1994 .... **£45.00**

SHELBY COBRA - The Shelby American Original Color
Archives 1963-1965. ....0 87938 757 2
Dave Friedman. Original colour photographs from the official
team and company photographer chronicle the development,
production and racing of Caroll Shelby's great Cobra that
redefined the sports car and made him a celebrity. The text
tells the behind-the-scene story of the Cobra. 160pp,
254 x 254mm, 150 colour, 50 b/w ills, hardbound.
July 1994.. **£22.95**

AUSTIN HEALEY. 1 85223 787 2
Graham Robson. Covers the design and development of the
'big Healeys' from the original mock-up to the final versions
of the Healey 3000. Includes a frank account of the bitter-
sweet relationship with Austin (latterly BMC). 192pp,
246 x 189mm, 8 colour pages, 150 b/w photos, hardback.
August 1994.. **£19.95**

TVR. 1 85223 796 1
John Tipler. In this comprehensive book John Tipler
examines the history, the cars, and the company's place in
today's market. Includes fully illustrated description of how
the cars are built. 192pp, 246 x 189mm, 8 colour pages,
150 b/w photos, hardback.
September 1994 .... **£19.95**

ASTON MARTIN V8 SERIES. 1 85223 808 9
David G Styles. This book starts with the DBSV8 and brings
the story up to date with the Virage of the 1990s. Company
history, details of all V8 models and derivatives, racing
exploits and full specifications. 192pp, 246 x 189mm,
8 colour pages, 150 b/w photos, hardbound.
October 1994 .... **£19.95**

DIRECTORY OF CAR CLUBS

If you would like your Club to be included in next year's directory, or have a change of address or telephone number, please inform us by December 31st 1994. Entries will be repeated unless we are requested otherwise.

ABC Owners Club, D.S. Hales, Registrar, 20 Langbourne Way, Claygate, Esher, Surrey.

A.C. Owners Club, B.C. Clark, The Flint Barn, Upper Wooton, Nr Basingstoke, Hants. Tel: 0256 851243

A.J.S. & Matchless Owners Club, 36 Childsbridge Lane, Kemsing, Sevenoaks, Kent.

Alexis Racing and Trials Car Register, Duncan Rabagliati, 4 Wool Road, Wimbledon, London SW20

Alfa Romeo Section (VSCC Ltd), Allan & Angela Cherrett, Old Forge, Quarr, Nr Gillingham, Dorset.

Alfa Romeo 1900 Register, Peter Marshall, Mariners, Courtlands Avenue, Esher, Surrey. Tel: 0223 894300

Alfa Romeo 2600/2000 Register, Roger Monk, Knighton, Church Close, West Runton, Cromer, Norfolk.

Alfa Romeo Owners Club, Michael Lindsay, 97 High Street, Linton, Cambs.

Allard Owners Club, Miss P. Hulse, 1 Dalmeny Avenue, Tufnell Park, London N7

Alvis 12/50 Register, Mr J. Willis, The Vinery, Wanborough Manor, Nr Guildford, Surrey. Tel: 0483 810308

Alvis Owners Club, 1 Forge Cottages, Bayham Road, Little Bayham, Nr Lamberhurst, Kent.

American Auto Club, G. Harris, PO Box 56, Redditch.

Pre-'50 American Auto Club, Alan Murphy, 41 Eastham Rake, Eastham, S. Wirral. Tel: 051 327 1392

Amilcar Salmson Register, R.A.F. King, The Apple House, Wilmoor Lane, Sherfield on Lodden, Hants.

Armstrong Siddeley Owners Club Ltd, Peter Sheppard, 57 Berberry Close, Bourneville, Birmingham.

Aston Martin Owners Club Ltd, Jim Whyman, AMOC Ltd, 1A High Street, Sutton, Nr Ely, Cambs. Tel: 0353 777353

Atlas Register, 38 Ridgeway, Southwell, Notts.

Austin J40 Car Club, B.G. Swann, 19 Lavender Avenue, Coudon, Coventry CV6 1DA.

Austin Atlantic Owners Club, Den Barlow, 10 Jennings Way, Diss, Norfolk. Tel: 0379 642460

A40 Farina Club, Membership Secretary, 113 Chastilian Road, Dartford, Kent.

1100 Club, Paul Vincent, 32 Medgbury Road, Swindon, Wilts.

Austin Cambridge/Westminster Car Club, Mr J. Curtis, 4 Russell Close, East Budleigh, Budleigh Salterton, Devon.

Austin Big 7 Register, R.E. Taylor, 101 Derby Road, Chellaston, Derby.

Austin Counties Car Club, David Stoves, 32 Vernolds Common, Craven Arms, Shropshire. Tel: 058 47 7459

Austin Eight Register, 3 La Grange Martin, St Martin, Jersey.

Austin Gipsy Register 1958-1968, Mike Gilbert, 24 Green Close, Rixon, Sturminster Newton, Dorset.

Austin Healey Club, Mrs P.C. Marks, 171 Coldharbour Road, Bristol.

750 Motor Club, 16 Woodstock Road, Witney, Oxon. Tel: 0993 702285

Austin Seven Mulliner Register, Mike Tebbett, Little Wyche, Walwyn Road, Upper Colwall, Nr Malvern, Worcs.

Austin Seven Owners Club (London), Mr and Mrs Simpkins, 5 Brook Cottages, Riding Lane, Hildenborough, Kent.

Austin Seven Sports Register, C.J. Taylor, 222 Prescot Road, Aughton, Ormskirk, Lancs.

Austin Seven Van Register, 1923-29, N.B. Baldry, 32 Wentborough Road, Maidenhead, Berks.

Austin Swallow Register, G.L. Walker, School House, Great Haseley, Oxford.

Austin Healey Club, Midland Centre, Mike Ward, 9 Stag Walk, Sutton Coldfield. Tel: 021-382 3223

Austin A30-35 Owners Club, Andy Levis, 26 White Barn Lane, Dagenham, Essex. Tel: 081-517 0198

Austin Maxi Club, Mr I. Botting, 144 Village Way, Beckenham, Kent.

Pre-War Austin Seven Club Ltd, Mr J. Tantum, 90 Dovedale Avenue, Long Eaton, Nottingham. Tel: 0602 727626

Austin Ten Drivers Club Ltd, Mrs Patricia East, Brambledene, 53 Oxted Green, Milford, Godalming, Surrey.

Bristol Austin Seven Club Ltd, 1 Silsbury Cottages, West Kennett, Marlborough, Wilts.

Vintage Austin Register, Frank Smith, The Briars, Four Lane Ends, Oakerthorpe, Alfreton, Derbyshire. Tel: 0773 831646

Scottish Austin Seven Club, 16 Victoria Gardens, Victoria Park, Kilmalcolm, Renfrew.

Solent Austin Seven Club Ltd, F. Claxton, 185 Warsash Road, Warsash, Hants.

South Wales Austin Seven Club, Mr and Mrs J. Neill, 302 Peniel Green Road, Llansamlet, Swansea.

Wanderers (Pre-War Austin Sevens), D. Tedham, Newhouse Farm, Baveney Wood, Cleobury, Mortimer, Kidderminster, Worcs.

Autovia Car Club, Alan Williams, Birchanger Hall, Birchanger, Nr Bishops Stortford, Herts.

Battery Vehicle Society, Keith Roberts, 29 Ambergate Drive, North Pentwyn, Cardiff.

Bean Car Club, G. Harris, Villa Rosa, Templewood Lane, Farnham Common, Bucks.

Old Bean Society, P.P. Cole, 165 Denbigh Drive, Hately Heath, West Bromwich, W. Midlands.

Bentley Drivers Club, 16 Chearsley Road, Long Crendon, Aylesbury, Bucks.

Berkeley Enthusiasts Club, Paul Fitness, 9 Hellards Road, Stevenage, Herts. Tel: 0438 724164

Biggin Hill Car Club, Peter Adams, Jasmine House, Jasmine Grove, Anerley, London SE20. Tel: 081 778 3537

BMW Car Club, PO Box 328, Andover, Hants. Tel: 0264 337883

BMW Drivers Club, Sue Hicks, Bavaria House, PO Box 8, Dereham, Norfolk. Tel: 0362 694459

Bond Owners Club, Stan Cornock, 42 Beaufort Avenue, Hodge Hill, Birmingham.

Borgward Drivers Club, Ian Cave, Nateley House, Ridgway, Pyrford, Woking, Surrey. Tel: 0932 342341

Brabham Register, E.D. Walker, The Old Bull, 5 Woodmancote, Dursley, Glos. Tel: 0453 543243

Bristol Owners Club, John Emery, Uesutor, Marringden Road, Billingshurst, West Sussex.

British Ambulance Preservation Society, Roger Leonard, 21 Victoria Road, Horley, Surrey.

British Automobile Racing Club Ltd, Miss T. Milton, Thruxton Circuit, Andover, Hants.

British Racing and Sports Car Club Ltd,
Brands Hatch, Fawkham, Dartford, Kent.
Brooklands Society Ltd, 38 Windmill Way,
Reigate, Surrey.
Brough Superior Club, P. Staughton (Secretary),
4 Summerfields, Northampton.
Bugatti Owners Club Ltd, Sue Ward, Prescott
Hill, Gotherington, Cheltenham, Glos.
U.K. Buick Club, Alf Gascoine, 47 Higham Road,
Woodford Green, Essex. Tel: 081-505 7347
Buckler Car Register, Stan Hibberd,
52 Greenacres, Woolton Hill, Newbury, Berks.
Tel: 0635 254162
Bullnose Morris Club, Richard Harris,
PO Box 383, Hove, East Sussex.
C.A. Bedford Owners Club, G.W. Seller,
7 Grasmere Road, Benfleet, Essex.
Cambridge-Oxford Owners Club,
COOC Membership, 6 Hurst Road, Slough.
Citroën Car Club. D.C. Saville, 49 Mungo Park
Way, Orpington, Kent. Tel: 0689 823639
Traction Owners Club, Peter Riggs, 2 Appleby
Gardens, Dunstable, Beds.
Traction Enthusiasts Club, Preston House
Studio, Preston, Canterbury, Kent.
2CVGB Deux Chevaux Club of GB,
PO Box 602, Crick, Northampton.
(Citroën) The Traction Owners Club,
Steve Reed, 1 Terwick Cottage, Rogate,
Nr Petersfield, Hants
Clan Owners Club, Chris Clay, 48 Valley Road,
Littleover, Derby. Tel: 0332 767410
Classic Corvette Club (UK), Ashley Pickering,
The Gables, Christchurch Road, Tring, Herts.
Classic Crossbred Club, 29 Parry Close,
Stanford Le Hope, Essex. Tel: 0375 671843
Classic and Historic Motor Club Ltd,
Tricia Burridge, The Smithy, High Street,
Ston Easton, Bath.
Classic Saloon Car Club, 7 Dunstable Road,
Caddington, Luton. Tel: 0582 31642
Classic Z Register, Lynne Godber, Thistledown,
Old Stockbridge Road, Kentsboro, Wallop,
Stockbridge, Hants. Tel: 0264 781979
Clyno Register, J.J. Salt, New Farm, Startley,
Chippenham, Wilts. Tel: 0249 720271
**Friends of The British Commercial Vehicle
Museum,** c/o B.C.V.M., King Street, Leyland,
Preston.
**Commercial Vehicle and Road Transport
Club,** Steven Wimbush, 8 Tachbrook Road,
Uxbridge, Middx.
Connaught Register, Duncan Rabagliati,
4 Wool Road, Wimbledon, London SW20.
Crayford Convertible Car Club, Rory Cronin,
68 Manor Road, Worthing, West Sussex.
Tel: 0903 212828
Cougar Club of America, Barrie S. Dixon,
11 Dean Close, Partington, Manchester.
Crossley Climax Register, Mr G. Harvey,
7 Meadow Road, Basingstoke, Hants.
Crossley Register, Geoff Lee, 'Arlyn', Brickwall
Lane, Ruislip, Middx, and M. Jenner, 244 Odessa
Road, Forest Gate, London E7.
DAF Owners Club, S.K. Bidwell (Club Secretary),
56 Ridgedate Road, Bolsover, Chesterfield,
Derbyshire.
Datsun Z Club, Mark or Margaret Bukowska.
Tel: 081-998 9616
Daimler and Lanchester Owners Club,
John Ridley, The Manor House, Trewyn,
Abergavenny, Gwent. Tel: 0873 890737
Delage Section VSCC Ltd, Douglas Macmillan,
Brook Farm, Broadway-on-Teme, Worcs.
Delahaye Club GB, A.F. Harrison, 34 Marine
Parade, Hythe, Kent. Tel: 0303 261016
Dellow Register, Douglas Temple Design Group,
4 Roumella Lane, Bournemouth, Dorset.
Tel: 0202 304641
De Tomaso Drivers Club, Chris Statham, 2-4
Bank Road, Bredbury, Stockport. Tel: 061-430 5052

Diva Register, Steve Pethybridge, 8 Wait End
Road, Waterlooville, Hants. Tel: 0705 251485
DKW Owners Club, C.P. Nixon, Rose Cottage,
Rodford, Westerleigh, Bristol.
Dutton Owners Club, Rob Powell, 20 Burford
Road, Baswich, Stafford, Staffs. Tel: 0785 56835
Elva Owners Club, R.A. Dunbar, Maple Tree
Lodge, The Hawthorns, Smock Alley, West Alley,
West Chiltington, West Sussex.
E.R.A. Club, Guy Spollon, Arden Grange,
Tanworth-in-Arden, Warwicks.
Facel Vega Owners Club, Roy Scandrett,
'Windrush', 16 Paddock Gardens, East Grinstead,
Sussex.
Fairthorpe Sports Car Club, Tony Hill,
9 Lynhurst Crescent, Hillingdon, Middx.
Ferrari Owners Club, 35 Market Place,
Snettisham, King's Lynn, Norfolk.
Fiat 130 Owners Club, Michael Reid, 28 Warwick
Mansions, Cromwell Crescent, London SW5.
Tel: 071-373 9740
Fiat Dino Register, Mr Morris, 59 Sandown Park,
Tunbridge Wells, Kent.
Fiat Motor Club (GB), H.A. Collyer, Barnside,
Chikwell Street, Glastonbury, Somerset.
Tel: 0458 31443
Fiat Osca Register, Mr M. Elliott, 36 Maypole
Drive, Chigwell, Essex. Tel: 081-500 7127
Fiat Twin-Cam Register, Graham Morrish,
19 Oakley Wood Road, Bishops Tachbrook,
Leamington Spa, Warwicks.
X/19 Owners Club, Sally Shearman, 86 Mill Lane,
Dorridge, Solihull.
Fire Service Preservation Group, Andrew Scott,
50 Old Slade Lane, Iver, Bucks.
Pre-67 Ford Owners Club, Mrs A. Miller,
100 Main Street, Cairneyhill, Fife.
Five Hundred Owners Club Association,
David Docherty, 'Oakley', 68 Upton Park, Upton-by-
Chester, Chester, Cheshire. Tel: 0244 382789
Ford 105E Owners Club, Sally Harris, 30 Gower
Road, Sedgley, Dudley. Tel: 0902 671071
Ford Mk III Zephyr and Zodiac Owners Club,
John Wilding, 10 Waltondale, Woodside, Telford,
Salop. Tel: 0952 580746
Zephyr and Zodiac Mk IV Owners Club,
Richard Cordle, 29 Ruskin Drive, Worcester Park,
Surrey. Tel: 081-330 2159
Model A Ford Club of Great Britain,
R. Phillippo, The Bakehouse, Church Street,
Harston, Cambs.
Ford Avo Owners Club, D. Hibbin, 53 Hallsfield
Road, Bridgewood, Chatham, Kent.
Ford Classic and Capri Owners Club,
Roy Lawrence, 15 Tom Davies House, Coronation
Avenue, Braintree, Essex. Tel: 0376 43934
Ford Corsair Owners Club, Mrs E. Checkley,
7 Barnfield, New Malden, Surrey.
Capri Club International, Field House, Redditch,
Worcs. Tel: 0527 502066
Ford Capri Enthusiasts Register, Liz Barnes,
46 Manningtree Road, South Ruislip, Middx.
Tel: 081-842 0102
Capri Drivers Association, Mrs Moira Farrelly
(Secretary), 9 Lyndhurst Road, Coulsdon, Surrey.
Mk I Consul, Zephyr and Zodiac Club,
180 Gypsy Road, Welling, Kent. Tel: 081-301 3709
Mk II Consul, Zephyr, and Zodiac Club,
170 Conisborough Crescent, Catford.
Mk I Cortina Owners Club, R.J. Raisey,
51 Studley Rise, Trowbridge, Wilts.
Cortina Mk II Register, Mark Blows,
78 Church Avenue, Broomfield, Chelmsford, Essex.
Ford GT Owners, c/o Riverside School,
Ferry Road, Hullbridge, Hockley, Essex.
Ford Cortina 1600E Owners Club,
Dave Marson, 23 Cumberland Road, Bilston,
West Midlands. Tel: Bilston 405055
Ford Cortina 1600E Enthusiasts Club,
D. Wright, 32 St Leonards Avenue, Hove, Sussex.

Savage Register, Trevor Smith, Hillcrest, Top Road, Little Cawthorpe, Louth, Lincs.

Sporting Escort Owners Club, 26 Huntingdon Crescent, off Madresfield Drive, Halesowen, West Midlands.

Ford Escort 1300E Owners Club, Robert Watt, 55 Lindley Road, Walton-on-Thames, Surrey.

Ford Executive Owners Register, Jenny Whitehouse, 3 Shanklin Road, Stonehouse Estate, Coventry.

Ford Granada Mk I Owners Club, Paul Bussey, Bay Tree House, 15 Thornbera Road, Bishop's Stortford, Herts.

Granada Mk II Enthusiasts' Club, (incorporating Mk III Register), P. Gupwell, 515A Bristol Road, Selly Oak, Birmingham.

Ford RS Owners Club, Ford RSOC, 18 Downsview Road, Sevenoaks, Kent. Tel: 0732 450539

Ford Sidevalve Owners Club, Membership Secretary, 30 Earls Close, Bishopstoke, Eastleigh, Hants.

Ford Model 'T' Ford Register of G.B, Mrs Julia Armer, 3 Riverside, Strong Close, Keighley, W. Yorks. Tel: 0535 607978

Mk II Independent O/C, 173 Sparrow Farm Drive, Feltham, Middx.

XR Owners Club, Paul Townend, 50 Wood Street, Castleford, W. Yorks.

Ford Y and C Model Register, Bob Wilkinson, Castle Farm, Main Street, Pollington, Nr Goole, Humberside. Tel: 0405 860836

Frazer-Nash Section of the VSCC, Mrs J. Blake, Daisy Head Farm, Caulcott, Oxford.

The Gentry Register, Frank Tuck, 1 Kinross Avenue, South Ascot, Berks. Tel: 0990 24637

Gilbern Owners Club, P.C. Fawkes, 24 Mayfield, Buckden, Huntingdon, Cambs. Tel: 0480 812066

Ginetta Owners Club, Dave Baker, 24 Wallace Mill Gardens, Mid Calder, West Lothian. Tel: 0506 8883129

Gordon Keeble Owners Club, Ann Knott, Westminster Road, Brackley, Northants. Tel: 0280 702311

Gwynne Register, K. Good, 9 Lancaster Avenue, Hadley Wood, Barnet, Herts.

Association of Healey Owners, Don Griffiths, The White House, Hill Pound, Swan More, Hants. Tel: 0489 895813

Heinkel Trojan Owners and Enthusiasts Club, Y. Luty, Carisbrooke, Wood End Lane, Fillongley, Coventry.

Hillman Commer Karrier Club, A. Freakes, 3 Kingfisher Court, East Molesey, Surrey. Tel: 081-941 0604

Historic Commercial Vehicle Society, H.C.V.S, Iden Grange, Cranbrook Road, Staplehurst, Kent.

Historic Sports Car Club, Cold Harbour, Kington Langley, Wilts.

Historic Rally Car Register RAC, Alison Woolley, Tibberton Court, Tibberton, Glos. Tel: 0452 79648

HRG Association, I.J. Dussek, Little Allens, Allens Lane, Plaxtol, Sevenoaks, Kent.

Holden U.K. Register, G.R.C. Hardy, Clun Felin, Woll's Castle, Haverfordwest, Pembrokeshire, Dyfed, Wales.

Honda S800 Sports Car Club, Chris Wallwork, 23a High Street, Steeton, W. Yorks. Tel: 0535 53845

Humber Register, Hugh Gregory, 176 London Road, St Albans, Herts.

Post Vintage Humber Car Club, T. Bayliss, 30 Norbury Road, Fallings Park, Wolverhampton.

The Imp Club, Jackie Clark, Cossington Field Farm, Bell Lane, Boxley, Kent. Tel: 0634 201807

Isetta Owners Club, Brian Orriss, 30 Durham Road, Sidcup, Kent.

Jaguar Car Club, R. Pugh, 19 Eldorado Crescent, Cheltenham, Glos.

Jaguar/Daimler Owners Club, 130/132 Bordesley Green, Birmingham B9 4SU. Tel: 021 426 2346

Jaguar Drivers Club, JDC Jaguar House, 18 Stuart Street, Luton, Beds. Tel: 0582 419332

Jaguar Enthusiasts Club, G.G. Searle, Sherborne, Mead Road, Stoke Gifford, Bristol. Tel: 0272 698186

Jensen Owners Club, Florence, 45 Station Road, Stoke Mandeville, Bucks. Tel: 0296 614072

Jowett Car Club, Frank Cooke, 152 Leicester Road, Loughborough, Leics. Tel: 0509 212473

Junior Zagato Register, Kenfield Hall, Petham, Nr Canterbury, Kent. Tel: 0227 700555

Jupiter Owners Auto Club, Steve Keil, 16 Empress Avenue, Woodford Green, Essex. Tel: 081-505 2215

Karmann Ghia Owners Club (GB), Eliza Conway, 269 Woodborough Road, Nottingham.

Kieft Racing and Sports Car Club, Duncan Rabagliati, 4 Wool Road, Wimbledon SW20.

Lagonda Club, Mrs Valerie May, 68 Saville Road, Lindfield, Haywards Heath, Sussex.

Landcrab Owners Club International, Bill Frazer, PO Box 218, Cardiff.

Land Rover Register (1947-1951), Membership Secretary, High House, Ladbrooke, Nr Leamington Spa.

Land Rover Series One Club, David Bowyer, East Foldhay, Zeal Monachorum, Crediton, Devon. Tel: 0363 82666

Land Rover Series Two Club, PO Box 1609, Yatton, Bristol.

Lancia Motor Club, The Old Shire House, Aylton, Ledbury, Herefordshire.

Lea Francis Owners Club, R. Sawers, French's, Long Wittenham, Abingdon, Oxon.

Lincoln-Zephyr Owners Club, Colin Spong, 22 New North Road, Hainault, Ilford, Essex.

London Bus Preservation Trust, Cobham Bus Museum, Redhill Road, Cobham, Surrey.

London Vintage Taxi Association, Keith White, 6 Alterton Close, Woking, Surrey.

Lotus Cortina Register, 'Fernleigh', Homash Lane, Shadoxhurst, Ashford, Kent.

Lotus Drivers Club, Lee Barton, 15 Pleasant Way, Leamington Spa. Tel: 0926 313514

Lotus Seven Owners Club, David Miryless, 18 St James, Beaminster, Dorset.

Club Lotus, PO Box 8, Dereham, Norfolk. Tel: 0362 694459

Historic Lotus Register, Mike Marsden, Orchard House, Wotton Road, Rangeworthy, Bristol.

Marcos Owners Club, 62 Culverley Road, Catford, London SE6. Tel: 081-697 2988

Club Marcos International, Mrs I. Chivers, Membership Secretary, 8 Ludmead Road, Corsham, Wilts. Tel: 0249 713769

Marendaz Special Car Register, John Shaw, 107 Old Bath Road, Cheltenham. Tel: 0242 526310

The Marina/Ital Drivers Club, Mr J.G. Lawson, 12 Nithsdale Road, Liverpool.

Marlin Owners Club, Mrs J. Cordrey, 14 Farthings West, Capel St. Mary, Ipswich.

Maserati Club, Michael Miles, The Paddock, Old Salisbury Road, Abbotts Ann, Andover, Hants. Tel: 0264 710312

Masters Club, Barry Knight, 2 Ranmore Avenue, East Croydon.

Matra Enthusiasts Club, M.E.C, 19 Abbotsbury, Orton Goldhay, Peterborough, Cambs. Tel: 0733 234555

Mercedes-Benz Club Ltd, P. Bellamy, 75 Theydon Grove, Epping, Essex. Tel: Epping 73304

Messerschmitt Owners Club, Mrs Eileen Hallam, The Birches, Ashmores Lane, Rusper, West Sussex.

Messerschmitt Enthusiasts Club, Graham Taylor, 5 The Green, Highworth, Swindon, Wilts.

Metropolitan Owners Club, Mr N. Savage, Goat Cottage, Nutbourne Common, Pulborough, Sussex. Tel: 07981 3921

The MG Car Club, PO Box 251 Abingdon, Oxon. Tel: 0235 555552

MG Octagon Car Club, Harry Crutchley, 36 Queensville Avenue, Stafford. Tel: 0785 51014

MG Owners Club, R. S. Bentley, 2/4 Station Road, Swavesey, Cambs. Tel: 0954 31125

The MG 'Y' Type Register, Mr J. G. Lawson, 12 Nithsdale Road, Liverpool.

Midget and Sprite Club, Nigel Williams, 15 Foxcote, Kingswood, Bristol. Tel: 0272 612759

Register of Unusual Micro-Cars, Jean Hammond, School House Farm, Hawkenbury, Staplehurst, Kent.

The Military Vehicle Trust, Nigel Godfrey, 8 Selborne Close, Blackwater, Camberley, Surrey.

Mini Cooper Club, Joyce Holman, 1 Weavers Cottages, Church Hill, West Hoathly, Sussex

Mini Cooper Register, Lisa Thornton, 1 Rich Close, Warwick. Tel: 0926 496934

Mini Marcos Owners Club, Roger Garland, 28 Meadow Road, Claines, Worcester. Tel: 0905 58533

Mini Moke Club, Paul Beard, 13 Ashdene Close, Hartlebury, Worcs.

Mini Owners Club, 15 Birchwood Road, Lichfield, Staffs.

Morgan Sports Car Club, Mrs Christine Healey, 41 Cordwell Close, Castle Donington, Derby.

Morgan Three-Wheeler Club Ltd, K. Robinson, Correction Farm, Middlewood, Poynton, Cheshire.

Morris Cowley and Oxford Club, Derek Andrews, 202 Chantry Gardens, Southwick, Trowbridge, Wilts.

Morris 12 Club, D. Hedge, Crossways, Potton Road, Hilton, Huntingdon.

Morris Marina Owners Club, Nigel Butler, Llys-Aled, 63 Junction Road, Stourbridge, West Midlands.

Morris Minor Owners Club, Jane White, 127-129 Green Lane, Derbyshire.

Morris Register, Arthur Peeling, 171 Levita House, Chalton Street, London.

Moss Owners Club, David Pegler, Pinewood, Weston Lane, Bath. Tel: 0225 331509

National Autocycle & Cyclemotor Club, c/o R. Harknett, 1 Parkfields, Roydon, Harlow, Essex.

Norton Owners Club, Dave Fenner, Beeches, Durley Brook Road, Durley, Southampton.

Nova Owners Club, Ray Nicholls, 19 Bute Avenue, Hathershaw, Oldham, Lancs.

NSU Owners Club, Rosemarie Crowley, 58 Tadorne Road, Tadworth, Surrey. Tel: 073781 2412

The Ogle Register, Chris Gow, 108 Potters Lane, Burgess Hill, Sussex. Tel: 0444 248439

Opel GT UK Owners Club, Martyn and Karen, PO Box 171, Derby. Tel: 0773 45086

Opel Manta Club, 14 Rockstowes Way, Westbury-on-Trym, Bristol.

Opel Vauxhall Drivers Club, The Old Mill, Borrow Hall, Dereham, Norfolk. Tel: 0362 694459

Manta A Series Register, Mark Kinnon, 87 Village Way, Beckenham, Kent.

Les Amis de Panhard et Levassor GB, Denise Polley, 11 Arterial Avenue, Rainham Essex. Tel: 04027 24425

Panther Car Club Ltd, 35 York Road, Farnborough, Hants. Tel: 0252 540217

Pedal Car Collectors Club, c/o A. P. Gayler, 4-4a Chapel Terrace Mews, Kemp Town, Brighton, Sussex.

Club Peugeot UK, Dick Kitchingman, Pelham, Chideock, Bridport, Dorset.

Piper (Sports and Racing Car) Club, Clive Davies, Pipers Oak, Lopham Road, East Harling, Norfolk. Tel: 0953 717813

Porsche Club Great Britain, Ayton House, West End, Northleach, Glos. Tel: 0451 60792

Post Office Vehicle Club, 7 Bignal Rand Drive, Wells, Somerset.

Post 45 Group, Mr R. Cox, 6 Nile Street, Norwich, Norfolk.

Potteries Vintage and Classic Car Club, B. Theobold, 78 Reeves Avenue, Cross Heath, Newcastle, Staffs.

Post-War Thoroughbred Car Club, 87 London Street, Chertsey, Surrey

The Radford Register, Chris Gow, 108 Potters Lane, Burgess Hill, West Sussex. Tel: 0444 248439

Railton Owners Club, Fairmiles, Barnes Hall Road, Burncross, Sheffield. Tel: 0742 468357

Raleigh Safety Seven and Early Reliant Owners Club, Mick Sleap, 17 Courtland Avenue, London E4.

Range Rover Register, Chris Tomley, Cwm/Cochen, Bettws, Newtown, Powys.

Rapier Register, D.C.H. Williams, Smithy, Tregynon, Newton Powys. Tel: 068687 396

Reliant Owners Club, Graham Close, 19 Smithey Close, High Green, Sheffield.

Reliant Rebel Register, M. Bentley, 70 Woodhall Lane, Calverley, Pudsey, West Yorks. Tel: 0532 570512

Reliant Sabre and Scimitar Owners Club, RSSOC, PO Box 67, Northampton NN2 6EE. Tel: 0604 791148

Rear Engine Renault Club, R. Woodall, 346 Crewe Road, Cresty, Crewe, Cheshire.

Renault Frères, J. G. Kemsley, Yew Tree House, Jubilee Road, Chelsfield, Kent.

Renault Owners Club, C. Marsden, Chevin House, Main Street, Burley-in-Wharfedale, Ilkley, West Yorks. Tel: 0943 862700

Riley Motor Club Ltd, A. J. Draper, 99 Farmer Ward Road, Kenilworth, Warwicks. Tel: 0926 57275

Riley R. M. Club, Bill Harris, 57 Cluny Gardens, Edinburgh.

Riley Register, J. A. Clarke, 56 Cheltenham Road, Bishops Cleeve, Cheltenham, Glos.

Ro80 Club GB, Simon Kremer, Mill Stone Cottage, Woodside Road, Windsor Forest, Windsor, Berks. Tel: 0344 890411

Rochdale Owners Club, Brian Tomlinson, 57 West Avenue, Birmingham.

Rolls-Royce Enthusiasts, Lt. Col. Eric Barrass, The Hunt House, Paulersbury, Northants.

Rootes Easidrive Register, M. Molley, 35 Glenesk Road, London SE9.

Rover P4 Drivers Guild, Colin Blowers (PC), 32 Arundel Road, Luton, Beds.

Rover P5 Owners Club, G. Moorshead, 13 Glen Avenue, Ashford, Middx. Tel: 0784 258166

Rover P6 Owners Club, PO Box 11, Heanor, Derbys.

Rover Sports Register, A. Mitchell, 42 Cecil Road, Ilford, Essex.

British Saab Enthusiasts, Mr M. Hodges, 75 Upper Road, Parkstone, Poole, Dorset.

The Saab Owners Club of GB Ltd, Mrs K. E. Piper, 16 Denewood Close, Watford, Herts. Tel: 0923 229945

British Salmson Owners Club, John Maddison, 86 Broadway North, Walsall, West Midlands. Tel: 0922 29677

Salmons Tickford Enthusiasts Club, Keith Griggs, 40 Duffins Orchard, Ottershaw, Surrey.

Scootacar Register, Stephen Boyd, Pamanste, 18 Holman Close, Aylsham, Norwich, Norfolk.

Simca Owners Register, David Chapman, 18 Cavendish Gardens, Redhill, Surrey.

Scimitar Drivers Club, c/o Mick Frost, Pegasus, Main Road, Woodham Ferrers, Essex. Tel: 0245 320734

Singer O.C., Martyn Wray, 11 Ermine Rise, Great Casterton, Stamford, Lincs. Tel: 0780 62740

Association of Singer Car Owners (A.S.C.O.),
Paul Stockwell, 119 Camelot Close, King Arthur's
Way, Andover, Hants.
Skoda Owners Club of Great Britain,
Ray White, 78 Montague Road, Leytonstone, E11
South Devon Commercial Vehicle Club,
Bob Gale, Avonwick Station, Diptford, Totnes,
Devon. Tel: 0364 73130
South Hants Model Auto Club, C. Derbyshire,
21 Aintree Road, Calmore, Southampton, Hants.
Spartan Owners Club, Steve Andrews,
28 Ashford Drive, Ravenhead, Notts.
Tel: 0623 793742
Stag Owners Club, Mr H. Vesey, 53 Cyprus Road,
Faversham, Kent. Tel: 0795 534376
Standard Motor Club, Tony Pingriff, 57 Main
Road, Meriden, Coventry. Tel: 0675 22181
Star, Starling, Stuart and Briton Register,
D. E. A. Evans, New Woodlodge, Hyperion Road,
Stourton, Stourbridge, Worcs.
Sunbeam Alpine Owners Club, Pauline Leese,
53 Wood Street, Mow Cop, Stoke-on-Trent.
Tel: 0782 519865
Sunbeam Rapier Owners Club, Peter Meech,
12 Greenacres, Downton, Salisbury, Wilts.
Tel: 0725 21140
Sunbeam Talbot Alpine Register,
Peter Shimmell, 183 Needlers End Lane, Balsall
Common, West Midlands. Tel: 0676 33304
Sunbeam Talbot Darracq Register, R. Lawson,
West Emlett Cottage, Black Dog, Crediton, Devon.
Sunbeam Tigers Owners Club, Brian Postle,
Beechwood, 8 Villa Real Estate, Consett,
Co. Durham.
The Swift Club and Swift Register, John
Harrison, 70 Eastwick Drive, Great Bookham,
Leatherhead, Surrey. Tel: 0372 52120
Tame Valley Vintage and Classic Car Club,
Mrs. S. Ogden, 13 Valley New Road, Royton,
Oldham OL2 6BP.
Tornado Register, Dave Malins, 48 St Monica's
Avenue, Luton, Beds. Tel: 0582 37641
TR Drivers Club, Bryan Harber, 19 Irene Road,
Orpington, Kent. Tel: 0689 73776
The TR Register, Rosy Good, 271 High Street,
Berkhamstead, Herts.
Tel: 0442 870471
Trident Car Club, Ken Morgan, Rose Cottage,
45 Newtown Road, Verwood, Nr Wimborne, Dorset.
Tel: 0202 822697
Club Triumph Eastern, Mrs S. Hurrell,
7 Weavers Drive, Glemsford, Suffolk.
Tel: 0787 282176
Club Triumph North London, D. Pollock,
86 Waggon Road, Hadley Wood, Herts.
Triumph Mayflower Club, T. Gordon,
12 Manor Close, Hoghton, Preston, Lancs.
Pre-1940 Triumph Owners Club, Alan Davis,
33 Blenheim Place, Aylesbury, Bucks.
Triumph Razoredge Owners Club, Stewart
Langton, 62 Seaward Avenue, Barton-on-Sea,
Hants. Tel: 0425 618074
The Triumph Roadster Club, Paul Hawkins,
186 Mawnay Road, Romford, Essex.
Tel: 0708 760745
Triumph Spitfire Club, Johan Hendricksen,
Begijnenakker 49, 4241 CK Prinsenbeek,
The Netherlands.
Triumph Sports Six Club Ltd,
121B St Mary's Road, Market Harborough, Leics.
Tel: 0858 34424
Triumph Sporting Owners Club, G. R. King,
16 Windsor Road, Hazel Grove, Stockport, Cheshire.
Triumph 2000/2500/2.5 Register, G. Aldous,
42 Hall Orchards, Middleton, King's Lynn, Norfolk.
Tel: 0553 841700
The Triumph Dolomite Club, 39 Mill Lane,
Arncott, Bicester, Oxon.
Tel: 0869 242847
Turner Register, Dave Scott, 21 Ellsworth Road,
High Wycombe, Bucks.

The Trojan Owners Club, Mrs Christine Potter
(Secretary), 64 Old Turnpike, Fareham, Hants.
Tel: 0329 231073
TVR Car Club, c/o David Gerald, TVR Sports
Cars, The Green, Inkberrow, Worcs. Tel: 0386
793239
United States Army Vehicle Club,
Dave Boocock, 31 Valley View Close, Bogthorn,
Oakworth Road, Keighley, Yorks.
Vanden Plas Owners Club, Nigel Stephens, The
Briars, Lawson Leas, Barrowby, Grantham, Lincs.
Vanguard 1 & 2 Owners Club, R. Jones,
The Villa, 11 The Down, Alviston, Avon.
Tel: 0454 419232
Droop Snoot Group, 41 Horsham Avenue,
Finchley, London N12. Tel: 081-368 1884
'F' and 'F.B.' Victor Owners Club,
Wayne Parkhouse, 5 Farnell Road, Staines, Middx.
Victor 101 FC (1964-1967), 12 Cliff Crescent,
Ellerdine, Telford, Shropshire.
The F-Victor Owners Club, Alan Victor Pope,
34 Hawkesbury Drive, Mill Lane, Calcot, Reading,
Berks. Tel: 0635 43532
Vauxhall Cavalier Convertible Club,
Ron Goddard, 47 Brooklands Close, Luton, Beds.
Vauxhall Owners Club, Brian J. Mundell,
2 Flaxton Court, St Leonards Road, Ayr, Scotland.
Vauxhall PA/PB/PC/E Owners Club,
G. Lonsdale, 77 Pilling Lane, Preesall, Lancs.
Tel: 0253 810866
Vauxhall VX4/90 Drivers Club,
c/o 43 Stroudwater Park, Weybridge, Surrey.
Vectis Historic Vehicle Club, 10 Paddock Drive,
Bembridge, Isle of Wight.
The Viva Owners Club, Adrian Miller,
The Thatches, Snetterton North End, Snetterton,
Norwich.
Veteran Car Club of Great Britain,
Jessamine House, High Street, Ashwell, Herts.
Vintage Sports Car Club Ltd, The Secretary,
121 Russell Road, Newbury, Berks.
Tel: 0635 44411
The Association of British Volkswagen Clubs,
Dept PC, 66 Pinewood Green, Iver Heath, Bucks.
Volkswagen Cabriolet Owners Club (GB),
Emma Palfreyman (Secretary), Dishley Mill,
Derby Road, Loughborough, Leics.
Historic Volkswagen Clubs, 11a Thornbury
Lane, Church Hill, Redditch, Worcs.
Tel: 0527 591883
Volkswagen Owners Club GB, R. Houghton,
49 Addington Road, Irthlingborough, Northants.
Volkswagen Owners Caravan Club (GB),
Mrs Shirley Oxley, 18 Willow Walk, Hockley, Essex.
Volkswagen Split Screen Van Club,
Brian Hobson, 12 Kirkfield Crescent, Thorner, Leeds.
Volkswagen '50-67' Transporter Club,
Peter Nicholson, 11 Lowton Road,
Lytham St Annes, Lancs. Tel: 0253 720023
VW Type 3 and 4 Club, Jane Terry, Pear Tree
Bungalow, Exted, Elham, Canterbury, Kent.
Volvo Enthusiasts Club, Kevin Price, 4 Goonbell,
St Agnes, Cornwall.
Volvo Owners Club, Mrs Suzanne Groves,
90 Down Road, Merrow, Guildford, Surrey.
Tel: 0483 37624
Vulcan Register, D. Hales, 20 Langbourne Way,
Claygate, Esher, Surrey.
The Wartburg Owners Club, Bernard Trevena,
56 Spiceall Estate, Compton, Guildford, Surrey.
Tel: 0483 810493
Wolseley 6/80 and Morris Oxford Club,
John Billinger, 67 Fleetgate, Barton-on-Humber,
North Lincs. Tel: 0652 635138
The Wolseley Hornet-Special Club,
Mrs P. Eames, Jasmin Cottage, Weston,
Nr Sidmouth, Devon.
Wolseley Register, B. Eley, 60 Garfield Avenue,
Dorchester, Dorset.
XR Owners Club, 20a Swithland Lane, Rothley,
Leics.

DIRECTORY OF AUCTIONEERS

United Kingdom

ADT Auctions Ltd., Blackbushe Airport, Blackwater, Camberley, Surrey.
Tel: 0252 878555

Alcocks, Wyeval House, 42 Bridge Street, Hereford.
Tel: 0432 344322

Bonhams, 65-69 Lots Road, London SW10.
Tel: 071-351 7111

Brooks, 81 Westside, London SW4.
Tel: 071-228 8000

Central Motor Auctions PLC, Central House, Pontefract Road, Rothwell, Leeds.
Tel: 0532 820707

Christie's, 8 King Street, St James's, London SW1.
Tel: 071-839 9060

Classic Motor Auctions, PO Box 20, Fishponds, Bristol.
Tel: 0272 701370

Coys of Kensington, 2-4 Queens Gate Mews, London SW7.
Tel: 071-584 7444

Eccles Auctions.
Tel: Cambridge 0223 561518.

Evans & Partridge, Agriculture House, High Street, Stockbridge, Hants.
Tel: 0264 810702

Greens Vintage and Classic Auction Sales, PO Box 25, Malvern, Worcs.
Tel: 0684 575902

Hampson Ltd., Road 4, Winsford Industrial Estate, Winsford, Cheshire.
Tel: 0606 559054

Hamptons Collectors Cars, 71 Church Street, Malvern Worcs.
Tel: 0684 893110

H & H Auctions, Rose Cottage, Roseneath Road, Urmston, Manchester.
Tel: 061 747 0561 & 0925 860471

Holloways, 49 Parsons Street, Banbury, Oxon.
Tel: 0295 253197

Husseys, Matford Park Road, Marsh Barton, Exeter.
Tel: 0392 425481

Lambert & Foster, 97 Commercial Road, Paddock Wood, Tonbridge, Kent.
Tel: 0892 832325

Phillips, West Two, 10 Salem Road, London W2.
Tel: 071-229 9090

RTS Auctions Ltd., 35 Primula Drive, Eaton, Norwich. Tel: 0603 505718

Shoreham Car Auctions, 5-6 Brighton Road, Kingston Wharf, Shoreham-by-Sea, West Sussex.
Tel: 0273 871871

Sotheby's, 34-35 New Bond Street, London W1.
Tel: 071-493 8080

Sotheby's, Summers Place, Billingshurst, West Sussex.
Tel: 0403 783933

Thimbleby & Shorland, PO Box 175, 31 Great Knollys Street, Reading, Berks.
Tel: 0734 508611

Truro Auction Centre, Calenick Street, Truro, Cornwall.
Tel: 0872 260020

International

'The Auction', 3535 Las Vegas Boulevard, South Las Vegas, Nevada 89101, USA.
Tel: 0101 702 794 3174

C. Boisgirard, 2 Rue de Provence, 75009 Paris, France.
Tel: 010 33 147708136

Carlisle Productions, The Flea Marketeers, 1000 Bryn Mawr Road, Carlisle, PA 17013-1588, USA

Christie's Australia Pty Ltd., 1 Darling Street, South Yarra, Melbourne, Victoria 3141.
Tel: 010 613 820 4311

Christie's (Monaco), S.A.M, Park Palace, 98000 Monte Carlo.
Tel: 010 339 325 1933

Christie, Manson & Woods International Inc., 502 Park Avenue, New York, NY 10022.
Tel: 0101 212 546 1000

Classic Automobile Auctions B.V., Goethestrasse 10, 6000 Frankfurt 1.
Tel: 010 49 69 28666/8

Kruse International Inc., PO Box 190-Co. Rd. 11-A, Auburn, Indiana, USA 46706.
Tel: 0101 219 925 5600

Paul McInnis Inc., Auction Gallery, Route 88, 356 Exeter Road, Hampton Falls, New Hampshire 03844, USA.
Tel: 0101 603 778 8989

Orion Auction House, Victoria Bldg-13, Bd. Princess Charlotte, Monte Carlo, MC 98000 Monaco.
Tel: 010 3393 301669

Silver Collector Car Auctions, E204, Spokane, Washington 99207, USA.
Tel: 0101 509 326 4485

Sotheby's, 1334 York Avenue, New York, NY 10021. Tel: 0101 212 606 7000

Sotheby's, B.P. 45, Le Sporting d'Hiver, Place du Casino, MC 98001 Monaco/Cedex.
Tel: 0101 3393 30 88 80

DIRECTORY OF MUSEUMS

Avon

Bristol Industrial Museum, Princes Wharf, City Docks, Bristol 1. Tel: 0272 251470

Bedfordshire

Shuttleworth Collection, Old Warden Aerodrome, Nr Biggleswade. Tel: 096 727 288

Buckinghamshire

West Wycombe Motor Museum, Cockshoot Farm, Chorley Road, West Wycombe.

Cambridgeshire

Vintage M/C Museum, South Witham, Nr Peterborough.

Cheshire

Mouldsworth Motor Museum, Smithy Lane, Mouldsworth. Tel: 0928 31781

Cornwall

Automobilia Motor Museum, The Old Mill, St Stephen, St Austell.

Co. Durham

North of England Open Air Museum, Beamish.

Cumbria

Lakeland Motor Museum, Holker Hall, Cark-in-Cartmel, Nr Grange-over-Sands. Tel: 0448 53314

Cars of the Stars Motor Museum, Standish Street, Keswick. Tel: 07687 73757

Derbyshire

The Donington Collection, Donington Park, Castle Donington. Tel: 0332 810048

Devon

Totnes Motor Museum, Steamer Quay, Totnes. Tel: 0803 862777

Essex

Ford Historic Car Collection, Ford Motor Co, Eagle Way, Brentwood.

Gloucestershire

The Bugatti Trust, Prescott, Gotherington, Cheltenham. Tel: 0242 677201

Cotswold Motor Museum, Old Mill, Bourton-on-the-Water, Nr Cheltenham. Tel: 0451 821255

Hampshire

Gangbridge Collection, Gangbridge House, St Mary Bourne, Andover.

The National Motor Museum, Beaulieu. Tel: 0590 612345

Humberside

Peter Black Collection, Lawkholme Lane, Keighley.

Bradford Industrial Museum, Moorside Mills, Moorside Road, Bradford. Tel: 0274 631756

Hull Transport Museum, 36 High Street, Kingston-upon-Hull. Tel: 0482 22311

Museum of Army Transport, Flemingate, Beverley. Tel: 0482 860445

Sandtoft Transport Centre, Sandtoft, Nr Doncaster.

Kent

Historic Vehicles Collection of C. M. Booth, Falstaff Antiques, High Street, Rolvenden.

The Motor Museum, Dargate, Nr Faversham.

Ramsgate Motor Museum, West Cliff Hall, Ramsgate. Tel: 0843 581948

Lancashire

The British Commercial Vehicles Museum, King Street, Leyland, Preston. Tel: 0772 451011

Bury Transport Museum, Castlecroft Road, off Bolton Street, Bury.

Manchester Museum of Transport, Boyle Street, Manchester.

Tameside Transport Collection, Warlow Brook, Frietland, Greenfield, Oldham.

Leicestershire

Stanford Hall Motorcycle Museum, Stanford Hall, Lutterworth. Tel: 0788 860250

Lincolnshire

Geeson Brothers Motorcycle Museum and Workshop, South Witham, Grantham. Tel: 057 283 280/386.

London

British Motor Industry, Heritage Trust, Syon Park, Brentford. Tel: 081-560 1378

Science Museum, South Kensington, SW7. Tel: 071-938 8000.

Norfolk

Caister Castle Car Collection, Caister-on-Sea, Nr Great Yarmouth. Tel: 0572 84251/84202.

Sandringham Museum, Sandringham. Tel: 0553 772675

Nottinghamshire

Nottingham Industrial Museum, Courtyard Buildings, Wallaton Park.

Shropshire

Midland Motor Museum, Stourbridge Road, Bridgnorth. Tel: 0746 761761

Somerset

Haynes Sparkford Motor Museum, Sparkford, Nr Yeovil. Tel: 0963 40804

Surrey

Brooklands Museum, Brooklands Road, Weybridge. Tel: 0932 859000

Dunsfold Land Rover Museum, Alfold Road, Dunsfold. Tel: 0483 200567

Sussex

Bentley Motor Museum, Bentley Wildfowl Trust, Halland. Tel: 082 584 711.

Effingham Motor Museum, Effingham Park, Copthorne.

Filching Manor Museum, Filching Manor, Jevington Road, Wannock, Polegate. Tel: 0323 487838/487933/487124

Tyne and Wear

Newburn Hall Motor Museum, 35 Townfield Garden, Newburn.

Warwickshire

Heritage Motor Centre, Banbury Road, Gaydon. Tel: 0926 641188

West Midlands

Birmingham Museum of Science and Industry, Newhall Street, Birmingham. Tel: 021-235 1661

Black Country Museum, Tipton Road, Dudley.

Museum of British Road Transport, St Agnes Lane, Hales Street, Coventry. Tel: 0203 832425

Autoworld at The Patrick Collection, 180 Lifford Lane, King's Norton, Birmingham. Tel: 021-459 9111

West Yorkshire

Automobilia Transport Museum, Billy Lane, Old Town, Hebden Bridge. Tel: 0422 844775

Wiltshire

Science Museum, Red Barn Gate, Wroughton, Nr Swindon. Tel: 0793 814466

Eire

The National Museum of Irish Transport, Scotts Garden, Killarney, Co Kerry.

Kilgarvan Motor Museum, Kilgarvan, Co Kerry. Tel: 010 353 64 85346

Isle of Man

Manx Motor Museum, Crosby. Tel: 0624 851236

Port Erin Motor Museum, High Street, Port Erin. Tel: 0624 832964

Jersey

Jersey Motor Museum, St Peter's Village

Northern Ireland

Ulster Folk and Transport Museum, Cultra Manor, Holywood, Co Down. Tel: 0232 428428

Scotland

Doune Motor Museum, Carse of Cambus, Doune, Perthshire. Tel: 078 684 203

Grampian Transport Museum, Alford, Aberdeenshire. Tel: 0336 2292

Highland Motor Heritage, Bankford, Perthshire.

Melrose Motor Museum, Annay Road, Melrose. Tel: 089 6822 2624

Moray Motor Museum, Bridge Street, Elgin. Tel: 0343 544933

Museum of Transport, Kelvin Hall, Bunhouse Road, Glasgow. Tel: 041-357 3929

Myreton Motor Museum, Aberlady, East Lothian. Tel: 087 57288

Royal Museum of Scotland, Chambers Street, Edinburgh. Tel: 031-225 7534

Wales

Conwy Valley Railway Museum Ltd, The Old Goods Yard, Betws-y-Coed, Gwynedd. Tel: 0690 710568

INDEX TO ADVERTISERS

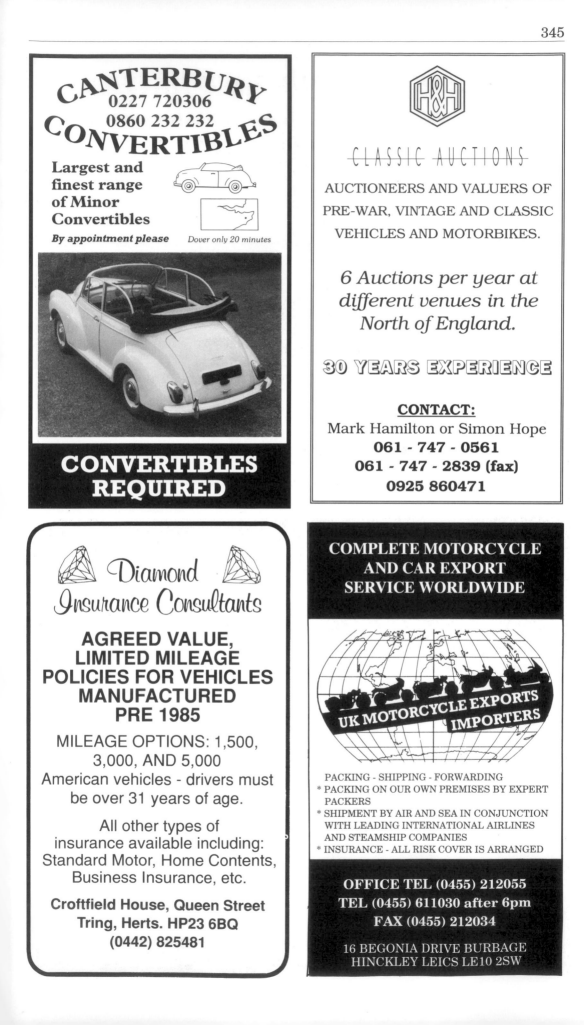

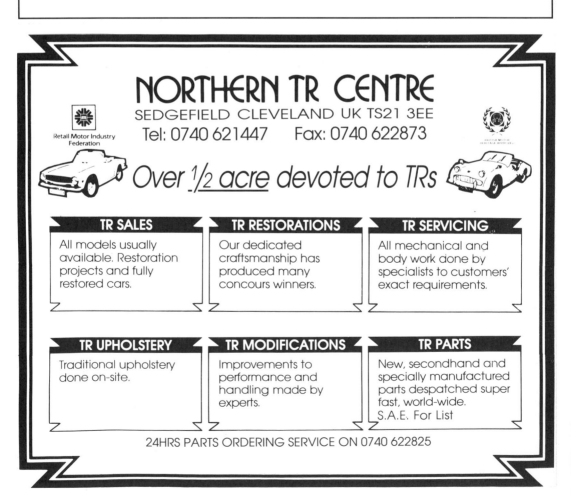

INDEX